TOURISM AND HOSPITALITY

Food and Beverage Service-Food Production

TOURISM AND HOSPITALITY

Food and Beverage Service-Food Production

Set of 4 Parts

(Part - 1)

Dr. Annamalai Murugan

Assistant Professor
Department of Tourism,
Tagore Government Arts and Science College,
Pondicherry

AVON PUBLICATIONS

NEW DELHI

Published by

AVON PUBLICATIONS
1/9938, West Gorakh Park, Street No. 3A,
Shahdara, Delhi- 110032
Showroom:
5A-12, Ground Floor, Ansari Road
Daryaganj, New Delhi 110002 (India)
Ph: 011- 23265366, 7210090042
E-mail: avonpublications72@gmail.com

TOURISM AND HOSPITALITY

Food and Beverage Service-Food Production

First Edition: 2018

ISBN: 978-81-9375-193-0 (Set of 4 Parts)

PRINTED IN INDIA

Printed at: New Delhi

Preface

The Indian Food and Beverage Services market is expanding rapidly at higher rate. The annual rate of growth is expected at 30 percent and will continue to grow with similar pace in the next few years. The overall scenario of the F&B service market has evolved over the past few years. There was a time when handful of brands were available in the market to eat out. But today, the customers are plenty of choices. We have witnessed lots of activities in F&B Services industry in the last 5 years, including exciting new service ideas, food and beverage offerings and new and innovative service ideas. Therefore, what are the emerging and current trends in the F&B Services industry? How will people eat, behave and be served in coming years? In this document we look at some of these emerging trends that will become part of everyday life soon.

TRANSFORMATION OF CUISINE:

Despite India's great tradition of food, eating out was not as common as in the West until recently. Now, eating out is a regular form of culture, especially in the metros, mini-metros driven by increase in income, greater number of nuclear families and working women, and urbanization. Ingredients like truffles, artichokes, asparagus, Blending of cuisines, e.g. Italian with Thai is another customer choice. People are ready to experiment with food& drinks in todays time. To cater to these guest or customer more innovation are done in food & beverage sector live kitchen has replaced old traditional kitchen. in todays world people wants to prepare their food with the help of professional chef. The trend is increasing for customers to choose cuisines that reflect their lifestyle, and in the process reject the traditional options.. On the other hand, customers are also being delighted with "street food" options served in a hygienic setting and good ambience. Another industry innovation is the dual format, e.g., café + library bar, café + grill item, bar +music lounge, etc. Multi-cuisine restaurants, which offer a non-specialized feel, are however losing ground to specialist players with customers willing to pay more but unwilling to compromise on quality. The way forward is likely to be an adoption& innovation of both lesser known Indian flavors from the northeatern and tribal belts ,village traditional food as well as other international cuisines like Korean, Burmese, lankan, bali etc.. While South Indian, Punjabi and Mughlai cuisines tended to dominate the Indian offerings, there is now also demand for such dishes as Andhra Chicken Pepper Fry. Similarly, Bhutanese, African and Korean cuisines can also find acceptance among customers. Thus, there is opportunity for F&B players to innovate the traditional and new Indian flavors while offering both individually. Further, while a niche segment may be created for international cuisines, customization may be needed to ensure that they suit the Indian palate. In modern day people want more choice in each segment.

ONLINE FOOD AND BEVERAGE SERVICE:

Modern trends which is functioning very popular in today's scenario online food& beverage order. People in metros donot have time for food or to venture out to new restaurant. to cater to those people taste bud various online food joint like FOOD PANDA, TINY OWL, Curry n bowl has come where people can order their food online or through mobile apps. Food will be served in stipulated time.cash on delivery option available for customer. whole range of choice will be given to customer. Customer can order cuisines such as Continental, Chinese, Indian, Thai etc.

EVOLUTION OF BEVERAGE AS GAME CHANGER:

Most people in India are exposed to a variety of beverages from an early age: mothers serve homemade milkshakes, sharbats, chocolate drinks etc. However, beverages are themselves only a "sidekick" and at best served as fillers in-between meals.. This emergence began with the introduction of coffee chains more than a decade ago. This was also a first in terms of organized beverage retail, since the segment was earlier dominated by small local players like juice shops. In the past few years, coffee has become a fashion statement among the youth. With both Indian and international coffee chains mushrooming across the country, cafés are playing a key role in customer preferences. This growth has also prompted bigger international brands like Starbucks and Dunkin' Donuts to foray into the Indian market. Indian coffee chain cafe coffee day, cuppa coffee day, barista has gain popularity among young Indians& it has become meeting points for then. A lot can happen over a coffee talk a lot about Indian people who wants discuss every thing on the sun over coffee.

Tea has gain popularity in recants times with more outlet such as Chai bar, tea point, meeting point,99 variety of tea has come into place. nowadays we can various flavouirs tea like chocolate, strawberry, lime, peach, orange, mandarin flav. we also have fruit & herb flavours tea very popular among all section of society.

However, consumers are keen on trying out new variants such as flavoured and herbal teas. awareness of the health benefits attributed to tea is another factor driving the expansion of tea-based chains like Chapatti, Passion – My Cup of Tea, Tapri, Infinitea, Chai Point, Tea Junction, Tea Pot, Tea Centre, Cha Bar. In modern world people are least bothered about the style of service. whether it is silver service or American service. the service is done from ,left hand side or right hand side of the guest. They are bothered about quality of food being served to the guest in nice environment with exceptional behaviour. they want entertainment while they visit restaurant the service staff should be humble, passionate about work, fun loving person, discipline & can make them feel home away from home. That is why most of the guest wants to celebrate birthday, marriage anniversary in hotel or restaurant. Staff should be able to connect with guest & they should enjoy their moment with staff.

In today's world most of the people lives lonely, so they want to celebrate it with others .to enjoy those moments they want to go to hotel.so the staff should make their moment enjoyable by having fun games with games, singing birthday songs with complimentary cakes. these all make come to the restaurant regularly.

INCREASING INFUSION OF ENTERTAINMENT IN F&B SERVICE SECTOR:

The development of the organized F&B market in India has taken time, due to which brands are still focusing on getting the fundamentals (the menu, the service etc.) .modern trend is that people do not want to go to particular place only for food & beverage, but they want entertainment in terms of sports, music, live performances. Many bar will have sports equipment like snookers, pools, table tennis, live gaming zone.

Brands which were primarily entertainment oriented, with F&B elements as add-ons. E.g., Sports bars, bookstore cafés. By adding entertainment options, F&B brands give customers another reason to spend more time at the dinner table, thus improving the average spend per visit. While some forms of entertainment are offered free of cost (for instance, live music), others games such as snooker require some additional payment. Traditionally, restaurants were rated in terms of theme and ambience; now they are offering varied entertainment. Modern trends require food& entertainment for the customer to be get attracted. People can play indoor as well as outdoor games supplied with various food & beverage in order to make the guest relaxed & enjoy from a hectic business schedule.

Infusion in Food & Beverage sector in India:

In today's time, world has become a global village. People are ready to try various cuisines, drinks, local food etc. They are ready to experiment with various cuisines& drinks. some of the innovative drinks& food which has been introduced recently were, pasta with butter chicken, lasagne pander do piazza, karma samosa, 99 variety of dosas which include Indian, south Indian, Chinese ,continental stuffing's. etc. People are ready to try herbal infusion drinks such as orange juice mixed with carrot juice, beetroot juice mixed with watermelon juice& flavoured with mint& lime. cucumber refreshing juice with alovera juice. Emerging trend in food & beverage sector focus more on customer or guest centric. customer has to be involved during the whole process to make their outing as enjoyable experience. we have to remember that guest are ready to pay price for quality product. They should get value for their money. entertainment, fun sports, gaming, music, healthy & innovative dishes with world class plateresentation. They should have wow moment after coming to our place.

The book has given a comprehensive textbook to the Food and Beverage Service designed to cater to the needs of the students of degree-diploma courses of hotel management and certificate courses of food craft institutes. It covers all aspects of the food and beverage department (F&B), as required by the syllabi of hotel management courses. Food and Beverage Service book is specifically tailored to meet the requirements of the students of hotel management courses. Due to its exhaustive coverage and practical approach, this textbook is suitable not only for students, but also for professionals.

Dr. Annamalai Murugan

Acknowledgments

Several individuals have contributed to prepare the manuscript of this book. The authors gratefully acknowledge contributions of each one of them. I owe much as well to *AVON PUBLICATIONS, New Delhi* who first encouraged me to take on this task and then prodded me to complete it in good time. I appreciate to the entire editorial team at *AVON PUBLICATIONS,* without their efforts this edition would not have been in the form in which it is at present.

Dr. Annamalai Murugan

Contents

Part - 1

Part - 2

Part - 3

Part - 4

CHAPTER 1

Food & Beverage Service Industry

The food & beverage industry is usually defined by it output of products, to satisfy the various demands of food & drinks of people. Bu it doesn't include the manufacturing of food & drink and its retailing. In today's world, the food & beverage service industry has expanded a lot and nowadays, it is serving more than 100million meals per day.

It has spread across all walks – of life. Hotel, restaurants, industrial canteen, hospital canteen, railway, airways, all are now part of food & beverage service industry.

The basic function of this industry is to serve food & drink to people, to satisfy their various types of needs. The main aim is to achieve customer satisfaction. The needs that customer might be seeking to satisfy are:

Physiological: the need of special food items

Economic: the need for good value for the price paid

Social: a friendly atmosphere, to express feelings frankly

Psychological: the need for enhancement of self esteem

Convenience: the desire for someone else to do the work.

These various needs play a major role in deciding the factors responsible for defining the different type of service methods in Food & Beverage service industry.

The service of food and beverage may be carried out in many ways depending on a number of factors:

The type of establishment

The type of customer to be served

The time available for the meal

The turnover of customer expected

The type of menu presented

The cost of meal served

The site of establishment

Food & beverage service can also be viewed from the customer's perspective. Essentially, the customer enters a food service area, orders or selects his/ her choice and then is served (the customer may pay either at this point or later). Food and beverages are then consumed, following which the area is cleared.

A steward is a food and beverage service employee who does everything possible, within reason, to make each guest's dining experience exactly how he/she wants is to be, and who exceeds guest expectations whenever possible.

In this content you will learn the following:

Duties and Responsibilities of a Steward/Waiter.

Competencies of a steward

Tools of a Steward

Duties & Responsibilities of Steward

Reporting to senior/captain to receive instructions for the shift and for any menu changes.

Attending briefings conducted by the manager/senior captain.

Setting the assigned tables and ensuring that the service area too is well stocked with linen, chinaware, glassware, etc. He sets up any special displays that may be used for the meal period.

Greeting guests and assisting the host/hostess in seating guests.

Filling water glasses, serving, beverages, answering questions about about menu items and making suggestions about dishes and drinks if the customer requests or desires.

Taking orders on an order pad, giving over the order with specifications to the chefs with considerations to the timing of the preceding courses. A steward picks up all food and other required items from various stations.

Serving food the serving dishes into the guest's plate.

Replenishing water, beverages and other food items as and when required.

Observing the guests in order to anticipate any additional request and to notice when the meal has been completed.

After all the guests have finished each course and before the next one is served, the waiter/waitress should remove all soiled dishes.

When guests have finished the meal, the table is cleared, reset and readied for the next customer.

Performing any other tasks as directed by the captain.

Competencies of a Steward

Grooming and personal Hygiene

How you appear and the first impression you create is more often than not seen as a reflection of the hygiene standards of your establishment and the quality of service to come.

Good Memory

Sound memory is an asset for any food and beverage service staff. It helps in providing excellent customer service.

Knowledge of food and beverage and technical ability

Knowledge of all the items on the menu and drink lists for making suggestions.

Knowledge and technical ability of how to serve each dish on the menu, its accompaniments, the correct cover, make-up of the dish and garnish.

Knowledge of various wines and drinks and its service in the correct glasses and at the right temperature.

Punctuality

To be punctual is all-important. If the staff is continually late it shows a lack of interest in their work and a lack of respect for the management and customers.

Local knowledge

The staff must be knowledgeable of the area in which they work so they may be able to advise and guide guests correctly.

Personality

The staff must be tactful, courteous, good humored and of even temper. The ability to converse with guests in a pleasing manner by smiling at the right places, adds greatly to the customers' dining experience.

Conduct

Staff conduct should be impeccable at all times, especially in front of customers. The rules and regulations of an establishment must be followed and respect must be shown to all senior members of staff.

Attitude

The staff must exhibit a joy in serving people.
Pride in one's work brings excellence.
Initiative is valued competency nowadays.

Honesty

Trust and respect in the triangle of staff, customer and management relationship fosters an atmosphere of work which encourages efficiency and good team spirit.

Loyalty

The staff's obligations and loyalty are firstly to the establishment to which they are employed and its management.

Sales Ability

The staff must have complete knowledge of all forms of food and drink and their correct service, to be able to contribute to personal selling and merchandising.

Sense of urgency

In order for the establishment to generate the maximum amount of business over the service period, with as high a net profit as possible, staff must develop a sense of urgency.

Handling complaints

Staff must show courtesy, tact, an even temper and good humour when handling complaints.

Customer satisfaction

The food and beverage staff must anticipate guest needs and ensure that the guest is completely satisfied.

Contribution to the team

Teams have become the cornerstones of food service operations. Poor team performance damage the establishment's reputation. An effective team, harnesses complimentary skills of other members and have trust in their competency.

Tools of a Steward

As as Steward, you should always carry the following tools with you. These tools are also referred as waiter's friend.

1: Waiter's Cloth

A very handy tool, a waiter's cloth is carried over the left wrist.

It is used for holding hot plates and dishes, crumbing, wiping spills, serving wine, and is wrapped around water jugs, etc.

It must be spotless and should never be used for personal purposes.

2: Ballpoint click Pen

It is used to take down an order and helps the waiter to write faster. It can be operated using a single hand.

3: Wine Opener

It is an important piece of equipment with multiple uses. It combines a knife for cutting the foil of a wine bottle, cork screw and a bottle opener.

4: Clean handkerchief

It is used for personal use, to wife perspiration for example.

5: Match box/lighter

This always comes in handy for lighting up the guest's cigar/cigarette.

6: KOT/BOT pad

The Kitchen Order Ticket and Beverage Order Ticket pad is used for taking down food and beverage orders respectively. However, many establishments use the same pad for food and beverage orders.

7: Nameplate

This comes with the establishment's logo and is usually in brass and sometimes in plastic. It is fixed to the left of the uniform over the chest.

SOME BASIC PRINCIPLES OF SERVICE

When the food is served at the table from a dish to a guest's plate, it is done from the left.

When food is pre-plated, the service to the guest is done from the right.

All beverages are served from the right.

Soups are served from the right unless poured from a soup tureen in which case it is done from the left.

Ladies are always served first.

Soiled plates are always cleared from the right.

Fresh cutlery and crockery is always served from the right.

Never reach across the guest

Dealing with guests during service.

Greetings such as 'Good morning' and 'Good evening' should be used upon receiving guests or when the member of staff first comes into contact with the customer, for example when lounge service staff attends people already seated in the lounge.

The list below identifies examples of interpersonal skills needed at particular points during the service.

Showing guests to their table: always lead and walk with them at their pace.

Seating customers: ladies first, descending in age unless the host is a lady.

Handling coats/wraps: handle with obvious care.

Handling menus/wine lists to customers: Offer the list right way round, open for the customer and wait for the customer to take it.

Opening and placing a napkin: Open carefully, do not shake it like a duster, place it on the customer's lap after saying 'excuse me' to the customer.

Talking to customer: Only talk when standing next to them and looking at them.

Offering water or rolls: Say, for example, 'Excuse me Sir/Madam, may i offer you a bread roll?'

Explaining food and beverage items: Use terms the customer understands, not technical terms such as turned vegetable or pane. Use terms that make the item sound attractive such as casserole not stew, creamed or purée potatoes not mashed. Don not use abbreviations, for example, 'veg'.

Being culturally aware: Meeting the needs of customers from other cultures will affect the ways in which staff need to be aware of the dietary requirements of the various religious faiths.

Serving and clearing: Always say 'Excuse me' before serving or clearing and 'Thank you' after you have finished with each customer.

Offering Accompaniments: Only offer them if you have them at the table. Offering them when they are not at the table usually means 'I will get them if you really want them!'

An Introduction to Hospitality

The hospitality industry is a part of a larger enterprise known as travel and tourism industry. The travel and tourism industry is a vast group of business with one goal in common : providing necessary or desired services to travelers. Advances in transportation enabled more people to travel greater distances at less cost spreading tourism across the globe. From modest origins, hospitality and tourism rose to become two of the largest world wide industries.

Warriors or traders were the early travelers but they did not have hotels to accommodate them. The warriors used tents but the merchants seeking to trade tools, clothing and livestock, traded merchandise for lodging. The inns offered little more than a cot or a bench in the corner of a room or a stable. Most of them were private residences that offered temporary residence or lodging to strangers. Guests stayed in large communal rooms where sanitation and privacy were non-existent. After the establishment of money in 6th century BC, innkeeping was one of the first commercial enterprises and hospitality was one of the first services for which money was exchanged.

In the third century AD, Roman Empire developed an extensive system of brick paved roads throughout Europe and Asia minor. Small road side lodges were constructed due to increase in the road transport. During the Industrial Revolution in 1700s, the Europeans began to combine food and beverage service with lodging. No attention was given to sanitation and beds as well as rooms had to be shared with other travelers. These early European inns were unsuitable for aristocrats. To accommodate wealthy travelers, luxurious structures were erected. These offered private rooms, individual sanitation and all comforts of a European castle. These elegant new establishments adopted the French name for mansion, 'hotel'. The rates they charged were very high and well beyond the means of common citizens.

In colonial America, inns were modeled after European inns. Beds and rooms had to be shared with strangers. Throughout 1800s, American innkeepers improved their services and continued to build larger properties.

Most of these were located in seaport town since sea transport was very widely used mode or travel and transport then. The first American hotel the 'City Hotel', opened in 1794 in the New York city. It was one of the largest building in the city and was built exclusively for hotel purpose. It had 73 guest rooms. 'Adelphi Hotel' in New York was the first high-rise structure in the city.

In 1829, a large new hotel was constructed in Boston. 'Tremont House' was the earliest first class hotel in America and brought revolution in the hospitality industry. This hotel was the first to offer private rooms with locking doors. Each guest room had a wash basin and a water pitcher and a bar of soap. Other innovations included a full time service staff, a French restaurant which was located in the lobby, etc. These American hotels became important social centers and unlike their European counterparts, welcomed anyone who could afford the reasonable rates. Meanwhile in Europe, sanitary lodging continued to be regarded as a privilege to be enjoyed only by the aristocracy. But in democratic America clean and comfortable accommodation was available to any middle class worker or family.

In early 1900s, a new type of traveler entered the picture, the traveling businessman. For him the world class hotels were too expensive and the old style inns too unsanitary. A new type of lodging establishment was opened for these type of guests - 'the commercial hotels'. It was opened by Mr. E. M. Statler, at Buffalo, New York, in Jan. 1908. It was the beginning of the chain hotel concept. This hotel provided private sanitary rooms with private bathroom. The guest received a pitcher of ice water and morning newspaper everyday. "A room and a bath for a dollar and a half " was well known among American travelers.

The great Depression nearly wiped out the hotel industry. But one hotel operator, Conrad Hilton, managed to stay afloat as a result of his oil and gas investments. Around 1940 - 1950, the Hilton Hotel corporation built or bought numerous luxury hotels around the world and competed with the largest hotel chains of the time Sheraton and Statler.

With the end of world war II, the hotel industry unexpectedly entered a new era of prosperity, Americans began traveling as never before. With an automobile in every garage, Americans began touring the country with their families. For this new type of traveler - the vacationing family unit - the formality of a traditional hotel was inappropriate. Families traveling in their cars needed casual lodging that was accessible from major highways and had ample facilities for parking. The early these properties were small and had fewer than 50 rooms. Most of them were owned and operated by a couple and were called Mom and Pop properties. By 1960, the motor hotel or the motel, had become an permanent and influential part of the hospitality industry. By this time the motels had over 100 rooms with a separate parking space for each unit.

In 1960s, a new type of lodging outlet - the economy, or budget hotel entered the picture. These lodging establishments sold only room space without F & B service. To save on construction cost, the economy hotels were built on inexpensive land and had small lobbies. They also hired minimum staff. By minimizing costs the budget hotels were able to give much lower room rates than their competitors. The first successful economy hotel, 'Travelodge', opened in Tacoma, Washington, in 1956 but the chain expanded nationwide by 1966. By early 1970s the idea of low rate motel/s hotels had captured the imagination of investors mini bars are the standard amenities of most budget hotels. These hotels / motels are also called as no-frills hotels.

By 1973, the no. of travelers staying in motels surpassed the no. of people staying in full-service hotels. To compete with these low end properties, mid-market hotel chains introduced their own limited service hotels. Theses hotels combined some of the features of the full service hotels with the cost saving of the budget hotels / motels. eg. Holiday created the limited service Hampton Inn chain and Marriott created Courtyard hotels. In these hotels all the rooms have separate living and sleeping areas. The lodging trend of the 1990s is towards epanded services made possible through consolidation of responsibilities. Guest services departments are found in hotels of all classes. These departments combine services that traditionally were performed by bell or door attendent, a concierge and an in house travel agent. Two new concepts in the hotel industry are 'The All Suite Hotels' and 'The Residential Hotels'.

TOURISM

Definition

- It is the movement of people from their normal place of residence & work for a period of not less than 24 hours and not more than 1 year. (according to W.T.O.)
- The sum of phenomenon and relationship arising from the travel as it does not lead to permanent residence and is not connected to any earning activity. (by Henniker & Kroff)
- Tourism covers the social activity of those who travel for a period of 24 hours or more in a country other than the one the person usually lives in (The league of nations in 1937)
- Tourism is a temporary, short term movement of people to destinations outside the places where they normally live and work and their activities during their stay at these destinations, including day visit & excursion. (By tourism society of Britain)
- Tourism may be defined in terms of particular activities selected by choice and undertaken outside the home environment. Tourism may or may not involve overnight stay away from home. (A.I.E.S.T, 1981)

- Tourism – The activity of temporary visitors staying at least 24 hours for leisure, business, family or meeting.
- Excursion – The activity of temporary visitors staying less than 24 hours but excluding people in transit.

TOURISM INDUSTRY

I. Comprised of a broad range of business and organizations that are related to virtually all the areas of economy.

« The components include all suppliers of goods and services which the tourists require.(according to Mr. A.J. Bunkart)

II. Tourism industry comprises those organizations that are :

« In the business of providing goods and services, to meet the distinctive needs of some identifiable collection of tourists.

« Cooperate with one another to some degree in doing so.

(According to Mr. Leiper)

III. According to Kaiser and others there is no such thing as tourism industry.

What happens is a collection of several industries that function separately with various types of links with tourists. These links can be both incidental as well as purposeful, direct or indirect.

In the seventh 5year plan (1985-90) tourism was given the status of an industry by govt. of India.

Hence as a plan objective its development was listed for the first time in the planning process. In May 1992, National Action plan was drawn for its growth and development.

Primary and secondary constituents

Primary or major constituents :

1. Transport
2. Accommodation
3. Intermediaries
4. catering and food
5. Govt. Dept., tourists information centers (tourists organizations)

Secondary constituents :

1. Shops and emporiums
2. Handicrafts and souvenirs
3. Local transportation
4. Coolie and transport assistance
5. Communication services.
6. Advertisement agencies
7. Publishing industry
8. Artists, musicians and performers

TOURISM

International tourism - When the travel is from one country to another.

Domestic tourism – When the travel is within the country that is trip taken

by a tourist within his/her own country or where the origin and destination are in the same country.

Inbound - It refers to tourists entering a country.

Outbound – It refers to tourists leaving their country of origin to another.

CLASSIFICATION BASED ON MOTIVES OF TRAVEL

TOURISM

Leisure Business
1.Pleasure 1.Conventions
2.Relaxation, rest, recreational. 2.Conferences
(holiday, vocational, tourism) 3.Seminars
4.Meetings
àCultural tourism
àSpiritual & religious tourism
àEthnic & family tourism
àSports & adventure tourism
àHealth tourism
«Miscellaneous Motives
àStatus & prestige
àFor the sheer joy of traveling
àShopping

ECO TOURISM

All tourism comprises either mass tourism or alternative tourism. Eco tourism is another subset of natural area and may combine elements of both nature based and adventure travel.

Eco tourism is responsible is responsible travel to natural areas which conserves the environment and improves the welfare of the local people.

PRINCIPLES OF ECO TOURISM

Eco tourism comprises of a number of inter-related components, all of which should be present for authentic eco tourism to occur. There are five key principles which are fundamental to eco-tourism.

1. Nature Based: Based on natural environment with a focus on its biological, physical and cultural features.
2. Ecologically Sustainable: All tourism should be sustainable ecologically, socially and environmentally.
3. Environmentally Educative: It attracts people who wish to interact with the environment in order to develop their knowledge, awareness and appreciation of it.
4. Locally Beneficial: It not only benefits the community and the environment but also improves the quality of tourist experience. Local communities can provide knowledge, services, facilities and products.
5. Tourist Satisfaction: Satisfaction of visitors is essential in long term viability. Visitor safety in regard to political stability. The eco tourism experience should match or exceed the realistic expectations of the visitor.

IV. EMERGING STYLES OF ECO TOURISM

1. Frontier Eco tourism: It involves individuals or small groups (10 or less) people who utilise non-motorised forms of transport. E.g., walking or canoeing.
2. Small Group Eco tourism: Involves individuals or relatively small group (15 or less) who utilise motorised forms of Transport. E.g., four wheel drive.
3. Popular Eco tourism: It involves larger number of visitors to, through or across a country's best known and most popular natural attractions. It relies on high capacity mechanised forms of transport. E.g., buses, large boats.

V. ECO TOURISM IN INDIA

In the last 20 years India has opened its doors to international visitors and is now fostering tourism largely to gain an increase in foreign exchange earnings to help its economy.

In 1996, 2.2 million international tourists visited the country. However India's tourism infrastructure is barely keeping pace with the industry increase and problems are evident in accommodation, transport and personnel sectors. In addition, India has real problem with environmental pollution and tourist pressures causing substantial damages to its natural treasures.

India's focus should be better redirected towards sustainable tourism. Strong elements in support of this approach include India's natural and cultural attractions, its unique blend of natural and cultural environment and its expertise in small package tours.

Another key for India would be to become involved in the Indian Ocean Tourism Organisation. India should plan the regions so that a balance is maintained among the natural, cultural and economic environment.

HOTEL

A hotel or inn may be defined as an establishment whose primary business is providing lodging facilities for the general public and which furnishes one or more of the following services.

- Housekeeping service
- Food and beverage service
- Bell and door attendant service
- Laundry and dry cleaning
- Concierge
- Use of furniture and fixtures

Hotels range from 50 to 2000 rooms, sometimes more. Inns usually have between 5 to 50 rooms.

CLASSIFICATION OF HOTELS

Hotels are classified on the basis of :

1. SIZE: Depending on the number of rooms, hotels are classified as

- Under 150 rooms
- 150 to 299 rooms
- 300 to 600 rooms
- More than 600 rooms

2.TARGET MARKET: Depending on the clientele hotels are classified as

- Commercial hotels- business clientele.
- Airport hotels- transient or stop over for airline passengers.
- Suite hotels- VVIPS, dignitaries, long staying guests.
- Extended stay hotels- Long staying guests.
- Residential hotels- generally for diplomats.
- Resorts- Recreation and leisure for holiday makers.
- Bed and breakfast- travelers.
- Timeshare and condominiums- Holiday makers.
- Conference centers / Convention hotels- for conferences, seminars and conventions.
- Casino- gambling / games.
- Alternate lodging properties- budget travelers.

3. LEVELS OF SERVICE:

- World class service- luxury service
- Mid range service
- Economy / limited service.

4. OWNERSHIP AND AFFILIATION:

- Independent hotels- single / stand alone properties
- Chain hotels- more than hotel being part of a group.
- Management contracts- Owners hire a management company to run their hotel.
- Franchise- using the name of a established chain of hotels by paying a fee.
- Referral groups- Independent hotels get together, form a group and assist one another in getting business.

Hotel

Definition

A hotel or inn may be defined as an establishment whose primary business is providing lodging facilities for the general public & which furnishes one or more of the following services.

Services

a) Food & Beverage b) Housekeeping c) Concierge d) Bell & Door attendant service e) Laundry & dry cleaning f) use of furniture & fixtures.

Hotels range from 50 to 2000 rooms & sometimes more. Inns usually have b/w 5 to 50 rooms.

Hotels are classified on the bases of :

SIZE

Includes no. of rooms & are classified as :

Small - upto 150 rooms
mid sized - 150 - 299 # s
large - 300 - 600 # s
very large - 600 + # s

II. TARGET MARKET

Clientele the hotel has or the clients they serve to.

a) Commercial Hotels

i. **Location** - Commercial area, down town areas, business districts & also in the heart of the city.
ii. **Clientele** - Businessmen or corporate.
iii. **Services / Facilities** - Good communication rooms conference rooms & also secretarial services. Highly specialised Business Centres.

Facilities in Business centers

Lounge with reception area, sitting area, with newspaper, national & international, magazines, televisions, Reuters, Conference Rooms ranging from capacity of 2 to 25 people, Secretarial Services, Stationary, Photo Copier, Fax, Binding, Lamination, Interpreters can also be arranged. Computers & internet connectivity also a guest can hire mobile phones & laptops from business centers. It may also have a small library.

Facilities in Club / Business Floors

2 phonelines ii) Fax Machine iii) Coffee Maker iv) Internet Facilities v) Business Kit & Large Study Table vi) Mostly junior suites vii) Separate reception to save time c/ a club lounge or club reception area.

These are mainly for Businessmen Lounge may serve breakfast, high tea & cocktails too. eg. Oberios, Taj, Hilton towers.

b. Airport Hotels

i. Location - Near airports
ii. Clientele - Stopovers, airline staff.
iii. Service / Facilities - Exchange rate / airport transverse travel desk (book tickets & updated High Schedule), more staff at night shift.

Also c/a transit hotels, length of stay is not long.

e.g. - The Leela, the Grand Hyatt

c. Suite Hotels

i. Location - not in commercial areas, but in posh areas.
ii. Clientele - VIPs, diplomats
iii. Services - High profile hotels, not very high facilities e.g. Lotus suite.

d. Extended Stay Hotels

i. Location - near by a residential area.
ii. Clientele - Journalists, Students doing research.
iii. Services - Extremely less services, may have a not so costly. e.g. Lodges.

e. Residential / Apartment hotels

i. Location - upmarket residential area
ii. Clientele - families staying for maybe 2 - 4 years.
iii. Services / facilities - Ample parking, Swimming pool, Gym, Housekeeping, Butter Services, Laundry Services it also has a complete kitchen. Are like apartments can have 1 to 4 bedrooms. e.g. Taj Apartments.

f. Resort

i. Location - Near scenic beauty, can be by a beach or mountains.
ii. Clientele - Holiday markers, travelers, families.
iii. Services - Recreation & Leisure facilities Swimming pool, Gym, Indoor & Out-door Game, Sight Seeing facilities, Spa.

e.g. Retreat, the Resorts, Taj Holiday Village.

g. Bread & Breakfast Hotels

Also known as 'Mom & Pop' hotels

i. Location - located in cultural centers
ii. Clientele - travelers
iii. Service - breakfast & accommodation

Advantages

- No sharing of profit.
- It can have a goodwill.
- Avoiding of bureaucracy

Disadvantages

- the decision may not be the best \ not lot of thought \ the experience is not much.
- losses can't be shared.
- the loyalty may not be much.
- no advantage of bulk production.

no sharing of reservation network

h. Timeshare and Condominium

(the unit under which these 2 work).

ô RCI - Resort Condominium international

Location - Mostly Resort \ out of the city.

Services - In timeshare the money investors are allowed a free stary.

Timeshare - People invest in a timeshare company & depending on the amount of investment, they get membership for certain duration of time. The members get to stay at the time share property (resort) once a year for a week. Members can exchange their holidays with members from other time share companies. This can be done by the time share company. e.g. Club Mahindra.

Condominium - Each member owns a unit c/a condo. The owner can stay at the unit for as long as he/she wants & when he is not staying at the resort / property, the unit can be given out to the general public when it is done so, a part of the revenue goes to the owner. They can also exchange their holidays. e.g. Royal Palms, RCI resorts.

- Timeshare & Condominiums are the members of RCI
- Cliental - Holiday makers
- Services - that of a resort

i. Casino

- These are the hotels which provide accommodation. Difference types of games, entertainment, different cuisine etc.
- Legalised gambling is the major part to the clients.

Headliner entertainment is also a part of casino
Casinos are also a major part of hotel industries.
e.g. has Vegas, Monte Carlo, Kathmandu.
River boat casino - These are the casino mostly in water b/w 2 lands probably where gambling is not allowed.

j. Conference Centres - Convention

Location - Out of the city for security reasons.

Clientele

Companies, Corporate
floor space for exhibition also a good business center.
Convention - These centre will have convention hall facility.
Location - Away from city for security reason.
Clientele - Delegates & VIPs & decision maker service - have large convention hall with all — facilities, Accommodation High security.
MICE
Meetings, Incentive Travel, Conferences & Exhibition.

k. Alternate Lodging Properties

Supplementary Accommodation
Either heritage hotels, cruise liners or house boats.
Ø & high cost for advertising.
e.g.: Mid town Pritam in Dadar (E).

III Levels of Service - Depending on the standard of service provided the hotels are classified as

a. World class service hotels

- LHW - Leading Hotels of the world (based in NY)
- LSHW - Leading small hotels of the world.
- For India the organisation
- HRACC - Hotel & Restaurant Approval Classification Committee
- FHRAI - Federation of Hotel & Restaurant Association of India like LHW another organisation.
- AAA - American Automobile Association - this organisation also classify the hotels \ all associates and corporates judge the hotels hence they give diamond rating.
- Grand Tourism - South American's (Mexico) organisation to classify the hotels.
- Under world class service hotels

5 star & 5 star deluxe.

b. Mid ranged service hotels

3 star & 4 star hotels
They provide with good service but not luxurious
The organisation which classifies these hotels is
SRS - Steingenberger Reservation System
(Germany based)

c. Economy / limited service / No. frills hotels.

- Good service but no extra facility.
- It is an economic hotel.
- not too much of luxury.
- but no compromise of an cleanliness & hygiene.
- 1 & 2 Star hotels

e.g. Indi 1 (Taj), Trident (Oberoi's)
India 1
The top brands are going for economic hotels to reach the masses.
The highest rating in India is 5 star deluxe.

IV OWNERSHIP & AFFILIATION HOTELS

Depending on who owns the hotels & type of ownership they've classified as

a. **Independent Hotels:** In this there is only single property.
b. **Chain Hotels:** Multi - property owned by a group of individual

Advantage

- brand loyalty
- sharing of losses
- adv. of bulk purchasing
- Reservation net & marketing & advertising can be shared.
- better & planned decision making.
- experimentation
- exchange of employ & training.

Disadvantages

- Profit is shared
- Reputation at stake if 1 property does not perform well.
- decision making is slow.
- bureaucracy is applicable.
- No individuality
- Internal Competition may not be healthy.

difficult controlling for 1 hotel may not be applicable or profitable for the other.

c. Management Contracted Hotels

Owners hire management companies to run the hotel for them conditions are written in the contract.

1. Pay Specific fee to Management Company the income is the owner.
2. The management company pays a specific amount to owners & the income is theirs.

e.g. Hilton.

d. Franchise

Using the name of a brand that has developed a distant way of doing business by paying a fee.

The brand that lends the name - franchiser
The hotel that buys the name - franchisee
e.g. Hilton Towers, Grand Maratha Sheraton.

Advantage

- Ø flexible
- quick decision making
- span of control

e. Referral group

The independent hotels get together & form an association to overcome the disadvantage of being an independent property.

The hotels help each other getting business share reservation net; marketing & advertising even purchases.

e.g. LHW (is a referral of leading hotels of the world).

CLASSIFICATION OF HOTELS (Star Classification)

The department of Tourism classification functioning hotels under the star system, into five categories from 1-star to 5-star for this purpose a permanent Committee, the Hotel and Restaurant Approval and Classification Committee has been set up which inspects the applicant hotels to assess their suitability or otherwise for award of the star category and are placed on the approved list of the Department. Approved hotels become eligible to various fiscal relief and benefits. The department intercedes on behalf of such hotels whenever necessary to ensure that their needs get priority consideration from various concerned authorities. These hotels also get worldwide publicity through tourist literature published by the Department of Tourism and distributed by the Government of India Tourist Offices in India and abroad. Approved hotels become eligible for foreign exchange for their import of essential equipment and provisions and for their advertising, publicity and promotion under the Hotel Incentive Quota Scheme.

To be eligible to apply for classification hotel must fulfill the following minimum basic requirements:

i) The Hotel must have at least 10 lettable bedrooms.

ii) Carpet areas in respect of rooms and areas of bathroom should by and large adhere to the following limits: -

Categories of Hotel	Area standard for bedrooms/bathrooms
· 5 Star/5 Star Deluxe Hotels	180 sq.ft.
Single -	200 sq.ft.
Double -	45 sq.ft.
Bathrooms -	
· 4 Star & 3 Star Hotels	120 sq.ft.
Single A/C and	140 sq.ft.
Single Non A/C -	(Extra area may be provided if twin beds are to
Double A/C and Double Non A/C -	be provided)
Bathrooms -	36 sq.ft.
· 2 Star & 1Star Hotels	100 sq.ft.
Single A/C and	120 sq.ft.
Single Non A/C -	(All rooms should have proper ventilationAnd
Double A/C and Double Non A/C -	ceiling fans)
Bathrooms -	30 sq.ft. Orsubject to local bye-laws

Failure to satisfy these conditions will disqualify a hotel for consideration.

The general features, facilities and services expected of hotels in the different star categories are broadly described below:

FIVE STAR CATEGORY

General features: The facade, architectural features and general construction of the hotel building should have the distinctive qualities of a luxury hotel of this category. The locality, including the immediate approach and environments, should be suitable for a luxury hotel of this category and there should be adequate parking space for the cars. The hotel should have at least 25 lettable rooms, all with attached bathrooms with long bath or the most modern shower chambers. All public rooms and private rooms should be fully air-conditioned and should be well equipped with superior quality carpets, curtains, furniture, fittings, etc. in good taste. It would be advisable to employ the services of professionally qualified and experienced interior designers of repute for this purpose. There should be an adequate no. of efficient lifts in the building of more than two storeys (including the ground floor), with 24 hrs. service. There should be a well-designed and properly equipped swimming pool.

Facilities: There should be a reception; cash and information counter attended by highly qualified, trained and experienced personnel and conference facilities in the form of one or more conference rooms, banquet hall and private dining rooms. There should be a bookstall, a beauty parlor, barbershop, recognised travel agency, florist and a shop for toilet requisites and medicines on the premises. There should be a telephone in each room and a facility of radio or relayed music in each room. There should be a well-equipped, well-furnished and well-maintained dining room, restaurant on premises and whenever permissible by law, there should be an elegant, well-equipped bar/ permit room. The pantry and cold storage should be professionally designed to ensure efficiency of operation and should be well equipped.

Services: The hotel should offer both International and Indian cuisine and the food and beverage service should be of highest standard. There should be professionally qualified, efficient and courteous staff in smart, clean uniforms. The staff coming in contact with the guests should understand English. The supervisory staff knowing at least one continental language should be rotated on duty at all times. There should be 24 hrs. Services for reception, information and telephones. There should be provision for reliable laundry and dry cleaning services. Housekeeping at the Hotel should be of the highest possible standard and there should be plentiful supply of linen, blankets, towels, etc., which should be of the highest quality available. Each bedroom should be provided with a good vacuum jug thermos flask with ice cold, boiled drinking water except where centrally chilled purified drinking water is provided. There should be special restaurant/dining room where facilities for dancing, orchestra are provided.

FOUR STAR CATEGORY

General Features: The architectural features and general construction of the building should be distinctive and the locality including the immediate approach should be suitable for a hotel of this category. There should be adequate parking facilities for cars.

The hotel should have 25 lettable rooms all with attached bathrooms. At least 50% of bathrooms must have long baths of the most modern shower chambers, with 24 hrs service of hot and cold running water. All public areas and private rooms should be well furnished with carpets, curtains, furniture, fittings etc. in good state. It would be advisable to employ the services of professionally qualified and experienced interior designer of repute for this purpose. There should be an adequate number of efficient lifts in building of more than two storeys (including ground floor). There should be well-appointed lobby and ladies, gents cloak rooms equipped with fittings and furniture of the highest standard.

Facilities: There should be a reception, cash and information counter attended by, trained and experienced personnel. There should be bookstall, recognised travel agency, money changing and safe deposit facilities and a left luggage room on the premises. There should be a telephone in each room and provision for a radio or relayed music in each room. There should a well-equipped, well-furnished and well-appointed dining room/restaurant on the premises and where ever permissible by law, there should be an elegant and well-equipped bar/permit room. The kitchen, the pantry, cold storage should be professionally designed to ensure efficiency of operation and should be well equipped.

Service: The hotel should offer both International and Indian cuisine and the food and beverage service should be of highest standard. There should be professionally qualified, efficient and courteous staff in smart, clean uniforms. The staff coming in contact with the guests should understand English. It will be desirable for some of the staff to posses the knowledge of foreign language and staff knowing at least one continental language should be rotated on duty at all times. There should be 24 hrs services for reception, information and telephones. There should be provision for reliable laundry and dry cleaning services. Housekeeping at the Hotel should be of the highest possible standard and there should be plentiful supply of linen, blankets, towels, etc., which should be of the highest quality available. Similarly the cutlery and the glass wear should be of the highest quality available. Each bedroom should be provided with a good vacuum jug thermos flask with ice cold, boiled drinking water except where centrally chilled purified drinking water is provided. There should be special restaurant/dining room where facilities for dancing, orchestra are provided.

THREE STAR CATEGORIES

General features: The architectural features and general construction of the building should be of a very good standard and the locality including the immediate approach should be suitable for very good hotel of this category. There should be adequate parking facilities for cars. The hotel should have at least 20 let table rooms all with attached bathrooms with bathtubs and/or showers. The bathrooms should be with hot and cold running water. At least 50% of the rooms should be air-conditioned and the furniture and furnishings such as carpets, curtains, etc., should be of a very good standard and design. There should be adequate number of lifts in the building with more than two storeys (including the ground floor). There should be a well appointed lounge and separate ladies and gentlemen's cloak room equipped with fittings of a good standard.

Facilities: There should be a reception and an formation counter attended by qualified staff, and a bookstall recognised travel agency, money changing and safe deposit facilities on the premises. There should be a telephone in each room (except in seasonal hotels where there would be a call bell in each room and a telephone on each floor for the use of hotel. There should be a well equipped and well maintained

Air-conditioned dining rooms /restaurant and where permissible by law, there should be a bar/permit rooms. The kitchen, pantry and cold storage should be a clean organised for orderliness and efficiency.

Service: The hotels should offer good quality cuisine both Indian as well as continental and the food and beverage service should be of a good standard. There should be qualified, trained, experienced, efficient and courteous staff coming in contact with the guests should be provision for laundry and dry cleaning service. Housekeeping at the hotel should be of a very good standard and there should be adequate supply of linen, blankets, towels etc., of good quality. Similarly, cutlery, crockery, glassware should be of a good quality. Each bedroom should be provided with vacuum jug/thermos flask with cold, boiled drinking water. The hotel should provide orchestra and hall room facilities and should attempt to present specially choreographed Indian Cabaret.

TWO STAR CATEGORY

General Features: The building should be well constructed and the locality and environs including the approach should be suitable for a good hotel. The hotel should be at least 10 lettable bedrooms of which at least 75% should have attached bathrooms with showers and a bathroom for every four of the remaining rooms and should be with modern sanitation and running cold water with adequate supply of hot water, soap and toilet papers. 25% of the rooms should be air-conditioned (where there should be heating arrangements in all the rooms) and all rooms must be properly ventilated clean and comfortable with all the necessary items of furniture. There should be a well-furnished lounge.

Facilities: There should be a reception counter with a telephone. There should be a telephone or call bell in each room and has a separate telephone. There should be a well-maintained and well-equipped dining room / restaurant serving good, clean wholesome food and a clean, hygienic and well-equipped kitchen and pantry.

Service: There should be experienced, courteous and efficient staff in smart and clean uniforms. The Supervisory staff coming in contact with guests should understand English. There should be provision for laundry and dry cleaning services. Housekeeping at the hotel should be of good standard and good quality linen, blankets, towels etc., should be provided. Similarly, crockery, cutlery and glassware should be of a good quality.

ONE STAR CATEGORY

General Features: The general construction of building should be good and the locality and environs, including immediate approach should be suitable. The hotel should have at least 10 lettable bedrooms of which at least 25% should have attached bathrooms with a bathroom for every 4 of the remaining rooms. At least 25% of the bathrooms should have western style WCs. All bathrooms should have modern sanitation and running cold-water wit adequate supply of hot water, soap and toilet paper. The rooms should be properly ventilated and should have clean and comfortable bed and furniture.

Facilities: There should be a reception counter with a telephone and a telephone for the use of guests and visitors. There should be clean and wholesome food and there should be a clean well equipped kitchen and pantry.

Services: There should be experienced, courteous and efficient staff in smart and clean uniforms and the senior staff coming in contact with guests should possess working knowledge of English. Housekeeping at the hotel should be of a good standard and clean and good quality linen, blankets, towels etc., should be supplied. Similarly, crockery cutlery and glassware should be of good quality.

A classification fee at the following rate is payable by the hotels supplying for classification:

Star Category Amount in Rs.

One star 2000/-

Two star 3000/-

Three star 4000/-

Four star 6000/-

Five star 8000/-

Five star deluxe 10000/-

The classification fee is payable by means of a demand draft drawn in favour of the Pay & Accounts Officer, Department of Tourism, New Delhi. For Re-classification, fee will be 50% of the above fee.

The application for One, Two and Three star category Hotels should be addressed to The Regional Director, Government of India Tourist Office, M. Karve road, Mumbai 400 020. Where as the applications for Four, Five and Five Deluxe category hotels should be addressed to The Assistant Director (Hotels), Department of Tourism, Government of India C-I Hutments, Dalhousie Road, New Delhi, 110011.

For each of these categories of star classification the hotel have to fulfill three classes of criteria, E - Essential, N - Necessary, D - Desirable. For each of these criteria there are maximum marks allotted.

Supplementary Accommodation

This consists of all types of accommodation other than the conventional hotel type. This can be described as premises which offer accommodation but not the extra services of a hotel. It is a very economical type of accommodation.

Main distinguishing features :

1. The standard of comforts is modest as compared to that of a hotel.
2. The accommodation is sold at a very low price.
3. They have an informal atmosphere and freedom regarding dress code.
4. There is more emphasis on recreation, entertainment and sports.

Supplementary accommodation plays a very important role in the total available tourist accommodation in the country. It caters to both international & domestic tourist traffic.

Types of supplementary accommodation :

- Sarais / Dharamshalas (inns)
- Youth hostels e.g. YMCA

- Camping sites.
- Circuit houses / Dak bunglows — Govt. accommodation.
- Tourist bungalows — M.T.D.C. holiday camps.
- Traveler's lodges or Forest lodges.
- Dormitories.
- Paying guest accommodation.
- Rotels (hotels on wheels e.g. Palace on wheels)
- Floatels (Hotels on Water e.g. House boats)

TYPES OF ROOMS

1. **SINGLE ROOM :** Room having a single bed. Room meant for one person. Abbreviation - or s.
2. **DOUBLE ROOM :** Room having a double bed (one large bed). It is meant for two persons. Abbreviation + or D.
3. **TWIN ROOM :** Room having two single beds, separated from each other. The room is meant for two persons. Abbreviation = or T.
4. **TWIN DOUBLE ROOM :** Room with two double beds, separated from each other and meant for four persons. It is also called as double double room.
5. **HOLLYWOOD TWIN ROOM :** Room with two single beds having common head board. It is meant for two persons.
6. **PARLOR :** Sitting or living room not used as a bed room.
7. **STUDIO ROOM :** Parlor set-up with one or two studio beds or sofa-cum-beds.
8. **SUITE :** Parlor connected with one or more bedrooms. Expensive, being larger with more rooms for privacy. Has more facilities like TV, fridge, mini bar, extra complementary, etc.
9. **LANAI :** Hawaiian term for a room with a balcony that overlooks a garden or swimming pool.
10. **JUNIOR SUITE :** One large room partitioned into a parlor and a bed room.
11. **EFFICIENCY ROOM :** Room with a kitchenette attached. Mainly found in motels and residential hotels.
12. **DUPLEX :** Set of rooms which are not at the same level but are situated on two different floors. The parlor and the bed room are connected with a staircase. One of the most expensive suites.
13. **PENTHOUSE SUITE :** Suite located to on the topmost floor of the hotel. A part of the room can be open to the sky or with a glass roof. Very expensive and exclusive suite.
14. **CABANA :** Located close to the swimming pool or beach. Has shower and changing facilities. May have been furnished in bamboo for attractive appearance.
15. **INTERCONNECTING ROOMS :** Two adjacent rooms allowing entry from one to the other through a connecting door. The connecting door is kept locked if the rooms have to be sold to two different guests separately.
16. **HOSPITALITY ROOM :** A room hired by a guest on hourly basis to entertain his guest. It is generally a banquet room.

17. **ADJOINING ROOMS :** Rooms with a common wall but no connecting door.
18. **ADJACENT ROOMS :** Rooms close to each other, perhaps across the hall or the corridor.

DEPARTMENTAL ORGANISATION OF A HOTEL

A hotel is an organisation made up of different departments all of which have to work in close co-ordination for the efficient working of the organisation.

Some departments are more important as far as revenue is concerned, some do not produce revenue but are very important from the operational point of view. Thus the departments of the hotels can be classified under three main headings. They are

1. Operating and Revenue producing.
2. Operating and Non revenue producing.
3. Non operating and Revenue producing.

Operating and Revenue producing departments (O.R.P.)

Minor revenue producing departments

a) Laundry : The hotel may have it's own laundry or may have a contract with an outside laundry. In any case laundry of guest clothing is a facility provided by the hotel & is charged for.
b) Telephone department : Guests are charged for the local and trunk or STD calls. Charging can be done either by the telephone operator or in case of direct billing by telephone meters. In a small hotel, there would be just a small switch board, probably operated by the receptionist. In large hotels, there exists a separate telephone department, where the board is manned by operators working in shifts.
c) Swimming pool : Though hotel guests are not charged for using the pool, their guests can be charged for this facility. Many hotels offer a free swim alongwith a buffet lunch (charged per head) setup near pool side.

Major revenue producing departments

1. Rooms departments : These are the departments concerned with the actual sale of rooms. This revenue producing section earns around 60% of the total hotel revenue. The departments under this section are Housekeeping and Front office.
2. Front office is concerned with actual sale of rooms and hence comes in direct contact with the guest. Housekeeping is concerned with keeping the guest rooms clean and in a position to be sold. Hence though Housekeeping is a behind the scene activity it is extremely important.
3. F & B Department : These are the departments concerned with the production of food & beverage items and their sale.
4. F & B Production includes all kitchens, bakery, confectionery, stores and pantry. All these are behind the scene and responsible to the total preparation of the food items right from the storage of raw material to the presentation of the final dish.
5. F & B Service includes all the service outlets where the food prepared by the production areas is sold to the guests. Theses areas can be listed as

- Restaurants - General as well as specialty restaurants. These restaurants have fixed hours of service.
- Coffee Shop - A coffee shop is open 24 hours of the day & serves mainly snacks & beverages. Heavy meals are generally served only during lunch and dinner time. A coffee shop generally has an informal atmosphere and plated service.
- Bar : Serves alcoholic and non alcoholic beverages along with snacks. A permit is required to operate it and there are fixed hours of operation.
- Room Service : 24 hours service in most large hotels.
- Banquets : It is the major revenue producing department, among the F&B service departments. Some of the banquet functions are Dinners, Lunches, Wedding receptions, Cocktail parties, Conferences, Club meetings, out door catering, etc.

Operating and Non revenue producing departments (O.N.R.P.)

1. Personnel : Deals with recruitment and training of staff, staff induction, promotions, welfare, etc.
2. Security : Deals with all unusual events in the hotel.
3. Maintenance : They are responsible for total maintenance and upkeep of rooms and public areas, i.e. Air-conditioning, Lifts, Plumbing, Electricity, Lighting, carpentry, etc.
4. Accounts : Receives a copy of all departmental vouchers & the guest bills. Maintains cash register, city ledger, etc. Prepares sales summary sheets for each day's sales.
5. Sales and Marketing : Sales is concerned with getting and maintaining clientele for both rooms and food & beverage.

Non operating and Revenue producing departments (N.O.R.P.)

They include travel agencies and airline offices, book shops, chemists, florists, bank, beauty parlor, etc. They either be let out on commission bases or on rental bases. These '**concessionaires**' should be reputable as for the guests they are a part of the hotel services.

FUNCTIONAL ORGANISATION OF FRONT OFFICE

The Front Office department can be divided into different sections according to the nature of their functions. They are :-

1. Reservations.
2. Reception.
3. Information.
4. Cashiers.
5. Bell desk.
6. Telephones.

1. Reservations

It is often referred to as the nerve center of the department. All booking requests are received and processed here. Prior arrangement for guest arrival can be made from the information processed at reservations which facilitates efficient and satisfactory service to the guests.

2. Reception

It is responsible for receiving the guests with warmth and a genuine smile. Registration of guests during check in, sensible and efficient dealing with situations which may arise at the counter are important tasks for the reception staff.

3. Information : The main functions of this section are :

a. To maintain an alphabetical guest index.
b. To receive messages for resident guests.
c. Handling guests room keys.
d. Handling guest mail, packages etc.
e. Paging for guests.
f. Providing relevant and accurate information to the guests and answering queries.

4. Cashier

Responsible for handling guest bills, where guests settle final bills either by cash, credit card or as charge settlement for their entire stay in the hotel. Expenses would include room, F & B service and charges for any other services or facilities used. These charges are recorded centrally upto the minute at the cashier's cabin. The cashier's role therefore is to post all guest charges and credits on the master bill so as to present the same duly totaled for payment at the time of guest departure. This section is also responsible for exchanging foreign currency and for safe deposit lockers provided for guest valuables.

5. Bell desk

Responsible for baggage handling at guest arrival or departure time and running errands during the guest's staying in the hotel.

6. Telephones

Handles all incoming and outgoing local calls and trunk and international calls for both guests and the hotel management.

DUTIES AND RESPONSIBILITIES OF THE FRONT OFFICE STAFF

A. Front Office Manager

- He is the head of the department.
- He ensures the smooth running of the department
- He sees to it that his staff reports to duty in time and in proper uniform.
- He ensures that courteous and personalized service is given to the guests by his staff.
- He deals with front office correspondence on reservations, enquiries, room booking etc.
- He is responsible for the up keep of the front desk, lobby manager's desk and their equipment.
- He deals with the complaints against his staff and other complaints of the guests.
- Participants in the selection of F O Personnel
- Conducts regularly scheduled meeting of F O Personnel.

B. Lobby Manager

- He ensures that all rooms are blocked as per reservation requests
- He keeps a check on room position
- He instructs the airport representatives regarding the list of arrivals to be met.
- He checks pre-registration cards
- He also checks house keeping discrepancy report
- He ensures that guest requests and complaints are followed up
- He follows up on group and crew movement
- He takes actions for all unusual events in the lobby like fire, accidents, etc.,
- He ensures the smooth running of the lobby.
- He sends "C" Forms to the FRRO.

C. Reception Supervisor

- To train all front office assistants on the job
- To make the duty roster for the staff
- To check the shift in-charge's list on a daily basis
- To check the next day's arrival list and to brief the staff accordingly
- He makes the requisition for the stationery required for the Front Office
- Ensures the smooth running of the reception
- Welcomes VIP guests
- Attends to guest complaints
- Assists the reception staff
- Maintains records of the reception

D. Reception Assistant

- To answer the queries of the guest to their satisfaction and to provide information
- To promptly register guests and to assign rooms to them
- To update the room rack regularly
- To complete pre-registration formalities for VIPs
- To execute government formalities regarding foreigners
- To prepare room reports and occupancy statistics
- Send messages to the guests
- To print the arrival list for the next day.

E. Reception Shift in-charge

- Performs the tasks of reception assistant
- Supervises and checks the entire Shift Operation
- Handles guest complaints
- Checks all the reports before the end of the shift
- Airline crew blocking and group blocking

F. Reservation Supervisor

- To help out Reservation Assistant in calls, courses and feeding reservation information.
- To supervise the staff under her and impart training
- To monitor all new movements
- To follow up on billing instructions and other special requests
- To check on credit facilities to Companies, discount policies and discounts offered to various companies.

- Co-ordination with Reception, Information, Sales and Marketing Departments and Tour Operator.
- Up-to-date information of the position of the house for the day and the next three days.
- She draws up a weekly, monthly and quarterly forecast
- Monitors VIP movements and informs all concerned
- Monitors house status and keep Front Office Manager informed of sold out dates.
- Deals with correspondence, vouchers, exchange orders, deposits, refund of deposits and actions thereon.
- She handles the group and conference booking.

G. Reservation Assistant

- To update regularly the reservation chart and computer
- To properly and courteously handle all reservation requests
- To keep all reservations correspondence up to date
- To handle amendments and cancellation of reservation.

H. Senior Bell Captain

- He controls the movements of Bell Captains and Bell Boys
- He briefs the Bell Boy and ensures that they are always well groomed
- Takes stock of the luggage, parcels and any other material
- Has thorough knowledge of the hotel, shops, airline offices, executive offices etc.
- Thorough procedure on arrival and departure
- To carry out different errands for the guests
- Responsible for the proper distribution of newspapers
- Keeping stock of the equipments, trolleys and ensuring that they are in good working order
- Vigilant and alert on duty
- To initiate action against guests having scanty baggage
- To assist in crew and group wake up call procedures

I. Bell Boy

- Take the baggage front the porch to the room
- Escort the guest to the rooms on arrival
- Place the baggage in the room
- Explain the operation of light switches, air conditioning control to the guests.
- Brings the baggage down in case of departures
- Checks the room to ensure that the guest has not left any articles in the room
- Obtain clearance from Front Office cashier on the errand card regarding the bill.
- Check that main and messages are distributed to the guests.

J. Front Office Cashier

- Operates front office posting equipment
- Completes cashier pre-shift supply checklist
- Completes guest check in procedures
- Post charges to guest account

- Handle paid-outs
- Completes guest check-out procedures
- Settles guest account
- Makes account adjustments

K. Night Auditor

- Posts room charges and taxes to guest accounts
- Processes guest charge vouchers and credit card vouchers
- Transfers charges and deposits to master accounts
- Verifies all account postings and balances
- Prepares a summary of cash, check and credit card activities
- Summarizes results of operations for management
- Knows how to operate position machines, typewriters and F O equipment
- Understands and knows how to perform check-in and check-out procedures
- Handle errands requested by guests and Front Office staff
- handle baggage of guests when they are shifting to another room
- Distribute news papers
- To page guests in the lobby
- To report guests with scantly baggage the bell captain
- To issue postage stamps against cash.

BASIS OF CHARGING

CHECK-IN/CHECK-OUT BASIS

As per this system, a particular time of the day is fixed as the check-out time. The most common is a 12 noon check-in / check-out system. According to this, the day starts at 12 noon daily and ends at 12 noon the next day, immaterial of the time at which the guest checks-in. If the guest has checked-in in the morning before 12 noon and intends to stay overnight, then from the point of his check-in, till 1200 hrs that day makes one day and from 1200 hrs till the next day, becomes another day. As a result, when the guest stays sometimes for 24 hours or lesser, he could be charged for more than a day. In other words, the same room may be sold twice in the same day.

Since it is not practical for any guest to check in at exactly 1200 hrs, most hotels permit a grace period (of about 2 hours), before and after checkout time. Though the system is good for the hotelier, many guests may think of this system as unreasonable. To ensure renewed patronage by the guests, many hotels today tell a guest that there exists a two hour grace period for check-in or check-out, but actually give a leeway of three hours to avoid disputes. Also, for an early morning check-in after 0600 hrs, instead of a full day extra to be charged, most hotels charge only a half day's charges. Following the same systems, when a guest checks-out as late as 1800 hrs, a half day tariff is again charged instead of a full day's charge. The logic that is explained in this system, is that the room cannot be sold after that point of the day. For an early morning check-in, the guest could be told that the room could not have been sold the previous night. However, the least amount charged is a minimum of one day's charge.

e.g., (1) Mr. A. checks-in on Sunday at 1200 hrs to room # 101.

Mr. A checks-out on Monday at 0030 hrs from room # 101.

Mr. B. checks-in on Monday at 0200 hrs to room # 101 and checks-out at 1200 hrs on Monday.

Mr. A. And Mr. B will both he charged for one day each.
e.g., (2) Mr. X checks - in at 0500 hrs on Monday.
Mr. X checks-out at 0600 hrs on Tuesday.
Mr. X will be charged for two days as per this system.

24 HOURS BASIS

As per this system, the guest is entitled to keep his room for a period of 24 hours from the point of the guest's check-in, for a day's charge. There is no fixed time of arrival for the guest. This system of charging is generally practised at resort hotels.

e.g. Mr. X checks-in at 1300 hrs on Tuesday. He will be charged for one day till 1300 hrs on Wednesday.

PER NIGHT BASIS

According to this system, the guest is charged on the basis of the number of nights he stays. This system has evolved from the 24 hours system of charging, and is not very much in use in the modern day hotels.

Very much connected to this system of charging is the concept of Day Rate or 'Day Use Rate'. This is a concessional rate given to guests who do not stay over-night in the hotel. Usually this is targeted at business clientele who use the room from 0900 hrs to 1800 hrs. The guest may check-in to the hotel for a wash and change in the morning, leave his baggage in the room and carry on for his business. He may return in the evening, have a wash and change, check-out and take the evening flight out.

FOOD PLANS

1. **European Plan (EP) :** This plan includes only the room charges and morning tea in some cases. All other charges are charged extra. Most commercial hotels run on this plan.
2. **Continental Plan (CP.) :** This plan includes room charges and a continental breakfast. All additional charges are considered extra. [A continental b/f consists of juices, toast or rolls, butter, cheese, jam, tea or coffee but no eggs.]
3. **Bermuda Plan (BP) :** This plan includes room charges optional early morning tea and an American breakfast. [American b/f is a buffet breakfast not served in the room]
4. **American Plan (AP) :** This plan includes all principal meals. It includes room charges with optional morning tea, English B/F, lunch, afternoon tea and dinner. It is mostly found in resort hotels and in commercial hotels catering to groups sent by airlines and companies or travel agents. This plan is also known as 'all inclusive plan' or 'full board' or 'en pension' [English breakfast has all courses like American B/F and ham, beacon, meat is also included].
5. **Modified American Plan (MAP) :** This plan has evolved out of the American plan. It includes room charges with optional morning tea, English B/F and an option of lunch or dinner. It is also called as 'demi pension' or 'half board'. This facilitates the guests to eat out for one meal. It is usually used for groups where meal coupons are provided to the guests (coupon is valid only for a day) and the coupon cost is included in the room rent.

The use of these plans:

· Commercial hotels prefer EP because:

1. Commercial hotels are situated in the urban areas, there are bound to be numerous restaurants in the vicinity. Hence the guest will prefer to keep his option open as far as meals are concerned. Moreover the hotel may not have a particular cuisine which the guest likes.
2. On the other hand hotel being situated in an urban area would get plenty of chance guests in their restaurants. Thus their F&B income is not restricted to only hotel residents. They do offer meal inclusive plans but only to groups sent by travel agents and company bookings for conventions, seminars, etc.

· Resort hotels prefer AP/ MAP because

1. They may be situated in an isolated area with hardly any restaurant in the vicinity. Guests therefore prefer to have meals in the hotel. For the tourists wishing to go sight seeing during the day, an MAP will be more appropriate.
2. The hotel itself benefits from this plan since the hotel relies only on the resident guests for their food and beverage income.

The CP. & BP lie between EP & AP So they can be offered by any hotel.

Above five are food plans.

There is another plan called 'GO PLAN'

It is not a food plan. It is an adjustment made in the settlement of accounts.

If a guest stays in different hotels of the same chain in the course of his tour, his bills will be forwarded to his next destination every time he changes the place of stay. The guest can make the payment at the last hotel he visits belonging to the same chain.

SPECIAL RATES

Very often a room may not be sold at the tariff quoted on the tariff sheet. The rooms may be discounted or special rates may be applied under certain conditions, or as a special case.

COMPANY VOLUME GUARANTEED RATE (CVGR)

Based on the room night potential of different companies, certain hotels give a special rate to those companies which contribute a large volume of room nights. This special rate offered came to be called as the 'Company Volume Guaranteed Rate' (C.V.G.R) or 'Company Guaranteed Rate' (C.G.R.). The higher the volume of business, the higher was the percentage of discount given. For this purpose, all those companies which offer a large quantum of business could be 'A' rated. As the contribution figure dipped, the company rating would also drop to 'B' or even 'C' for those with a relatively poor volume of business.

Many hotels today, in order to accommodate all category of employees from one particular organisation, have gone ahead and offered very low rates to the lower down officers, and higher rates to the top brass of the company, based on their entitlements and expenditure capabilities. A record of the room night contribution (R.N.C.) of individual companies are maintained either on a computerized system or manually by an alphabetically indented register. Periodically, the companies are informed of their volume contribution. If the expected room night contribution was not maintained by any one company, they would fall to a lower rating or even be left out of the C.G.R. list after the total period of assessment.

PACKAGE RATES

Many resort hotels (especially during lean/Off season periods) and some commercial hotels from time to time coin seasonal packages for different durations (e.g: two nights three days/three nights four days), which may include besides the room and meal, a complimentary airport transfer, sightseeing, entertainment etc.

OFF-SEASON RATES

Most resorts and other seasonal hotels have separate tariffs for peak and off-seasons. The off-season rates are much lower than regular or peak-season rates.

EMPLOYEE RATE

Employees of major hotel chains have a special employee rate for all employees at their member hotels within the chain. This is however based on the availability of space and policy of the individual hotel.

F.H.R.A.I DISCOUNT

The Federation of Hotel and Restaurants Association of India (F.H.R.A.I) is a major association ofhotels and restaurants in India. As a gesture of goodwill for members of the same fraternity, the association issues membership cards to the Proprietor / Partners / Chairman / M.Ds of these establishments, which entitles them to a special discount(presently 30% on room rent, food and beverage (excluding liquor), if paid by cash and 25% if settled through a credit card. The percentage of discount and other conditions are subject to change).

AIRLINE CREW

Most airlines enter into a contract with hotels in different cities where its flights commute, wherein staff of the airline (crew) are given a very special rate for a fixed period. Their duration of stay may be a few hours upto a maximum of 24 hours. There is also another special rate negotiated for the lay-over passengers. The food-plan applied would be based on the requirement, but the food element computed is also on a discounted basis.

GROUPS

Groups (G.I.T - Guest in Transit) are given special rates due to the number of rooms taken by them at a time. A group under standard stipulation, comprises of 15 guests or more. Based on the discretion of the Management, the group leader may be given a complimentary room for a minimum of 15 paying customers.

Guests who do not come into any of the above groups are called as 'F.I.Ts' or Free Individual Travellers. i.e., they are not part of any group or company enjoying special rates. When these are Indians or Domestic clientele, they are referred to as 'D.F.I.T'. or 'Domestic Free Individual Traveller'. Similarly, if the guest is not a domestic traveler i.e., if he is a foreigner, then he is called as 'F.F.I.T'. or 'Foreign Free Individual Traveller'.

CRIB RATE

This is a special rate applicable in some hotels to children. Most Indian hotels prefer to compliment upto a maximum of two children below the age of twelve.

EXTRA BED / EXTRA PERSON CHARGES

As most five star hotels today do not have single rooms, but have only double rooms which could accommodate a minimum of two guests, a third person if present, is given an extra bed and charged. This charge is in most hotels levied even if an extra bed is not given. The rate charged could be approximately 20 to 25% of the room rate.

Besides the above, special rates may also be given to a hoard of other category of people based on the discounting policies of the management. Some of these might be commercially important persons (C.I.Ps) for publicity and promotion purposes, influential persons like company directors, decision makers, top executives, travel writers, etc. Such discounts have to be authorised by a senior member of the Management.

CHAPTER 2

An Introduction to Hospitality

The hospitality industry is a part of a larger enterprise known as travel and tourism industry. The travel and tourism industry is a vast group of business with one goal in common : providing necessary or desired services to travelers. Advances in transportation enabled more people to travel greater distances at less cost spreading tourism across the globe. From modest origins, hospitality and tourism rose to become two of the largest world wide industries.

Warriors or traders were the early travelers but they did not have hotels to accommodate them. The warriors used tents but the merchants seeking to trade tools, clothing and livestock, traded merchandise for lodging. The inns offered little more than a cot or a bench in the corner of a room or a stable. Most of them were private residences that offered temporary residence or lodging to strangers. Guests stayed in large communal rooms where sanitation and privacy were non-existent. After the establishment of money in 6th century BC, innkeeping was one of the first commercial enterprises and hospitality was one of the first services for which money was exchanged.

In the third century AD, Roman Empire developed an extensive system of brick paved roads throughout Europe and Asia minor. Small road side lodges were constructed due to increase in the road transport. During the Industrial Revolution in 1700s, the Europeans began to combine food and beverage service with lodging. No attention was given to sanitation and beds as well as rooms had to be shared with other travelers. These early European inns were unsuitable for aristocrats. To accommodate wealthy travelers, luxurious structures were erected. These offered private rooms, individual sanitation and all comforts of a European castle. These elegant new establishments adopted the French name for mansion, 'hotel'. The rates they charged were very high and well beyond the means of common citizens.

In colonial America, inns were modeled after European inns. Beds and rooms had to be shared with strangers. Throughout 1800s, American innkeepers improved their services and continued to build larger properties.

Most of these were located in seaport town since sea transport was very widely used mode or travel and transport then. The first American hotel the 'City Hotel', opened in 1794 in the New York city. It was one of the largest building in the city and was built exclusively for hotel purpose. It had 73 guest rooms. 'Adelphi Hotel' in New York was the first high-rise structure in the city.

In 1829, a large new hotel was constructed in Boston. 'Tremont House' was the earliest first class hotel in America and brought revolution in the hospitality industry. This hotel was the first to offer private rooms with locking doors. Each guest room had a wash basin and a water pitcher and a bar of soap. Other innovations included a full time service staff, a French restaurant which was located in the lobby, etc. These American hotels became important social centers and unlike their European counterparts, welcomed anyone who could afford the reasonable rates. Meanwhile in Europe, sanitary lodging continued to be regarded as a privilege to be enjoyed only by the aristocracy. But in democratic America clean and comfortable accommodation was available to any middle class worker or family.

In early 1900s, a new type of traveler entered the picture, the traveling businessman. For him the world class hotels were too expensive and the old style inns too unsanitary. A new type of lodging establishment was opened for these type of guests - 'the commercial hotels'. It was opened by Mr. E. M. Statler, at Buffalo, New York, in Jan. 1908. It was the beginning of the chain hotel concept. This hotel provided private sanitary rooms with private bathroom. The guest received a pitcher of ice water and morning newspaper everyday. "A room and a bath for a dollar and a half " was well known among American travelers.

The great Depression nearly wiped out the hotel industry. But one hotel operator, Conrad Hilton, managed to stay afloat as a result of his oil and gas investments. Around 1940 - 1950, the Hilton Hotel corporation built or bought numerous luxury hotels around the world and competed with the largest hotel chains of the time Sheraton and Statler.

With the end of world war II, the hotel industry unexpectedly entered a new era of prosperity, Americans began traveling as never before. With an automobile in every garage, Americans began touring the country with their families. For this new type of traveler - the vacationing family unit - the formality of a traditional hotel was inappropriate. Families traveling in their cars needed casual lodging that was accessible from major highways and had ample facilities for parking. The early these properties were small and had fewer than 50 rooms. Most of them were owned and operated by a couple and were called Mom and Pop properties. By 1960, the motor hotel or the motel, had become an permanent and influential part of the hospitality industry. By this time the motels had over 100 rooms with a separate parking space for each unit.

In 1960s, a new type of lodging outlet - the economy, or budget hotel entered the picture. These lodging establishments sold only room space without F & B service. To save on construction cost, the economy hotels were built on inexpensive land and had small lobbies. They also hired minimum staff. By minimizing costs the budget hotels were able to give much lower room rates than their competitors. The first successful economy hotel, 'Travelodge', opened in Tacoma, Washington, in 1956 but the chain expanded nationwide by 1966. By early 1970s the idea of low rate motel/s hotels had captured the imagination of investors mini bars are the standard amenities of most budget hotels. These hotels / motels are also called as no-frills hotels.

By 1973, the no. of travelers staying in motels surpassed the no. of people staying in full-service hotels. To compete with these low end properties, mid-market hotel chains introduced their own limited service hotels. Theses hotels combined some of the features of the full service hotels with the cost saving of the budget hotels / motels. eg. Holiday created the limited service Hampton Inn chain and Marriott created Courtyard hotels. In these hotels all the rooms have separate living and sleeping areas. The lodging trend of the 1990s is towards epanded services made possible through consolidation of responsibilities. Guest services departments are found in hotels of all classes. These departments combine services that traditionally were performed by bell or door attendent, a concierge and an in house travel agent. Two new concepts in the hotel industry are 'The All Suite Hotels' and 'The Residential Hotels'.

THE HOTEL & CATERING INDUSTRY

Introduction to the Hotel Industry

The hotel industry is one of the oldest enterprises in the world that are closely associated to tour and travel. The primitive lodging houses or inns originated to cater the needs of the travellers and were managed by local people in their private homes. The history of hotel industry can tracked back to 3000 BC. Some of these inns were used to provide food stuffs as a regular need and wine as thirst quenchers. Sometimes, entertainment and recreation was provided by performing folk songs and dances.

- In 5th century BC, the invention of currency changed inn-keeping into a commercial activity.
- In 3rd century AD, mushrooming of lodging houses was on the boom throughout Asia and Europe and these lodging houses were known as *mansions.*
- In the middle ages, monasteries and abbeys were the first establishments to offer the lodging facilities to travellers on a regular basis.

Till the industrial revolution broke out in England in the 18th century the condition was similar. The development of travelling through railways and steamships during this time, made travelling more convenient and people started travelling for business rather than jus for social, educational and religious purposes.

The real growth of the hotel industry took place with the opening of ***City Hotel*** in New York, USA, in 1794. This was the first building especially built as a hotel with 73 rooms. The inauguration of this hotel marked the beginning of the present-day hotel industry.

The opening of ***Tremont House*** in Boston is another landmark in the evolution of the hotel industry. It offered en-suite bathrooms, locks on the doors and an a la carte menu.

In 1908, ***Statler hotel*** in Buffalo, New York with 450 rooms on multi-storeyed building was the pioneer in the hotel industry, as it was equipped with most of the modern facilities like en suite bathroom with running hot and cold water, electric lamp on the desk and radio.

Numerous hotels were established in the decades of 1920's not only in cities, but also in the mountains in the form of hill resorts. But suddenly in 1930's it was a disaster effect on the hotel industry due to world war- II and many hotels became bankrupt.

In 1950's the development of aircrafts and commercial passenger flight in the western world stimulated travel and hence the hotel industry got a positive responses.

In the modern world, lodging facilities got a diversification with the market segmentation and many classifications of hotel came in the existence.

Growth of the hotel Industry in India

The hotel industry in India traces its roots to ***dharamshalas*** and ***serais***, which used to provide food, accommodation to travellers, and stabling facilities for their horses or bollocks free of cost. India has come a long way since those times and taken considerable strides in the development of the hospitality sector.

In ancient India, since dates back from the 6th century BC trade and commerce in western and North-western region were well connected by road and sea routes and merchants used to stay in*serais* or rest houses located though the trade routes. The growth and development of catering and mass feeding for religious purposes aided its contribution in progress of hotel industry. India, being a known destination of educational hub during AD 320- 540, many of the popular universities like Nalanda, Taxila, Ujjain, and Ajanta the scholars used to travel across the country for research and advanced studies. Again these phenomenon developed impetus of community feeding and various types of cuisines to suit the diverse food habits and customers of the people.

During Medial India, invaders brought the dramatic change in food habits. Muslims conveyed the variety of meats and cereals in the staple diet, followed by many exotic cuisines from Persia and Iran, which with the blend of taste of India given a birth of Mughlai cuisine. Alcoholic drinks became a part of prestigious feast. In the emperor of ***SherShah Suri***, it was a lots of effort taken for development of *Serais* along with Grand Trunk road facilitated with trees asides and *dhabas*

In modern India Europeans brought French and English cuisines in high grade restaurants and wine making skills. During 19th century ***Pallonjee Pestonjee*** (1840) built the first Westren style hotel in Bombay, which was known for its excellent continental cuisine and fine wines. Calcutta had its famous ***Great Eastern Hotel***, earlier known as the *Auckland Hotel*. The ***Madras Connemara Hotel*** was a popular stay for British officers.

Jamshedji Ratanji Tata, formed the ***Indian Hotel Company*** in 1897 and built the exquisitely beautiful **Taj Mahal** Hotel in Bombay and opened in 1903. Later on many renowned international and national hotel chains such as Oberoi, Welcomegroup, Intercontinental, Sheraton, Hilton, Marriott, Imperial opened their units in India. KFC, Dominos , subways and MsDonald's started their operations in food joints.

Role of Catering establishment in the travel/tourism industry

The fast paced growth of the Indian tourism industry has immensely benefited the hospitality industry. The hospitality sector is an essential and dynamic component of the tourism industry. The hotel industry covers a wide range of accommodation services from full service luxury hotels to bed and breakfasts facilities. There are many types of catering operations ranging from wayside kiosks to exclusive fine dinning restaurants in a 5-star hotel and from meals for industrial workers to food and beverage services to airline passengers. These are also known as food service or catering sector scattered through various establishments, which is a major segment in Tourism industry, because of the dependability of meal for every body.

Sectors of the Food service Industry

The Catering establishment is any place that provides food and beverages to the public either on a commercial or non commercial basis. Establishments which are concerned with the provision of food and beverages as their prime aspect such as hotels and restaurants are termed as primary catering establishments. And establishments such as school and industrial canteens fall under the category of secondary catering establishment.

The food service industry can also be classified into the following sectors:

1. Commercial catering
2. Welfare catering
3. Transport catering

- **Commercial Catering:** These establishments are business oriented and run on the basis of profits. They may be residential or non residential. Hotels, Restaurants, Pubs, Takeaways, Drive-ins, Function catering, Clubs and Fast food operations fall in this category.
- **Welfare Catering:** These are non commercial catering establishments focused on nutrition and non-economic factors. Schools, hospitals, industries, defence service catering, prison catering, youth hostels are example of welfare catering. These are also known as secondary catering establishment as food is second concern here.
- **Transport catering:** The service of food and beverages to passengers before, during and after a journey on any mode of travel is termed as transport catering. It usually involves the feeding of a large number of customers arriving together at a catering facility and who need to be catered for a specific time period. These as Railway catering, Airline catering, marine catering and motorway .

EVOLUTION AND GROWTH OF HOTELS IN INDIA

- In 1964 Government of India set up three corporations
  - India Tourism and Hotel Corporation
  - India Tourism Corporation Ltd.
  - India Tourism and Transport corporation
- In 1966 Government of India merged these corporations and formed a new corporation INDIA TOURISM DEVELOPMENT CORPORATION (ITDC)
- Many hotels opened in India like Oberoi (1934), Welcome group (1975), Taj(1903), Sinclairs, Leela, Park Hotel, J.P. Hotels, and many more.

HOSPITALITY

The generous and cordial provision of service to a guest is known as hospitality. Dictionary defines hospitality as reception and entertainment of guest with liberality and goodwill. Hospitality organization provides accommodation, food and beverage, transportation, entertainment and health care. Hospitality industry mainly consist of all those businesses and institutions that provide food and lodging – such as hotels, motels, lodges, inns, cruise ships, restaurants, and the institutions of public services. In a broad sense, any group engaged in tourism, entertainment, transportation and lodging are covered under hospitality. Hospitality industry is part of travel and tourism industry. Hospitality industry is now both profit-making as well as non-profit making. For example, commercial hotels are profit making while canteens, cafeterias and religious catering outlets are non-profit making. Hospitality industry provides services which are need oriented and the services vary with the needs. For example, the need of a business executive shall be a business hotel while the needs of a student are generally a youth hostel.

ORIGIN- Early travellers were either warriors or traders or people in search of knowledge and there were no hotels for them to stay when they were away from their homes. They had to pitch tents for their accommodation and carry their food for entire duration of their journey. It was not always possible for everyone and so traders and people in search of knowledge had to place a high value on hospitality and sometimes traded their merchandise for lodging. Inn keeping can be said to be the first commercial enterprise and hospitality one of the first service for which money was exchanged. Inns of the Biblical times offered only a cot or a bench in the corner. Guests stayed in large communal rooms with no sanitation and privacy. The rates were, of course, reasonable. The company was rough. Travellers shared the same quarters with their horses and animals. These accommodations slowly and gradually improved.

HOTEL

A hotel is a public place that provides boarding and lodging to customer on payment. Common law states that "A hotel is a place where all who conduct themselves properly, and who being able to pay for their entertainment, are received, if there be accommodation for them," and who without any stipulated engagement as to the duration of their stay or as to the rate of compensation, are while there, supplied at a reasonable cost with their meals, lodging and other services and attention as are necessarily incident to the use as a temporary home.

A hotel may be called as an establishment where primary business is to provide to the general public lodging facilities and which may also furnish one or more of the various services such as food, beverage, laundry, uniformed services etc. As per dictionary, the term 'Hotel' refers to 'a house of entertainment of travellers'

Inn: Public houses in early times in England were called inns. Normally the term inn was meant for the finer establishments catering to the nobilities and clergy. In France these were called Hotelleries.

Tavern: The house frequented by common man was known as taverns. The important establishments in France were called Cabarets.

Hostel: Derived from the word host and was used very late. The head of the hostel was called Hostler in French, while in England he was called Inn-keeper.

HOTEL SERVICES

The present day modern concept of the hotel is not just a place to provide accommodation, food and beverage, but is like a city within a city and offering to its guests every possible facility, accommodation, service and convenience., such as rooms, restaurants, bars, cocktail lounges, banqueting facilities, convention and conference facilities, telephone, radio and television, laundry, valets, cigars and cigarettes, book shops, banking, parking, florists, chemist, gymnasium, beauty parlour, travel agents business centre, etc. Apart from these a vast shopping arcade providing various items like jewellery, men's wear, ladies' wear, toys, books news stand and magazine, etc. are also provided. In addition to these, personal services like babysitting, private detectives, planning of tour itineraries, railway / air booking and accommodation, booking in other hotels may also be provided along with Clubs and night club, health club, foreign exchange, swimming pool, library, car rental and chauffeurs, cinema and theatre ticketing, etc. All these facilities may occasionally be without additional charges to the guest but generally specifically charged.

GUEST

A person who purchases the services of the hotel and pays for them. Hotel guest may be defined as "people who have, who are, or who will be availing the services of hotel, for a particular period in order to satisfy their demand for accommodation, food and beverage or entertainment, for which they are willing to pay".

Initially a guest comes to a hotel for its good name and reputation about service and food, second time he comes to confirm his experiences and further keeps on coming for its comfortable and emphatic atmosphere and becomes a regular customer, because by now he is pretty confident about the hotel.

ANCILLARY DEPARTMENT

In any establishment a guest's first impression on entering the service area is of great importance. A guest can be won or lost on these impressions alone. There are many service areas behind the scene or what may be termed as back of the house which is required to be efficiently run, well organized, supervised and well stocked with appropriate equipments depending on the style of operation.

These service areas are usually between kitchen and the food service area. They are important areas in the make-up of the catering establishments acting as a link between kitchen and restaurants. These are also the meeting point for staffs of various sections as they carry out their duties and therefore there must be close liaison between the various members of staff and their respective departments.

In general, especially in large operations, five main back-of-the-house service areas can be identified:

1. Still room
2. Kitchen stewarding
3. Hot plate/ food pick up area
4. Linen room
5. Store

STILL ROOM/ PANTRY

The main function of the still room is to provide items of F&B required for the service of a meal and not created by any other major department like kitchen, patisserie, larder etc. Depending on the policy of the management and the volume of business at times it is supervised by a supervisor who may be a senior member of the f&b brigade.

When ordering goods from the main dry store, all requirements should be written on a requisition sheet in duplicate. The top copy goes to the store to be retained by the store-keeper after issuing the goods and the duplicate remains in the requisition book as a mean of checking the receipt of goods from the store by a member of the still room. The store keeper should not issue goods unless the still room supervisor or another person in authority has signed the requisition.

Equipments

Following are the equipments required for proper storage, preparation and presentation of the food by the still room-

a. Refrigerator- storing butter, milk, fruit juice, cream and so on
b. Beverage vending machine- soft drink, tea, coffee etc.
c. Large double sink
d. Salamander or toaster
e. Bread slicing machine
f. Working table and cutting board
g. Ice maker
h. Storage cupboard for all dry goods held in stock and for such miscellaneous items as doilies, paper napkin, straw etc.
i. Gas range or induction plate

As a basic guide the following food items would normally be dispensed from the still room-

1. All non-alcoholic beverages including tea, coffee, soft drinks, chocolate drinks etc.
2. Preserves like jam, jelly, marmalade, honey, butter etc.
3. Various bread rolls like brioche, croissants
4. Various breakfast cereals like cornflakes, wheat flakes etc.
5. Pastries, gateaux, sandwich, boiled eggs are also dispensed

A proper control is very important for the items which are dispensed from the still room. Therefore all items should be issued either against a requisition from the service area or against a waiter's check.

KITCHEN STEWARDING

The kitchen stewarding is basically divided into two areas:

a) Wash up area-

It is an important service area and should be ideally situated so that the brigade can work speedily and efficiently while passing from the food service area to the kitchen. The waiter should stack the trays of dirties correctly at the side board with all the same sized plates together and all the tableware stacked on one of the plates with the blades of the knives running under the arch of the forks. All glassware should be stacked on separate trays and taken to a separate wash up area. Wash up section should be the first place when the waiter enters the back area.

Hygiene is of utmost importance at the wash up area, as all sorts of germs can originate from here and can contaminate the food. This section is normally in the charge of the stewarding supervisor who may in turn have number of wash up boys as per need.

Dishwashing Methods

There are two main methods used for dishwashing for foodservice operations-

Manual (tank) method-

The dirty crockery is placed in a tank of hot water containing a soap detergent solution.

After washing, these are placed in wire racks and dipped into a second sterilizing tank containing clean hot water detergent at a temperature of approximately 75ÚC (179ÚF). The racks are left for two minutes and then lifted out and the crockery left to drain. If sterilized in water at this temperature the crockery will dry by itself without the use of drying up cloths. This is more hygienic. After drying the crockery is stacked into piles of the correct size and placed on shelves until required for further use.

Dishwashing machine

Used in larger establishments. Debris should be removed from the crockery before it is placed into the wire racks. The racks are then passed through the machine, the crockery being washed, rinsed and sterilized. Having passed through the machine the crockery is left to drain for two or three minutes and is then stacked and placed on shelves until required for further use.

b) Silver room/ plate room

In larger establishments the silver room or the plate room, as it is sometimes known, is a separate service area controlled by the kitchen stewarding supervisor. They take care of all the silverwares and the china wares stored in the silver room and are also responsible for silver polishing. The silver room should hold the complete stock of silverware required by the different department to meet the day to day requirements along with a surplus stock in case of emergency.

While stacking, large silver ware, like salver, flat platter etc. should be stored on shelves. When stacking heavier items should go on the shelves lower down and smaller and lighter items on the shelves higher up to prevent accidents. Flatware and cutlery should be kept in drawers lined with baize cloth to prevent them from moving about in the drawer and getting scratched or marked.

FOOD PICK UP AREA

This may be regarded as the meeting point between the food service staff and food preparation staff. It is very essential to ensure that there is an active cooperation and good relation between the staffs of these two areas. The aboyeur or the barker is in charge and controls the food pick up area during the service period. The aboyeur also controls the off board which tells the waiter immediately if any dish is off. It should be sited in a prominent position for all to see. The aboyeur receives the KOT from the waiter and places the order on the KOT to the respective kitchen area. He also helps the waiter to pick up the food.

Many a times all the crockery and hollowware are placed below the hot plate for easy meal service. The hot plate is operated electrically.

LINEN ROOM

It keeps a stock of various linen used in the restaurant/outlet. Example – table cloth, serviettes, guest napkin, slip cloth, baize etc.

Fresh linen is picked up by the restaurant staff in exchange of the soiled linen. Generally it is done once a day. But it might be more than once in case of coffee shop. A linen register is maintained on a daily basis for this purpose.

STORE

Store room is the area from where the F&B service staff requisite and receives items such as grocery and stationary that are required for smooth running of the day to day operation of the outlet.

WATER

An important nutrient .75 to 80 percent of our total body is water. The total body fluid is distributed among two major components

Extracellular fluid – contain sodium

Intercellular fluid – contain potassium

Water is made up of hydrogen & oxygen the ratio is 2:1

Sources visible & invisible water.

Visible water that we can see are- plain water, fruit juices, tea, milk, coffee etc

Invisible water that is inside the food s & metabolic water.

Function-

- Water quenched our thirst and is the most refreshing & cooling of all liquids.
- It is a structural component of all cell
- Water is a medium in which all chemical reaction takes place
- It is an essential components of all body fluid such as blood, ceribospinal fluid, bile,digestive fluid,urine.
- It acts like a lubricant & helps us to swallowed food or to digest food.
- It acts like a solvent for the products of digestion & help in transporting this product in different pare of body.
- It regulates the body temperature.
- It helps to throw the waste product from the body.

Water balance

In a normal individual, the maintenance of water balance is archived by adjusting both water intake & excretion as needed. The major inputs of water are –

- Fluids that we consume asbeverages, including water depending on climatic condition & habits.
- Different type of foods & fruits that we take as solid form.
- Metabolic water.

Output or loss of water from body

- Renal loss – Kidneys excrete about 1-2 liter of water daily
- Skin – The water loss from skin is through perspiration.
- Intestine – A small quantities of water is normally loss in faeces.
- Lungs – The air expired from the lungs also contains water.
- Sweat – It depends on the physical activity & environmental condition.

Daily intake & output of water

Intake ml/day Output ml/day

Fluid we take 2,200 Skin 350

From metabolism 200 Lungs 350

——————— Sweat 100

2,400 Faeces 100

Urine 1,500

2,400

Dehydration – It is defined as an excessive loss of body water. It may occur because of inadequate intake of, or abnormal loss of body water or a combination of both.

The symptoms of dehydration are

- Thirst
- Loss of appetite
- Decreased urination
- Nausea
- Impaired temperature regulation
- Muscular spasms
- Increased pulse rate

Symptoms of severe dehydration appear when Fluid level fall by more than 10 percent. A 20 percent loss of fluid from the body can be fatal.

A dehydrated person is usually managed by Oral Rehydration Therapy (ORT). The WHO recommended ORS (Oral Rehydration Salt) that are to be dissolved in 1 liter of water & make a Oral Rehydration Solution & have to be finished within 24 hours. He also can take HAF.(Home Available Fluid)

Home Available Fluid

Normally we prepared in home 1 glass of water + 2 spoon full of sugar + a pinch of salt + few drops of lime juice (lime juice contained potassium & salt contain sodium which help to maintained the equilibriums among intra cellular & extra cellular fluid .)

ORS (WHO) for 1 liter

Content amount in gm

Glucose 20.0

Sodium Chloride (salt) 3.5

Sodium bicarbonate (baking soda) 1.5

Potassium chloride 1.5

A minimum +8 glass of water is recommended daily.

Excess amount of water causes oedema. (Swelling of the skin).

Labels: Carbohydrates a Nutrient, ENERGY, Fat, Hotel Management, Hotel Management Study Materials Notes, Housekeeping, management college, PROTEIN, WATERnutrition

Fat

It belongs to lipids groups. We found as triglycerides in foods. It converts to Glycerid & fatty acid. It is made up of Carbone hydrogen & oxygen. Main source is providing energy i,e 9 kcal/gm. It is aster of fatty acid & glycerol.

The lipids are important to our health are fatty acid,fats,oils, phospholipids, sulpholipids& sterol.

Classification sources given in class

Saturated fatty acdis – These are found in animal food like meat, fish,eggyolk etc.No double bond, solid in nature.example- steric, palmitic,butyric etc.Maximum of 10 persent of our total calorie should come from our total calorie.

Unsaturated fatty acid – One, two or more double bonds, liquid in nature.

It is classified in 2 –

- MUFA- example Oleic acid & has one double bond .found in ground nut, olive oil; corn oiletc.they may help to lower the blood cholesterol level.
- PUFA – example- linoleic,lilonenic, arachidonic acid has two or more double bond. They help in lowering blood cholesterol levels & prevent atherosclerosis & coronary heart diseases.

Essential Fatty Acid: Poly unsaturated fatty acid cannot synthesized in our body. We have to take it through our diet. Example- linoleic, lilonenic, arachidonic acid.

Cholesterol - It is a fat like substance present in food. It is different in structure from triglycerids.It is present in all cell of the body & in large amount in brain & nervous tissue. The diseases related are cardiovascular disorder. The normal blood sugar level will be 200mg/100ml of blood.

Human get cholesterol from-

- Synthesis of liver
- Food rich in cholesterol

Functions of cholesterol are –

- It is precursor of all storied hormones
- A precursor of vit D, 7- dehydrochlosterol, is present in the skin which is irradiated by UV ray of sunlight to form vit D
- It is required for formation of bile
- It is an essential component of cell membrane.

PROTEIN

Definition – Protein come from a Greek word 'Proteo' means 'to take the first place.' are very complex nitrogenous organic compound. It is made up of carbon, hydrogen, oxygen, nitrogen. The present of nitrogen distinguished protein from carbohydrate& fats. Apart from nitrogen, elements like sulphur, phosphorous, copper, & iron are also found in some proteins. Lipid combined with protein formed lipo-protein.

The basic units from which protein are built are the amino acid. Each amino acid contains a carboxyl group (COOH) or acid group & an amino group or basic group.

Structure of amino acid given in class

Proteins consist of chains of amino acids that are linked to each other by a peptide linkage (-CO-NH-).

22 different amino acid are widely distributed in nature. The protein obtained from plants and animals are quite different both in amounts present & in quality. The protein contain of any food can be estimated by measuring the nitrogen contain of the food.

Essential Amino Acid – Those amino acids which cannot be synthesized in sufficient amounts by the body & must be provided by the diet are called essential amino acids. There are 10 essential amino acids. Among those 9 are essential for adults with it 1 for children.

Non essential amino acid – There are 12 non essential aminoacid.This Amino Acid can be synthesized in our body from other amino acid.(total – 22 amino acids)

Essential AminoAcid Non essential amino acid

Adults Additional for children Alanine

- Isoleucine Asparagine
- Leucine Arginine Aspartic acid
- Lysine Cystine
- Methionine Glutamine
- Phenylalanine Glutamic acid
- Threonine Trosine
- Tryptophan
- Valine
- Histidine

Classification of protein – (follow class note)

1. According to nature – plant & animal
2. According to quality - 1st class, 2nd class & incomplete
3. According to structure – Simple, compound& derived

Functions of protein - Protein performs three main functions

- Structural function
- Regulatory function
- Energy

Structural function –

Growth –

- Protein helps us in growth & development.
- All body fluid except urine & bile are made up of protein
- Proteins are the major constituent of muscles, organs, endocrine gland, & collagen.
- Collagen is the main structural protein of bone, ligament, skin etc.
- All enzymes, some hormones are like insulin are made up of proteins

Maintenance or wear & tear

It also helps to repair the dead cell.

Regulatory functions – Certain amino acid & protein have highly specialized functions in the regulation of body process & protection against disease.

Hemoglobin, an iron containing protein in the blood cells, performs an important role by transporting oxygen to the tissue cell.

Plasma protein maintains water balance & regulates the osmotic pressure in blood.

All enzymes & some hormones are made up of protein.

Energy – Like carbohydrate protein too provides 4kcal/gm.

Sources –

Food	gm/100gm
Rice	6.4
Wheat	11.8
Lentil	25.1
Rajmah	22.9
Cheese	24.1
Cow's milk	3.2
Egg (hen)	13.3
Mutton	18.5

Effect of deficiency & excess

It is known as PCM (Protein calorie malnutrition) OR PEM (Protein energy Malnutrition)

Protein deficiency is more marked during periods when protein needs are more specially among pre – school children in developing country.

Leads with only protein deficiency known as Kwashiorkor symptom moon face, oedema,pot belly, irritated in nature, red colour hair etc.

Marasmus is a combined disease of calorie + protein deficiency. Symptoms skeleton like features, very eager to take food,etc.

ENERGY

Food is digested, the complex nutrients i.e., carbohydrates, fats, protein are broken down into monosaccharides, fatty acids & glycerol, & amino acids, respectively. These simple forms are absorbed into the blood stream & supplied to the millions of cells in the body to be oxidized by series of complex steps to released energy.

Human being needs energy for the following:

- Basal metabolism
- Metabolic responses to food – thermo genesis / SDA
- Physical activities
- Growth
- For mothers in special conditions (pregnancy & lactation)

TEE = BMR (45 – 75percent) + Thermo genesis (10 percent) +
Physical activities (15 – 50 percent)

Factors affecting the BMR

BMR is the largest component of the daily energy demand representing 45 – 70 percent of daily total energy expenditure. It is highly variable & the cause of this variation include factors such as

- body size & composition ,
- age,

- gender,
- environmental condition,
- hormonal status,
- fever/illness/infection / injury,
- specific body conditions of mothers(pregnancy & lactation),
- other factors etc

Thermal effect of food (SDA)

Thermal effect of food (TEF) determined primarily by the amount of composition of food consumed .For example, is greater after consumption of carbohydrate & protein than after fat. It varies from 5-10 percent for carbohydrates, 0-5 percent for Fat, & 20 -30 percent for protein.

Physical Activity

Sedentary workers –persons taking, reading, watching TV, listening Radio, doing computer works specially sitting activities (teachers, office workers).

Moderate workers – with some activities servants, house cleaners, rural womans, students etc.

Heavy workers – Labour class.

Energy requirement

The amount of food needed to ensure good health will vary from one individual to another. All people do not requires the same amount of nutrients.Requirment vary depending upon age, gender, body size, activities, state of health etc.ICMR has prepared Recommended Dietary Allowances(RDA) for Indians.

Energy balance: Energy out put – Energy input

Energy balance is a condition in which the energy provided by food is nearly equal to energy expenditure by the body resulting in a steady body weight.

Over weight & under weight both are the abnormalities

Both measured by BMI (body Mass Index)

BMI = Weight in kilograms / height in meters squire

Housekeeping

Housekeeping is the act of cleaning the rooms and furnishings of a home. It is one of the many chores included in the term housework. Housecleaning includes activities such as disposing of rubbish, cleaning dirty surfaces, dusting and vacuuming. It may also involve some outdoor chores, such as removing leaves from rain gutters, washing windows and sweeping doormats. The term is often used also figuratively in politics and business, for the removal of unwanted personnel, methods or policies in an effort at reform or improvement. Effective housekeeping can eliminate some workplace hazards and help get a job done safely and properly. Poor housekeeping can frequently contribute to accidents by hiding hazards that cause injuries. If the sight of paper, debris, clutter and spills is accepted as normal, then other more serious health and safety hazards may be taken for granted.Housekeeping is not just cleanliness. It includes keeping work areas neat and orderly; maintaining halls and floors free of slip and trip hazards; and removing of waste materials (e.g., paper, cardboard) and other fire hazards from work areas. It also requires paying attention to important details such as the layout of the whole workplace, aisle marking, the adequacy of storage facilities, and maintenance. Good housekeeping is also a basic part of accident and fire prevention.Effective housekeeping is an ongoing operation: it is not a hit-and-miss cleanup done occasionally. Periodic "panic" cleanups are costly and ineffective in reducing accidents.

IMPORTANCE OF HOUSEKEEPING IN HOSPITALITY OPERATIONS

Housekeeping refers to 'keeping of the house and includes all those factors which lead to comfort, cleanliness and service of the people occupying the particular place, be it a hotel, resort, or a club house. It begins with cleaning of all furniture and furnishings, to their upkeep and maintenance, their selection and purchase and eventually their replacement. It takes more manpower and technique to accomplish housekeeping's almost countless functions than those of any other single department of the lodging industry.

The hospitality industry caters to two basic necessities – food and shelter. The standard of housekeeping plays an important role in the reputation of any establishment. Clientele repetition depends mainly on the level of cleanliness and upkeep of all areas. Guests go to any hotel for food or lodging, and both these services are emphasized by cleanliness, décor and new ideas. Studies indicate that guests give their main reason for returning or not returning to a hotel, to the cleanliness of the hotel. If the place is clean, not only will the guests come back but will also talk about it and recommend it to others.

The objective of housekeeping department is guest satisfaction. For this the 'sales appeal' of the guest rooms and public areas has to be maintained and the surroundings should be:

CLEAN COMFORTABLE ATTRACTIVE SAFE

Clean:- The primary function of housekeeping is cleaning of rooms and public areas. One cannot feel comfortable in an environment that is not clean and well ordered. One should also use clean and correct methods for cleaning. Even though undesirable architectural features and traffic problems may complicate the task, a combination of efficient procedures, appropriate tools, and trained staff can provide sparkling interiors. For e.g. even a costly cut-glass ashtray looses it's appeal if filled with used cigarette butts.

Comfort:- Similarly neatness is of no use if there is no comfort. The housekeeping department contributes to the comfortable furnishings and every minute tasks related to the convenience of the guests. For e.g. a sofa might be clean, but if not stuffed well or if the springs have become slack, no one would like to sit on it. Since the definition of comfort is a personal matter, it includes soft pillows as well as hard ones, soft mattresses as well as hard-boards. The linen provided is also very important as guest can feel the linen(bed sheets, towels etc.) and inferior quality would make the guest feel unhappy.

Attractive:-The décor of every room is important. Every guest room should have it's own mood and color and design are mood makers. Thus a well decorated, clean and well maintained surrounding is largely responsible for high occupancy rates. Some housekeepers take full responsibility, some take assistance of a professional designer and achieve a balance between beauty and practicality.

Safe:- Another aspect of housekeeping is ensuring the safety of the guests. The housekeeping staff try their utmost to ensure that the guest is not in danger, or susceptible to any accidents. They should be alert to accident causing conditions- loose tile, wobbly chair, burnt out exit light and get them rectified immediately.They also come very close to the personal items and documents of the guests during the cleaning of the rooms. Hence it is their responsibility to keep all the personal information a secret.

Along with clean, comfortable, attractive and safe surroundings, the staff of housekeeping department must also offer the guests a prompt, friendly and courteous service, and be of assistance whenever required. Not only must the equipment and methods be as clean as possible, but also the person who is doing the cleaning. Great care must be paid to personal hygiene of all the staff

To achieve all the above requirements, housekeeping has to plan their inputs of cleaning agents, equipment's manpower, etc.

In the hotel industry pressure has built up because of the tremendous increase in costs, not only in building, but also recurring costs of repair and maintenance. Housekeeping like all other indirect cost departments is involved in the struggle to keep the operating cost low, so as to maintain profitability. More important than costs is to meet the demands of today's guest. Maintenance and cleanliness of the hotel is one factor which precedes all others if profit is to continue. No amount of advertising, entertainment and glamour will compensate for poor housekeeping. Good housekeeping is a great asset to marketing as a well kept house becomes word of mouth publicity.

Another important aspect of housekeeping which tends to be overlooked is that, this is the only department with legitimate access to almost every area of the hotel, and thus obtains a singular view of the entire operation, including an almost unique insight into the ways that a guest might react to a facility, it's personnel, or services. The housekeeping can be the eyes and ears of the management. Therefore housekeeper's opinion and suggestion must be seriously considered.

Like in any other industry, hotel also has a line of products to sell and the quality, value and price of these products will decide if the business will be successful or not. In hotels this product line includes lobby, meeting rooms, restaurant, banquet rooms, etc., but the principle product is the guest room. Impressions are enhanced or completely destroyed as the guest moves from the reception counter, along the corridors towards the room.

Guest rooms are the heart of the hotel and a good professional housekeeper attaches a great deal of importance to their upkeep, quality of service and the appearance and courtesy of all housekeeping personnel. Comfort and design may impress the guest, but attitude and approach of the staff will decide the success in getting a potential customer.

A guest spends more time alone in his room than he spends in any other part of the hotel, and hence he can check up the cleanliness if he wants to. If he finds that it is only surface cleaning, he loses confidence in the hotel and it's methods. If a guest opens a drawer or cupboard and finds it not clean he would not feel like putting anything in the drawer. Also if there is anything forgotten by the last guest it proves careless checking and can really annoy a guest.A stained dirty or freshness looking carpet upsets a guest if he wishes to walk barefoot. Within the room special importance is given to the cleanliness of the bathroom as it is a breeding space for germs.

Also if the guest lets the room attendant clean his room while he is there and sees dirty methods like cleaning glasses with dirty dusters he would be feeling disappointed. So staff training and supervision can achieve and uphold high standards.

The International Traveler is a very fussy traveler so housekeeping plays a vital role in creating a impression of the hotel.Modern room supplies and services like express laundry and dry cleaning services show a guest that the hotel is considering the comfort and wishes to please him.

Not only does the resident guests get a large share of their impression of a hotel from the housekeeping through the rooms but also the guests who come to the restaurants and bars, guests invited to a function in the banquet halls, guests visiting the spas can feel the cleanliness level in the hotel from the lobby, public areas, restaurants, toilets, facilities, uniforms of staff and judge a lot about the hotel. Therefore we can conclude that this department contributes greatly to guest impressions of a hotel and is open to general inspection and cannot hide poor service.

If we look at any hotel from outside we can see that much visually seen is rooms and as rooms and public areas are completely under the maintenance of the Housekeeping Department to neglect this department is to neglect the building and property. Though maintenance is also involved in the maintenance and upkeep of the hotel but it's the duty of the housekeeping department to inspect the rooms and public areas and inform the maintenance department of the faults.

The importance of housekeeping's responsibility in the area of operating costs cannot be overlooked. Housekeeping department is the single largest employer in the hotel (labour and material). Housekeeper must be involved in day-to-day management planning.

Housekeeping consultant must be involved from the very initial planning stage of construction. Housekeeper's view must be obtained in the methods and cost of maintaining new or renovated structures, etc. She / he should be involved in meetings with the architects, design interiors and interior decorator.

Management must give serious consideration to the allocation of building space to housekeeping functions. Since every sq.-ft. is revenue producing, often building planning teams do not understand the functioning of housekeeping department well enough to allocate adequate space. Before any new facility planning, it is necessary for the management to decide how extensive it's housekeeping functions are going to be; what guest room conveniences will be provided, so that there is enough storage space, etc.

AREAS OF RESPONSIBILITY OF HOUSEKEEPING and PERSONALITY ATTRIBUTES OF HOUSEKEEPING STAFF and Layout of the housekeeping Department

AREAS OF RESPONSIBILITY OF HOUSEKEEPING:-

The primary function of the department is cleaning and servicing of guest rooms, suites, corridors, elevators, service and clean floors, stairways, ;public and banquet areas, staff cloak rooms, and back areas except the kitchen area.

1. The organization and co-ordination of the work,
2. Staff training,
3. Duty Rota,

4. Implementation of management and company policies in the department,
5. Guest and staff laundry and dry-cleaning,
6. Shoe cleaning facility
7. Floral arrangement,
8. Special decorations,
9. Operating linen room and Uniform room,
10. Mending linen and uniform,
11. Lost and found
12. Maintaining inventories and records
13. Purchasing:
    i. cleaning agent
    ii. cleaning equipments
    iii. linen: table and bed & bath
    iv. furnishings
14. Special cleaning
15. shampooing
16. Annual budget
17. Interviewing prospective candidates
18. Maintaining good working staff moral
19. Assessment of staff
20. Issue loaned article to guest
21. Dealing with guest queries
22. Baby sitting

PERSONALITY ATTRIBUTES OF HOUSEKEEPING STAFF:-

There are certain qualities which a housekeeping staff should possess in order to perform the housekeeping functions which are sometimes more important than the skill too.

i) Pleasant personality- The staff should have a good presentation of ones own self when interacting with guests. This reflect the quality of service and standards in an establishment.
ii) Physical fitness- The housekeeping staff should go through a thorough medical examination and should be fit to perform the housekeeping functions.
iii) Personal Hygiene- The housekeeping staff should have healthy skin, clean hair, eyes, teeth, nose, nails and fingers etc.
iv) Eye for detail- The staff should possess power of critical observation to make a flawless room and keen sense to inspect rooms for perfection.
v) Cooperation- The staff must cooperate with staff of other departments for team work and more efficiency.
vi) Adaptability- The staff should be able to adopt to new ideas and accept changing situations willingly
vii) Honesty- The housekeeping staff need to have this quality as they have access to all the rooms and guest belongings are left lying around. They also deal with various kinds of guest amenities that are very expensive. So they should have inherent discipline and integrity.

viii) Tactful and diplomatic- The housekeeping staff have to handle guest requests and complaints. The guests are fussy and can make unusual requests. The staff have to be tactful and diplomatic to handle these requests.

ix) Right attitude- The staff should have a right attitude which displays an even temper, courtesy and good humor and optimistic in nature.

x) Calm Behavior- Should be able to handle situations with composed personality and humbleness and politeness.

xi) Courteous- Should be courteous to both guests and colleagues

xii) Punctuality- Should have respect for time during working hours as this reflects on his/her sincerity.

xiii) Good memory- Should have good memory to remember staff likes, dislikes, needs and wishes of guests and especially repeat guests.

Layout of the housekeeping Department:-

Diagram-Done in class

The layout of the department indicates the different areas and subdivisions in the department. The layout of the department depends on following factors;-

#Total number of Guestrooms

No. of outlets and banquets

Amount of manpower required.

Following are the areas of the department:-

Executive Housekeepers Office- This is the Executive housekeepers office where the administrative work of the department is performed.

Housekeeping Desk- This is the control centre of the housekeeping and is manned 24 hrs a day. This is the area where housekeeping staff report for duty and sign out at the end of the shift. Notice boards, telephones, computers, storage shelves (for registers and files), lost and found cupboard, key racks etc. are present here.

Laundry- The place in the hotel where washing, pressing, dry cleaning, folding of linen and uniform of the hotel takes place.

Linen Room- The linen room is the place where the linen of the hotel are stored, collected & circulated throughout the hotel. Eg. of linen-bed sheets, towels, table covers etc.

Uniform Room- The place from where uniforms are collected, stored and distributed to the staff of the hotel.

Sewing room- The place in the department where stitching and repair of linen and uniforms takes place.

Housekeeping Stores- This is the storage area in the department where the cleaning agents, cleaning equipments, guest supplies are stored for the daily housekeeping functions and are securely locked.

Flower Room- Ideally should be an air-conditioned room to keep flowers fresh for arrangements in the hotel. It should have work tables, counters, sink, water supply, cupboards to store vases, stones etc.

Lost and found- The lost and found section in the department stores all the articles left by the guest and is stored for a specific period.

Floor Pantry- Located on each guest floor to stock the linen, cleaning supplies and guest supplies required for operations of the floor and should be securely locked.

INTERDEPARTMENTAL COORDINATION

No individual department in any hotel can work in isolation. The housekeeping department, is just one of the department in a hotel working towards the satisfaction of the guests, each department is dependent on others for information and services if its work is to be accomplished effectively.

Fig: Interdepartmental coordination

COORDINATION WITH FRONT OFFICE

- To ensure efficient rooming of guests, both housekeeping and front office must inform each other of changes in a room's status. Knowing whether a room is occupied, vacant, on change, out of order (OOO), under repair, or similar for proper room management
- There should be coordination to clean front office public areas
- There must be coordination between housekeeping and front office department to share information on occupancy levels which helps to forecast occupancy for the year and makes it easier to draw up a budget, establish par stock levels and estimate required staff strength.
- There should be coordination know about the daily room report and housekeeping discrepancy report.
- It also helps to gear renovations and spring cleaning to low occupancy periods there by preventing loss of revenue.
- The housekeeping and front office department also coordinate with each other for other important information which require special attention like
- VIPs in house: this information is essential so that the staff can take a little extra care and keener precautions in cleaning and supervising VIP rooms.
- Groups in the house: the group rooming list must be provided before the group's arrival to the housekeeping as groups tends to move together in terms of arrival, departure, sightseeing tours and meals. Their rooms need to be readied together in view of strict time parameters. Group rooming lists enable the hk department to organize their work and have the group's room ready on time.
- Crews in the house: Sometimes the arrival of a crew and the departure of another crew from the same airline may overlap. In such circumstances, it is important for the allotted rooms to be cleaned within a short period of time. Thus for this there should be a effective coordination between front office and housekeeping.

10. Flowers: sometimes the management extends its compliments to a guest with a special gesture of a flower arrangement in the room as recognition of the importance of a person. This requirement of flower arrangements for certain guests is conveyed to housekeeping by the front office on a daily basis.
11. Apart from the above communications the front office needs to depend on housekeeping for the provision of clean uniforms to its staff.

COORDINATION WITH FOOD AND BEVERAGE DEPARTMENT

- The coordination of housekeeping with the restaurants and banquet halls is mainly concerned with the provision of linen and uniforms.

- On his/her part the restaurant manager should ensure that the time set for the exchange of linen must be maintained and linen should not be lost or misused.
- There should be coordination to maintain minibar in guest rooms.
- The housekeeping should be well informed about the forthcoming banquet function in advance so that housekeeping will arrange everything to organize that function.
- House keeping may also have to arrange for flower decorations for banquets.
- The coordination between the two departments becomes particularly necessary in collection of trays from the guest corridors which are collected from the room, placement of fruit basket in special rooms.
- In many hotels housekeeping also looks after pest control in restaurants, kitchens, and stores attached to them. Special cleaning of these areas call for coordination with the housekeeping department.
- Both the restaurant and kitchen staff requires clean uniforms on a daily basis, for which too they need to coordinate with housekeeping.

COORDINATION STORE

- Coordination with stores ensures the availability of day-to –day necessities of housekeeping.
- Larger hotels have a store attached to the housekeeping department that stocks linen, supplies and so on.
- Smaller hotels may stock them in the general store, except for linen, which is sent to the housekeeping department on purchase.
- Communication with stores is by way of a requisition form, which housekeeping sends to when it requires certain items. The requisition form is called as store requisition form.

COORDINATION WITH PURCHASE DEPARTMENT

- The purchase department procures out –of–stock items for housekeeping, such as guest supplies and amenities, stationery, linen, cleaning materials and equipments etc.
- Housekeeping should convey their requirements to purchase by way of advance notice in the form of a purchase requisition.

COORDINATION WITH PERSONNEL DEPARTMENT

- Housekeeping coordinates with the personnel department for following reason
- Acquisition: human resource planning, recruitment, selection and induction/ socialization.
- Maintenance: compensation management e.g. pay/ salary, wages, over time, medical treatment etc.
- Motivation: performance appraisal system, reward management system and training and development.

COORDINATIONWITH SALES AND MARKETING DEPARTMENT

- There should be effective coordination between sales and marketing department and housekeeping to supply promotional items in guest rooms and other areas of hotel.

- The sales and marketing department informs housekeeping of the occupancy forecast for the entire year, which is broken up month wise. This enables house-keeping to budget for the necessary expenses
- An important contribution of the housekeeping staff to hotel sales is ensuring that repeat business is obtained by providing the level of cleanliness and service that meets or exceeds guest expectations.
- The sales and marketing team also have to depend on housekeeping for their uniforms.
- Two things are certain in the hotel business: no matter how many guests a sales-person brings in the door, if housekeeping does not execute its function with excellence the guests will not be coming back.
- Vice versa, no matter how well- kept the rooms, if the sales staff does not bring potential guests to the hotel, occupancy falls.

COORDINATION WITH MAINTENANCE DEPARTMENT

- The housekeeping department depends on maintenance to keep things in order.
- While carrying out their scheduled work, housekeeping employees may find some deficiencies in the hotel facilities, such as faulty electrical plugs, dripping faucets, leaking pipes or malfunctioning air-conditioning units etc.
- A need for urgent repairs is reported to maintenance over telephone and these requests are usually taken into action immediately.
- There are various heads under which maintenance work is done they are:
- Electrical work: air conditioning and heating; fused bulbs , lights and lamps that are not functioning ; defective plugs and plug points ; short circuits; and faulty geysers , refrigerators , and minibar fall under this category.
- Boiler work: this is necessary to maintain a supply of hot water to guestroom.
- Mechanical work: this entails repair or replacement of any faulty equipment, such as vacuum cleaners, ice-cube machines, and so on.
- Plumbing work: this deals with faulty faucets (taps), showers, drainage sys-tems, water closets, and so on.
- Carpentry work: broken of shaky furniture; mirrors and cupboards in less than peak condition, and fresh woodwork are all part of this.

COORDINATION WITH SECURITY DEPARTMENT

- The coordination here is mainly concerned with the prevention of fire and thefts and the safekeeping of keys and lost property.
- Housekeeping personnel should also report anything of a suspicious nature or movement in hotel immediately to the security staff.
- Housekeeping have to coordinate if they see any anti-social activities in the guest room such as gambling, smuggling and so on.
- The security department is responsible for conducting training sessions on han-dling emergency situations for the staff.e.g they conduct fire drill to train staff to gear up in a fire emergency.

USE OF COMPUTERS IN HOUSEKEEPING and List of Guest room supplies

USE OF COMPUTERS IN HOUSEKEEPING

Many hotels have invested heavily in information technology(IT) infrastructure and networking that use the latest technical advances in their operations.

The latest in IT amenities:-

The newer technologies that are gaining entry into the hospitality segment are:-

a) Wi-fi (Wireless fidelity),
b) Radio frequency identification
c) Tracking inventory and guest data through cellular and wireless technologies,
d) GPS(Global positioning System),
e) Handheld communication devices.
f) Wireless local area networks(WLANs) and
g) Mobile computers.

Wirelss connectivity is developing rapidly , enabling whole world to stay networked and connected. Business travellers in particular are always looking for ways to stay connected while on move and expect wireless connectivity at their hotels. Hotels are aware of the benefits of enabling broadband access throughout their facilities as wireless connections improve a guest experience by providing complete mobility. WLANs allow guests to share high speed internet connections, browse the web, access their corporate networks remotely yet securely access the business centre from their room, organize video conference, play games online etc.

Hotels provide Wi- Fi as a value added amenity to guests or offer the service at a cost to their guests. Wi- Fi is provided in guest rooms, public areas, lobbies, meeting rooms, lounges and so on. It permits users to roam unrestricted throughout the hotel facility, with real time access to critical information as and when required.

IT in the housekeeping department:-

WLAN technology is enabling a wide range of hospitality operations in the housekeeping department. Housekeeping staff can conduct room checks, after a guest vacates the room through a handheld Wi-Fi enabled device, to report the status of the room. They can also communicate with security personnel instantly over email in case of an emergency. Staff can also ensure that from remote spots, fire extinguishers are charged, emergency lights are functioning and so on, check and communicate, inventory information for guestroom supplies and stocking of minibars in order to ensure that provisions are replenished in an efficient manner. Housekeeping managers can also contact workers and identify their locations quickly resulting in quicker response times.

Computers are now being used in many housekeeping functions for rooms management , inventory control, linen management etc.Many software packages are now available in India that provide specific applications for housekeeping opearations. Computers can now be linked to the telephone systems in each individual guest rooms. This technology greatly reduces the cost of individual wiring in each guestroom. For instance an link can be created between the telephone system and CPU of hotels computer network by dialling specific sequence of numbers from a guestroom. Once dialled the computer can recognize the room number to which it is being connected. After the connection is established a specific list of dial up codes are aavaialbale to the GRA, by which he or she can transmit information to the computer system directly without any input devices in the rooms.

HOUSEKEEPING SOFTWARE

Housekeeping software modules are now an integral part of hotel management softwares. The module widely available includes applications such as forecasting GRA requirements, daily housekeeping scheduling, tracking housekeeping inventory, monitoring GRA performance.

1) Forecasting GRA requirements- This module is designed to forecast the total number of GRAs needed in each day in each shift, based on current in house occupancy and staffing and also keeping in mind the expected arrivals and departures. These modules can forecast staffing upto 365 days in advance.
2) Daily housekeeping scheduling- This application can automatically create and print a cleaning schedule each day for each GRA , based on number of dirty rooms, estimated cleaning time needed per room, number of GRAs available in the establishment. A housekeping status screen is the core element of this system, and tracks each housekeeper updating the status as rooms are cleaned and inspected. The module tracks the status from 'dirty' to 'ready for inspection' to 'clean and ready for guests'. This is made possible by marking the rooms clean using an in-room intercom or handheld wireless PDA (personal digital assistant)

If a optional housekeeper – phone interface is installed the room attendanr can press a key in the in- room phone to indicate they have started cleaning. This stamps the cleaning start time into the housekeeping history file. The room attendant can press a different key to indicate they have completed clenaing and which indicates the time that its ready to be inspected. Reports available can show the actual cleaning time per room, as well as expected cleaning time and checking time per room.

Room status can be changed in various ways:-

a) Room attendant can use the phone in the room to directly to change the room status from clean to dirty.
b) Room attendant can call the front desk or the housekeping deparment and ask them to change the room status using the houskeeping status screen.

3) Attending guest requests promptly-This module can also schedule the servicing of guest requests. For instance if a guest calls the front desk and requests a crib or extra towels, the front desk can input this requst into the computer and it then appears on the main houseekeeping monitor screen. The guest request information can also be informed to th most suitably placed GRA and can also be placed to a handheld wireless device(PDA) or cell phone and he also informs the desk as soon as the request is completed.
4) Monitoring GRA performance:-

This is a historical reporting module. It is possible to measure the peformance of GRA by tracking the estimatesd cleaning time and the actual cleaning time. This also gives the time required by supervisor to check the rooms. Thus reports are aavailable that show how much time was taken by room attendants preparing the room and supervisor completing the inspection. The executive housekeeper can thus track time and duration for each room cleaning by each person.

In case the room is not properly cleaned the room status can again be changed to dirty and the room can be assigned to the room attendant with comments like shower

neds proper cleaning and that can also help to track the GRA performance. Even if a guest has checked in into a room and if the guest has complained then housekeeper can determine the GRA or supervisor who has done the cleaning and inspected the room.
5)Indication of cleaning time:-

The housekeeping staff can also be alerted when a room is available for cleaning. In this application guests can click a button , which sets off another sensor , to indicate they are out of the room and the room can be cleaned.
6) Reporting maintenance problems through wireless devices:-

While doing the routine room checking , room attendant may notice that the WC is leaking and pick up the room phone and identify the specific problem and report it immediately to the maintenance person through his wireless phone.

List of Guest room supplies

Behind the door:

Fire exit map

"DND" card (do not disturb)

"Please clean my room" card

"Collect my laundry" card

In the wardrobe:

Iron board with iron

Coat brush

Hangers – three different types

Coat hangers

Satin padded hanger for ladies

Clip hangers

Laundry bag

Laundry list

Shoe tray with Room slipper, Shoe shiner/mitt, Shoe horn and complimentary card)

Safety locker (with a guideline card)

Minibar

Inside:

Mineral water

Aerated beverage and energy drink

Alcoholic beverage – gin, vodka, whiskey, dark rum, white rum, bear cans etc.

On top of the Minibar:

A snack tray on top with 3 nuts,(cashew, almond, pistachio), 2 wafers (moong dal, khatta mitha), 2 mints, 3 chocolate, 1 cookie, ice bucket, 2 old fashioned, 1 brandy balloon, 1 liquor glass, 2 drinking glass, 2 mineral water bottle(500 ml

Minibar menu (provides charges for alcoholic beverage and snacks)

Luggage rack :

Remains free of any item. (As guest is expected to put his baggage on luggage rack)

Writing table:

Guest folder-

1. Letter head (large, medium and small)

2. Envelope
3. Picture postcard
4. Fax form
5. Confidential form
6. Tariff card
7. Brochure
8. Pen

Business Kit- Pen, Pencil, Sharpener, cello tape, scissor, gems pin etc.

1 internet adaptor

Tea and coffee set up

1. Cups and saucer set – 2
2. Sugar sachet (three variant – plain suger, sugar free sugar & brown sugar)
3. Coffee sachet
4. Milk (condensed milk 10ml container)
5. Tea –(many variants – Green tea, Lemon, Ginger, Darjeeling tea, English Breakfast Tea, Earl Grey Tea, etc.)
6. Sugar free sachets

ON THE COFFEE TABLE

- Hotel Magazines (may be provided in magazine rack)
- Fruit Basket with quarter plate and fruit knife
- Ashtray and match box
- Newspaper (4-5 types – 02 national and 2-3 international newspaper)
- Room service menu card

ON THE BEDSIDE TABLE

- Mineral water bottle 500ml – 2no.
- Glass tumblers with coaster- 2no.
- Scribbling pad with pencil – I each
- In-house telephone directory
- "do not change my linen" card
- Telephone/ Internet tariff card
- Breakfast door knob order card
- Pillow menu (7-8 types are offered)
- City telephone directory
- Yellow pages book (it's a telephone directory with commercial no.)

INSIDE THE BEDSIDE TABLE DRAWER

A SLUMBER KIT:

- "anti stress" spray
- "sound sleep" spray
- eye mask
- ear plug
- Breakfast door knob card
- Holy book

ON THE BED

mattress pad
mattress
mattress protector
first sheet
second sheet
blanket
blanket cover/crinkle sheet
bed cover
pillows and cushions- 4-5no.
IN THE BATHROOM:-

VANITORY COUNTER

- Moisturizer- 30 ml bottle -2no
- Talcum Powder- 2 no.
- Hair oil – 1no.
- Shaving Kit- 1no
- Dental Kit-1 no.
- For your care Kit-(Band Aid, Ear buds, Nail filer)- 1no.
- Comb- 1no.
- Soap-30 gms – 1no.
- Tooth glass/Gurgle glass- 2no.
- Cotton balls in jar
- Tissue paper in box
- Hair Dryer-1 fixed on the wall
- Face towel- 2no.
- Hand towel- 2 nos.

NEXT TO WC

- Toilet roll in a toilet roll holder
- Sanibin- (a bin with lid) – two sanitary disposable bags a placed near sanibin
- Toilet soap
- Toilet strip/ WC band ("Disinfected for use" in printed on the strip)

NEXT TO BATH TUB:-

- Soap- 60 gms- 1no.
- Shampoo- 30 ml – 2no.
- Conditioner- 30 ml – 2no.
- Shower gel- 30 ml -2no.
- Loofah – 1no.
- Shower cap- 2no.
- Bath towel- 02 nos.
- Bubble bath 30ml – 2no.

INNOVATIVE SUPPLIES IN EVA FLOOR:-

- Wardrobe- Silk gowns, Iron and Iron Board
- Minibar- Gin and vodka(as preferred by ladies)
- Writing Table- Sewing Kit,
- Bedside table- Jewellery box

- Next to Bath tub and shower cubicles-Toiletries(Bath Gel, lotion, shampoo, conditioner are from Forest Essentials)Loofah, Pumice, honey soap.
- Vanitory counter- Amenity tray consists of nail filer, detangling comb, nail polish remover, lip balm, astringent, body talc, face wash, tweezer, Safety pin, face tissues known as SINGLE LADY KIT.
- Next to WC- Disposal bag.

CLEANING EQUIPMENTS

These are manual or mechanical devices which help in the cleaning process.

Selection Criteria for cleaning equipments:-

Efficient cleaning and maintenance and maximum work productivity are dependent on high quality cleaning equipments and selecting the ideal equipments plays major role in the cleaning process.

The selection criteria for equipments are:-

i) Safety in operation
ii) Suitability to type of area, surface, work, amount of obstruction and cleaning frequency.
iii) Versatility to do various types of cleaning.
iv) Work performance in terms of capacity of machine.
v) Ease of handling in terms of size, weight, height of machine and ease of operation.
vi) Portability in terms of ease of transfer between floors and provision of wheels and detachable parts.
vii) Durability of the equipment, sturdiness, life of the equipment etc.
viii) Noise level of the equipment
ix) Availability of spare parts, easy servicing conditions.
x) Protective design of the equipment without sharp edges.
xi) Easy to store in terms of dismantling parts and storage space required.
xii) Cost as initial costs, operating costs, maintenance

MANUAL EQUIPMENTS

Equipments which help in the cleaning process by directly using manual energy of the employees.

The common manual equipments are :-

1) Brooms 2) Brushes 3) Mops 4) Cloths 5) Containers 6) Box Sweepers

1) BROOMS:-

Brooms consist of long bristles gathered together and inserted into a handle. Bristles may be made of grass, corn, coconut fibers etc.

Types of brooms:-

Soft Bristled brooms- Brooms made of corn fiber, grass brooms, and used on smooth floors.

Hard bristled Brooms- Coconut fiber brooms or yard brooms are used on rough surfaces especially outdoors.

Wall brooms/ Tall Turks- These are used to remove cobwebs from ceilings. They have a soft head and a long handle.

2) BRUSHES:-

These are designed to remove dust and dirt from surfaces.

Parts of brush

a. Stock in which bristles are inserted made of wood, metal or plastic.
b. Bristles made of horse hair, nylon, jute or coir have chisel like action which dislodges the soil
c. Handle may also be made of wood or plastic and can be detachable or non detachable.

Types of Brushes:-

- Hard Brush- Stiff bristles and well spaced out. Removes heavy soil from rough surfaces.
- Soft brush- Softer bristles and set close together. Removes loose soil from smooth surfaces like carpets, furniture etc.
- Scrubbing Brushes- These have short, hard bristles designed for cleaning stains and heavy soil. Also known as T brushes.

Other brushes are Toilet Brushes/Johnny Mops, Bottle Brushes, Cloth scrubbing Brush, Carpet brushes, Feather Brush etc.

3) MOPS:-

Types of mops are dry mops and wet mops.

#Dry mops:-

Also called dust control mops. These are used to remove dust from floors, wall, ceiling. Mops have handle, to which a metal frame is attached. The mop head made of dense cotton fringes are inserted into the frame and stretched over it.

#Wet/damp mops:-

These mops are used along with buckets to remove dirt from the floor surfaces. The mop consists of a handle and cotton fringes or sponge which are capable of absorbing water.

Types of damp mop-

a) Do-all-mops- Consists strands of twisted cotton fixed to a circular metal plate which is fixed to a stock.
b) Kentucky mop-Cotton strands fixed to a length of cotton fabrics which is inserted into a metal stock
c) Foss mop-Dense cotton fringes inserted into a metal stock
d) Squeeze- Consists of a rubber blade attached to a metal handle to remove excess water from the floor.
e) Sponge mops- Consists of sponge fixed to a replaceable lever controlled head, hinged for removing the water and attached to a long handle.

4) CLOTHS

Various cloths are used in dry and wet cleaning. For efficient usage cloth can be color coded and used by staff for different usages.

Types of cloths-

a) Dusters/ cloths- Soft absorbent plain or checked cotton material or yellow flannelette used for dusting and buffing.
b) Swabs and Wipes- These are made of loosely woven cotton cloths which are soft, absorbent material used for wet cleaning of surface above floor level. Mainly used for cleaning bathtubs and washbasins.
c) Floor cloths – These are coarse knitted cotton cloths which are bigger, thicker and used to clean floors.

d) Glass Cloths/ Scrim- These are lint free loosely woven linen material and is used for cleaning glass and mirrors.
e) Cotton Rags or cloths-Disposable cotton or cloths used for applying polishes and cleaning agents.
f) Chamois leather- Obtained from chamois goat and used for cleaning windows and mirror, polishing silver.
g) Dust sheets- Made of thin cotton material which are discarded from linen room like bedsheets or curtains used to cover floor , furniture during renovation work.
h) Drug gets- Linen, canvas or plastic material placed on the floor in doorways to absorb excessive dirt caused during bad weather or renovation work.
i) Bucket cloths/Splash mats-Thick fabric placed under buckets to prevent water marks formation on surfaces.

5) CONTAINERS

The staff require containers to carry, transport, and store items of use and collect waste products.

Types of containers-

a) Buckets- Made of plastic or galvanized iron. Used to collect water and used with mops for cleaning.
b) Dustpans- Used along with brushes to collect dust and made of plastic or metal. The edge in contact with floor must be thin and sharp.
c) Dustbins- Made of plastics, wood, metals, leather , jute and placed in rooms, public areas and all back areas and lined with plastic bags.
d) Sani-bins-Metal or plastic bins with lids.
e) Spray bottles- Lightweight containers which deliver a fine mist of water or cleaning solution on the surface to be cleaned.
f) Hand caddies- Made of metal, wood or plastic consists of a tray with slots for storing chemical bottles and a handle to carry it.
g) Carts and trolleys-
i) Chambermaids trolley/Room Attendants cart/ Maids Trolley- Used to carry linen, cleaning agents, supplies, cleaning equipments required for guestroom cleaning and stored in the guest corridors and should be movable and strong.
ii) Janitorial trolley- Used for cleaning and storing cleaning supplies for public area cleaning.
iii) Mop wringer trolley- This piece of equipment consists of mop and buckets to carry cleaning solution and clean water mainly used for public areas.
iv) Linen trolley- Used for transfer of linen from guestrooms to laundry for washing and are made of cloth or metal with castor wheels.

6) **BOXSWEEPER**

These are manually operated carpet sweepers used for removing crumbs from the surfaces. It consists of a brush that revolves when equipment is pushed over the carpet and crumbs get collected in the dust-collector pan which are emptied when filled.

MECHANICAL EUIPMEMT

The equipments which work by motors powered by electricity.

Different mechanical equipments are:-

(I) VACUUM CLEANERS/SUCTION CLEANERS- Dust and crumbs are removed from surface by suction.

Vacuum cleaners can be classified on the basis of:-

- Shape of the machine- Cylindrical, upright, backpack, dustette
- Function- Dry pick up, wet pick up, dry and wet pick up, pile lifter
- Centralized vacuuming system

DIFFERENT VACUUM CLEANERS:-

a) CYLINDRICAL VACUUM CLEANER(DRY PICK UP):-

These machines work by suction. Electricity makes the motor work and dust is collected by high suction created by the motor and sucked in through the hose and collected in the dust bag inside the machine. Various attachments are used like floor cleaning head, crevice cleaning head, upholstery cleaning head etc for cleaning different areas. Most commonly used vacuum cleaners used for guest rooms.

b)UPRIGHT VACUUM CLEANER(DRY PICK UP)

The main body of the machine lies horizontally on the surface and does not have attachments but has built in hose for cleaning corners and upholstery. Mainly used for large carpeted areas

c) BACK PAC VACUUM CLEANER/PIGGYBACK VACUUMS/PAPOOSE(DRY PICK UP):-

Small lightweight vacuum cleaners which can be strapped at the back and used to clean upholstery, curtains

d)DUSTTETTES(DRY PICK UP) :-

Small lightweight battery operated vacuum cleaners used to vacuum clean upholstery, carpet edges, mattresses, curtain and stair cases etc. Can be carried in hand.

e)WET PICK UP VACUUM CLEANER :-

Picks up wet waste, excess waste water and used to pick up water from floor after scrubbing. This can also be used to remove excess moisture after shampooing the carpet. The machine has a squeeze head which is used to remove excess water and collected in a tank which is emptied after use.

f)LARGE TANK TYPE VACUUM CLEANER(DRY AND WET PICK UP)

Also called canister type vacuum cleaners or industrial vacuum cleaners and are used for dry and wet pick up both. Used for cleaning large areas like lobbies, banquet halls etc.

g) PILE LIFTER

It's a vacuum cleaner with two motors to make it extremely strong on action. The pile of the carpet usually flattens in use. Pile lifter grooms the pile of the carpet and restore their vertical orientation. It is not used daily. Mainly used before shampooing the carpet.

h) CENTRALIZED VACUUMING

Centralized vacuum cleaning system suction is generated at one point in a building. Soil is removed by suitable nozzles linked by flexible stretchable hoses to vacuum point. It is then conveyed by a network of pipes to a central container. This system is expensive to install and is generally done at the construction stage.

CARE AND STORAGE OF VACUUM CLEANERS:-

i) Wheels should be oiled regularly
ii) fter use dust bags or tanks should be emptied and cleaned.
iii) Clean attachment heads after cleaning work is done.
iv) If machine is dry pick up never try to pick wet waste.
v) Attachments should be stored in proper boxes.

(II) FLOOR MAINTENANCE MACHINE

This is a multi functional machine which can scrub, polish and buff the floors. The machines have driving discs (single disc or three small discs rotates on opposite directions) colored nylon pads, water tank, shampoo tank, sprayer which are used for different functions. Lighter the color of the pads lesser strong it is.

For scrubbing and stripping: Scrubbing is done with scrubbing brush or with scrubbing pad(black) attached to the disc which cut the soil.

For polishing: Red colored pads to apply polish on the floor

For buffing: beige or white pads are used to create high gloss finish.

(III) WET EXTRACTION MACHINES:-

Wet extraction machine are used to restore the surface appearance of carpet, upholstery and curtains. They remove deeply embedded soil not removed by suction cleaning.

Types of wet Extraction systems:-

a) Hot water extraction machine-They carry a hot water tank and detergent used for deep cleaning carpet with high pressure spray nozzles and a suction unit to remove soiled solution from the surface.
b) Solvent extraction machines- Used for cleaning upholstery and curtains.

(IV)SHAMPOOING MACHINES:-

Brushes are made of nylon as it needs to be strong to get through the carpet pile. They are fixed to the discs of the floor maintenance machine. There are special pressure tank along with a foam generator which produces the foam in dry form which cleans the carpet and suspends the soil. This way carpet does not get too wet.

(V)POWER SWEEPER:-

These are self or manually operated machines designed to remove debris and loose soil from floor, pavement, car park, and large areas.

(VI) SCARIFYING MACHINES:-Scarifying is a process of removing heavy grease, mud, thick deposits of dirt from floor by chisel like action with a wire brush cutting tool.

STORAGE AND CARE OF CLEANING EQUIPMENT:-

I) Equipment's should be stored in areas which are locked properly.
II) Proper records of issuing equipment's should be maintained(Area, attachments given, time issued, whom issued to, time of return)
III) Attachments and parts should be cleaned properly and stored after use.
IV) Brushes should never be faced downwards in the floor as it would damage the bristles.

CERAMICS

These materials are made from a mixture of sand and clay and are extremely porous unless a glaze or seal is applied to the outer surface during or after manufacture.

They are used both internally and externally as construction material as well as decorative finishes. They are also used as sanitary fittings, tableware and kitchenware. The most frequently found materials are: -

a) Earthenware
b) Stoneware
c) Vitreous china
d) Porcelain
e) Bone china
f) Brick
g) Marble
h) Concrete / cement
i) Terrazzo
j) Granolithic

Concrete and granolithic are mainly used as floor surfaces.

EARTHENWARE – This is a thick, heavy and very porous material, which is usually glazed for use. It chips easily and must be cleaned, stored & handled with care. It is cheap to produce. Used majorly for mugs, jugs, bowls, vases, goblets, ashtrays, etc.

STONEWARE – This is similar to earthenware but has more stone content. It is fire at very high temperature giving a stronger material, which is impervious, and so needs no glazing. Some stoneware is oven and flameproof.

VITEROUS CHINA – This is also fired at a very high temp than earthenware. It contains more flint, which makes it stronger but also very heavy. Some types of vitreous china have a high chip resistance and are used throughout hotels and institutions for crockery and sanitary ware.

PORCELAIN – This is a translucent earthenware containing china clay, stone and feldspar. It is very strong but also expensive and therefore rarely found in institutions. Mainly used for cups and saucers.

BONE CHINA – It is similar to porcelain but contains bone ash and less feldspar. It is fired at very high temperature, making it thin, strong and impervious. Mainly used for crockery.

CLEANING AND STORING

Great care should be taken in the cleaning and storage of these fine ceramic items to avoid chipping, cracking, scratching. Extreme temperatures should be avoided and they should be cleaned or soaked immediately after use to avoid harsh abrasives. A hot neutral synthetic detergent solution should be used followed by rinsing and drying, preferably in a dish washing machine where rinse aids can be used and drying occurs naturally. Stains, particularly those made by tea and coffee can be removed by rubbing a damp cloth and bicarbonate of soda.

LAYOUT OF GUEST ROOMS

Layout of guest might differ from room to room and from hotel to hotel. Layout entirely depends on the availability of space.

Most basic type of bed room in a hotel might consist of the following:

- Wardrobe
- Luggage rack

- Minibar
- Writing table cum dressing table.
- A chair for the writing table.
- A mirror attached to the wall for dressing.
- Two single seated sofa or a double seated sofa.
- A coffee table
- Bed/Beds with bedside table (bedside table may be termed as bedside console)
- Bedboard
- Proper upholstery
- Appropriate lighting
- A television
- A telephone

Bath will consist of the following:

- Vanitory unit (consist of wash basin)
- Mirror
- WC (water closet)
- Bidet(in some hotels)
- Bath tub
- Necessary faucets (taps & shower)
- Towel racks and holders
- Bottle opener and cloth hooks attached to the bath door.

Suite will have an additional living and dining space with sofa set and sofa side tables and also a dining table with chairs. Some suites also have different themes. Some suites also have bar set up or library space or a space with different fitness equipments etc.

More luxurious rooms (suite) may consist little extra:

A parlor (living room);

- Lounge (seating area with sofa/couch and centre table)
- Dinning room /dinning table
- A bar
- Reading space/ library
- Gym
- Small kitchenette
- Small wash room
- Balcony (optional)

The bed room:

- Luxurious bed
- Luxurious mattress
- Luxurious sofa/couch
- Coffee table
- Writing table and chair
- Minibar
- Luxurious soft furnishing

Dressing room:

- Wardrobes
- Mirror
- A stool

Bathroom:

- Vanitory unit (washbasin inbuilt)
- Mirror
- Hair drier
- Concave mirror
- Television
- Telephone
- Bathtub (may be of different shape and size)
- Towel racks
- Jacuzzi (whirlpool bath)
- Shower cubical

Toilet

- WC (water closet)
- Bidet (a unit to be used after using WC)
- News paper rack.
- Towel holder

FLOOR FINISHES

Floors are both functional and decorative and play an important part in the cleaning and maintenance program of any hotel. They cover a large area and are subjected to a great deal of wear and tear. Clean and well-kept floors indicate the standard of cleanliness throughout the establishment. Only in rare cases is the type of flooring chosen solely for luxury.Common considerations while choosing a flooring are: - Appearance – colour, design, cold, warmResistance to spills – water, grease, food, acid, etc.Ease of cleaning in relation to the type and amount of soilingSound and heat insulationNature and condition of sub floor.

Hard floors are usually sealed to give a non-absorbent, semi permanent gloss or finish which will wear off in time. Seal is applied on clean and dry floor. Before re-sealing any remaining seal has to be striped off. This is done with a chemical stripper, except in the case of wood and cork where sanding is done.

In order to preserve the seal, polish should be applied to sealed flooring. Polishes are usually spirit or water based. Spirit based floor polishes may be paste or liquid and require buffing when dry to produce a shine. Water based polishes are liquid and dries after application to give a shiny surface.

SUBFLOORS

In large modern buildings the subfloor is often made of concrete, but in older and smaller buildings it consists of soft wooden boards, nailed to wooden joints.

HARD FINISHES

Granolithic

Granolithic is hard floor finish of graded granite chips set in cement. It is used for basement corridors, storerooms, stairways and laundry. It is usually laid in tile form.

Terrazzo

This is also a hard floor finish, consisting of a mixture of marble and other decorative chipping set in fine cement that can be coloured. Marble is a rock (limestone) mainly found in Italy, and maybe white, black, green or brown. When used as a flooring it is laid in slabs. Marble is very expensive; terrazzo being only chips of marble is much cheaper. To prevent slipperiness self-polishing emulsions are applied. Terrazzo is used in foyers, cloakrooms and kitchens.

Removable pre-cast slabs can be made to cover service pipes for ease of maintenance.Coven edges facilitate cleaning.Not effected by water and may have a drain incorporated.Very durable.They are vermin proof, impervious to dry rot, and fire resistant.Cleaning is relatively easyInitial cost of granolithic is lower than terrazzo. : - Hard and noisyCold in appearanceTerrazzo is slippery when wet.Cracks may appear.Granolithic will chip, especially on stairs. In terrazzo, marble chipping may become loose.Acids and strong alkalis adversely effect terrazzo.

Clean regularlyAvoid strong alkalis on terrazzo.Attend to cracks and loose chipping immediately.

Magnesite

Magnesite flooring consists of wood floor and other fillers mixed with burnt magnesite, and laid in site (on the spot) or in form of small blocks. This finish is extremely porous and washing should be avoided as much as possible. It maybe sealed and /or polished to prevent the penetration of water and dirt, but then it becomes very slippery.

Moderately warmGood appearanceCleaning is relatively easyInitial cost is low

Hard and rather noisyLittle choice of colourBecomes slippery when polishedEasily harmed by water, acids, alkalis and abrasives.

Clean regularlyAvoid frequent washing

Bitumastic

This is a type of asphalt rolled on to a solid subfloor, in a hot plastic state. Conventionally found in black, red or brown colours only, it may have other colours rolled in, or surface maybe painted. It is used mainly in bathrooms to protect the floor from dampness.

Coven edges facilitate cleaningNot effected by water and may have a drain incorporated.Very durable.It is vermin proof and impervious to dry rot.Initial cost is low.Non-slippery.

Poor appearanceDents with heavy weightSoftens to heatHarmed by spirits, oils and acids.

Clean regularly Use special floor paint to restore colour whenever necessary.

Ceramic tiles

Ceramics are clayware and it's floor tiles are available in variety of qualities, colour and sizes. Tiles with a particularly hard glaze are used as more decorative floorings. A wide range of colours is available to harmonise with wall tiles. Tessellated tiles are small ceramic tiles often used as mosaic, giving highly decorative floor.

Removable pre-cast slabs can be made to cover service pipes for ease of maintenance.Coven edges facilitate cleaning.They are not affected by water and may have a drain incorporated.Available in many qualities, colours and size.Ridged and abrasive surfaced tiles can be used for a less slippery floor.Very durable. One loose tile may be replaced or reset.Not affected by acids, alkalis or grease.They are vermin proof, impervious to dry rot and fire resistant.Cleaning is very easy.

Hard and noisyCold in appearanceSlippery when wet or greasy.Under heavy weight, they crack or break easilyMarks are difficult to removeInitial cost is average.

Clean regularlyAttend to loose and broken tiles.

Wood

Wood finishes of good quality are among the most beautiful flooring, provided the variety of wood and size of the unit are chosen for effect. As floorings are to be laid bare and are subject to tremendous wear and tear, only hard wood must be used.

Strip wood flooring

A strip wood flooring consists of lengths of narrow strips (under 4"wide) of hard wood of good appearance. E.g. Maple. The boards are fixed to joists or to timber insets in concrete. This construction together with the length of strips, gives the floor it's resilience properties and makes it suitable for dance floors. A sprung floor has springs under the joists to increase the resilience.

Wood block flooring

A wood block flooring consists of rectangular blocks (e.g. 9"x3"or 12"x2") laid with an adhesive on a level concrete base. Blocks are generally laid to form a pattern. Wood used is generally oak, teak, jarrah, missanda, etc. When used in linen rooms, store rooms or staff halls, it is chosen for it's durability and insulation rather than for their appearance.

Parquet flooring

In appearance parquet flooring resembles wood block flooring. It also consists of rectangular pieces of wood but the blocks are much thinner (less than 3/8"in thickness) and are pinned and glued to a wooden subfloor, often in a herring bone pattern. It is used in foyers and lounges in conjunction with rugs. Cheaper parquet flooring may only have a veneer of a good quality wood on the surface and thus form a much less hardwearing surface.

Wood mosaics

Wood mosaics are generally made up in panels (18"sq formed of four ½"squares in basket pattern). It is backed with felt or aluminium. It is laid directly on concrete with an adhesive or as an overlay on an existing floor.

Available in varying colours and grainsGive a good appearance when used in strips or parquet.Hardwearing and does not require frequent repairs.Surface can be sanded and fresh surface exposed.Very good as heat insulator.

NoisyInflammable and susceptible to dry rot.Splinters if heavy item is dragged on itIf not sealed, they are absorbent and cleaning can become laborious and expensiveInitial cost is high

Clean regularly and polish with wax polish.Attend to loose blocks and splinters.Resurface by sanding when necessary

Available in variety of colours.Very durable.Easy cleaning.

Hard and hence noisy.Cold in appearance.Slippery when wet.Easily harmed by spirits, grease and coarse abrasives.Dent with heavy weights and soften with heat.Scratches occur with grit and sharp edges.Gets badly marked, especially with rubber heels.

Clean regularly.Use water base polish, not spirit based ones.Replace loose or broken tiles as soon as possible.

Relatively non-slip.Have great resistance to wear and tear, especially the flexible type.Generally grease and oil resistant.Resistant to acids and alkalis.More resistant to point load than thermoplastic tiles.Not easily scratched.Can be easily washed and polished.

SEMI-HARD FINISHES

Thermoplastic floor finish

Thermoplastic floor tiles are made from a variety of asphalt binders with inert fillers and pigments. The tiles are usually 9"square, and are laid on a clean, smooth, rigid surface, set as closely together as possible with the help of an adhesive. They are laid in warm pliable state (thermoplastic) but harden on cooling and may be carried up to the wall to form a small coven skirting. They are polished with water based polish, and are used in bathrooms, cloakrooms, corridors, offices, etc.

Vinyl

They are available in two main types.

Vinyl asbestos, which is obtained only in tile form, is slightly flexible and is manufactured from PVC or similar synthetic resins, inert fillers including short fiber asbestos, and pigments. It is available in wide range of colours and the tiles can be stuck to a solid subfloor with a suitable adhesive.

A flexible form is based on PVC or similar synthetic resins, inert fillers, pigments and plasticisers. It is available in tiles, or sheet form when it is sometimes mounted on canvas or other suitable backing material. There is coven skirting available and the sheet material can be used as a protective skirting.

Both types maybe used in bathrooms, cloakrooms, canteens, offices, etc.

GLASS

Glass is a complete mixture of several silicates; all glass contains silica. Common soda glass contains sodium and calcium silicates and has the approximate composition Na2O, CaO, 5SiO2. In addition to or in place of soda (Na2O) and lime (CaO), special glasses may contain potash (K2O), bartya (BaO), magnesia (MgO), lead oxide (PhO), and zinc oxide (ZnO). They may also sometimes contain borate and phosphates. The properties of glass are profoundly modified by it's composition, and hence based on composition glass can be classified into: -

1. Soft glass / Soda glass / Soda lime glass – It contains sodium and calcium sili cates. It is used for general-purpose glassware – flat or hollow glassware.
2. Lead crystal glass / Flint glass – It contains potassium and lead silicates and has high density and refractive index. Hence it is used in making lens prisms. It is also used for decorative purposes (as cut glass). It is very expensive and used mainly for bowls, drinking glasses, vases, etc., which are not in constant use. In flint glass very soft lead is used in the form of litharge (PhO) or red lead (Ph3O4).
3. Borosilicate glass / Jena glass / Pyrex glass – They are highly resistant to the action ofheat and chemical reagents and are used to make baking dishes.

- Jena Glass – Contains zinc and barium oxides and boron trioxide in place of some silica.

- Pyrex glass – Contains boron trioxide and is very rich in silica. It contains sodium and aluminium boro-silicates.

4. Flat glass – This is made from soda lime glass and is used for windows, shelves, etc. they are of two main types –

- Sheet glass – It is drawn continuously from the matter mass and passed through and annealing tower after which it can be cut into the required lengths.
- Float glass – It is like plate glass in many instances, but unlike plate glasses it doesn't need to be ground and polished after annealing.

  Both are made from very refined ingredients and provide clear, undistorted vision and are used for shop windows, mirrors and protective coverings on furniture. The edges are often leveled; i. e. cut at an angle, while those on shelves are ground and corners rounded.

5. Silvered glass – They are used for mirrors. It is made by coating one side of the glass panel with silver and some case copper, followed by a coat of paint and a layer of stove enamel. Silvered glass maybe used as tiles or mosaics or as reflective sheets.
6. Laminated safety glasses – Much used in automobiles, it is made by enameling together two sheets of thin plate glass with a layer of non-brittle plastic material (e.g. transparent cellulose acetate or polyvinyl butyral) in between. When glass breaks under impact, the fragments are held in place by the flexible inner layer.
7. Fiberglass – Glass is reduced to flexible filaments or threads. It is an excellent heat insulator. Fiberglass is woven into fabric for fireproof curtains. Glass is also spun into short fibers, known as glass wool.
8. Coloured glass – This is made by adding various metallic oxides which yield coloured silicates or other substances to the molten glass in course of it's manufacture.

Colour of glass
Colouring agent
Ruby red
Gold, selenium, cuprous oxide
Blue
Cobalt oxide, cupric acid
Milky
Fluorspar with felspar, tin dioxide or calcium phosphate
Yellow
Cadmium sulphide, uranium oxide
Green
Chromic oxide, ferric oxide
Amber
Carbonaceous material with sulphur or iron sulphide
Black
Excess of ferric oxide

MANUFACTURE

Ordinary glass is made by a fusion of a mixture of glass sand, soda ash and limestone (SiO2, Na2O, and CaO). Silica is the glass former, soda acts as flux, and lime is the stabilizer conferring durability to the glass. In addition small quantities of Sodium Sulphate, Sodium Nitrate, Flurospar Arsenic Oxide, etc are added to act as melting refining aids. As glass in molten state is a viscous liquid, it entraps bubbles (Co2, SO2, steam etc). Removal of these bubbles is called refining. Iron Oxide is the major impurity that enters into glass through raw materials and imparts unwanted colour to the glass.

The glass furnace is a rectangular chamber lined with superior quality refractory blocks that can withstand high temperature (1600degree C). It has two chambers – one for melting and refining; and the other for working where homogenised molten glass is withdrawn. A constant level of molten glass is maintained by introducing raw materials at one end and withdrawal of molten glass at other end. Somewhat colder molten glass is drawn from the working chamber and shaped into articles manually or by machine.

After shaping the glass article has to be cooled very carefully. This process is called annealing. Glass that is cooled rapidly is brittle due to the existence of internal strain and is liable to crack on heating, or receiving slight shocks or scratches. If cooled too slowly, glass denitrifies, i. e. some of the components start to crystallize out separately rendering the glass opaque. All glassware is therefore annealed to reduce the internal strain by heating for sometime at a temperature just below the softening point of glass (around 500 degrees C), so that the articles don't get deformed. Then they are slowly and uniformly cooled. Annealing oven is a tunnel like furnace, hot at one end and provided with a slowly moving frame holding the glassware. This might sometimes take days.

TYPES

Obscured and Safety glass: - Both are made from sheet or flat glass.

Obscured glass is required for bathrooms and other places where light requires passing without it being transparent, often having a pattern on one side. This is produced by passing molten glass between embossed rollers.

Safety glass maybe

Embossed glass with wire: Wire is incorporated during rolling process. Wire prevents glass fragments from falling when broken.

Laminated glass: Made by sticking two thin sheets of glass with a vinyl type plastic in between

Toughened glass: This is made by subjecting the glass to a temperature just below the softening point and then cooling the surface layer rapidly. This forms a skin on top of the glass and if broken the glass shatters into small, harmless fragments.

Toughened and laminated glass: This is five times stronger than any other types of safety glass.

Enamels: - Enamels are fusible glass rendered opaque by pacifiers like tin dioxide, titanium oxide and zirconium oxide, which are applied cold; and fused to the metal surface at red heat. The raw material for the enamel glass includes quartz, felspar & fluxes, borax and soda ash. Enameling of Iron or Brass ware prevents atmospheric corrosion. Enameled wares are in large demand as sanitary and cooking ware, nameplates, signboards, refrigerator and diary equipment, etc.

Glaze: - Glaze is a thin coating of easily fusible glass molted on to the surface of the more or less porous ceramic ware. The glaze composition includes refractory ingredients (felspar, silica, china clay & lime) and fluxes (soda, potash, borax, lead oxide) in different proportions.

MAINTAINING GLASS SURFACES

Daily care involves damp or dry dusting, preferably with lintfree cloth such as paper or scrim. High soiling and greasy finger marks can be removed by wiping with a solution of equal quantities of vinegar and water or a mixture of 18ml ammonia to half bucket of warm water. More stubborn marks such as make-up and toothpaste deposits found in mirrors can be removed by wiping with a solvent such as methylated spirit. Newspaper prints contain solvents and can be used to clean windowpanes and mirrors. Textured or engraved glass should be cleaned occasionally with a very soft brush. Use of abrasives should be avoided.

HARD SURFACES

Types used in Hotel Industry

1. Metals : Aluminum, Brass, Copper, Pewter, Gold, Silver, Steel, Stainless Steel, Tin, Iron, Bronze, EPNS (Electro plated nickel silver), Chromium, etc.
2. Wood : Solid, Plywood, Chipboard, Hardboard, Blackboard, Laminated sheet, Cork, Cane, Wicker, Bamboo, etc.
3. Plastic : Thermosetting and Thermoplastics.
4. Ceramics : Earthenware, Stoneware, Vitreous China, Porcelain, Bone China, Brick
5. Glass : Lead Crystal, Sodalime, Borosilicate, Glass Fiber
6. Rubber : Vulcanised.

The wide range found creates many problems for the Housekeeping as each requires different cleaning procedures. Measures are taken to standardise them in some way by applying protective coatings or finishes. Their maintenance can become very costly and time consuming. Hard surfaces will scratch, crack, chip, perish, splinter, blister and may become dangerously slippery.

Reasons for choosing hard surfaces –

- Hygienic
- Aesthetic appeal
- Insulation
- Easy for daily maintenance

METALS

Metal surfaces are generally protected to prevent tarnishing, scratching or rusting, depending on the reason it is being used for.

Methods of protecting metal surfaces :-

- Painting – It is usually applied to steel or wrought iron, which is used for decorative purpose. Paint prevents the metal from coming in contact with oxygen and moisture, which causes it to rust.
- Enameling – This method gives a colorful gloss or matt finish to steel or cast-iron pans, signboards, blackboards, etc. molten glass is applied to the surface which sets to form a tough easily cleanable surface.
- Plastic Coating – P.V.C, acrylic and polyester plastics can be used to cover handrails, table & chair legs, broom handles etc.

- Electroplating – Electrolysis is used to deposit metals such as chromium, copper, zinc, tin, silver & gold on surfaces as nickel, brass, steel and copper. This finish is widely used for cutlery, restaurant equipment, cooking equipment, furniture and fittings.
- Galvanising – The base metal is coated with a layer of zinc to reduce corrosion and is extensively used for mop buckets, dustbins, pot sinks,etc.
- Anodising – This is an Electro – chemical process which enhances the appearance of aluminum and increases it's resistance to soiling and corrosion. It is used for door and window fittings etc.
- Lacquering – This is usually applied to copper and brass by painting or spraying and effectively reduces tarnishing to a minimum.
- Tinplate – Items such as cheese graters, sieves, wire whisks and copper pans, etc.may be coated with or dipped into molten tin, as tin has good corrosion resistance.

SILVER

This is a relatively soft metal found naturally in the earth. It is a white metal, unaffected by water, pure air and majority of foodstuff. It is worn away by abrasion.

Sterling silver is an alloy containing 92.5% silver and the remainder substantially copper, which is added to harden the silver, and yet not change any properties of the metal. Sterling is obviously more expensive than silverplate and is seldom used in hotels and other establishments.

Silver plated wares are made from blanks or bodies of a nickel, silver and brass alloy. They are immersed in a complex solution of silver salts and by means of electrolysis, silver is transferred to the blanks. These articles are also called EPNS or electroplated nickel silver article.

The tarnishing of silver is due to the action of compounds of sulphur present in the atmosphere and in certain foodstuff such as eggs, onions, juices, pickles, etc. the tarnish is silver sulphide and varies in colour from yellow, through brown, to blue – black. Tarnish can be removed by –

Silver dips – Articles are dipped in an acidic solution of thiourea compound and then washed and dried. No friction is needed. This liquid attacks stainless steel and should be used only in a glass, earthenware, or plastic container.

Polivit method – the silver articles are immersed in a hot soda solution containing a sheet of aluminum for 10 min. During this period a chemical exchange takes place. The articles are then removed, washed and dried.

The silver after being cleaned by these methods should be polished to restore it's shine by any of the following methods –

Proprietary preparations – This is based on precipitated whiting and jewelers rouge. E.g. – Silvo.

A burnishing machine – Highly polished steel balls rubs against silver articles immersed in a detergent solution. The machine rotates and friction is applied on the articles by the steel balls. After this article is washed and dried.

Uses of Silver – cutlery, restaurant wares, ornaments, vases, bowls, etc.

COPPER

It can be used in solid form or plate applied on mild steel. Acids corrode it. It's tarnishing is a result of oxidation in a moist atmosphere to form green verdigris. Abrasives will scratch or wear away surfaces.

Uses : Table tops, wall panels / surfaces, utensils, decorative furniture, ornaments, etc.

Protective coating : Lacquering, long term polish (lacquering can be removed with acetone if necessary)

Clean with a paste made of equal quantities of vinegar, salt and flour. Polish with proprietary polish, e.g., Brasso.

BRASS

It's an alloy of copper and zinc. It maybe solid or plate applied on mild steel. Corroded by acids. Tarnishing occurs as a result of oxidation in a moist atmosphere to form green verdigris. Application of abrasives will scratch or wear away surface.

Composition : Cu – 60 – 80 %, Zn – 40 – 20 %

Uses : furniture, door and window fittings, foot rails, taps, object d'art, decorative finishes, ornaments, etc.

Protective coating : Lacquering, long term polish.

Tarnishing can be avoided by lacquering. Lacquered items can be maintained by buffing with flannel for a shine to develop. Unlacquered articles can be polished with a brass polish (e.g., Brasso) or a mixture of equal quantities of tamarind and salt..

Corroded brass should be treated with spirits of salts and then rinsed thoroughly. In very bad cases soak for 12 hrs in washing soda solution (approx. 50gms), then rinse and polish.

STEEL

Steel is iron containing little carbon and small quantities of other materials like nickel, chromium, vanadium, manganese, etc.

Uses : Used as pressed steel for bath sinks, etc.

To prevent corrosion it is often coated with enamel.

STAINLESS STEEL

It is an alloy of iron, chromium and nickel. Chromium is added to make it resistant to corrosion, acids & alkalis. It is tough, durable metal and usually has a mirror polish or satin finish. It can be harmed by silver dip solution, chlorine type bleaches, salt/ vinegar mixtures. These act on the surface and cause discoloration. Black deposits occur if left in contact with moist aluminum or galvanised surfaces due to deposition of zinc by electrochemical action. Stainless steel needs only simple washing and drying.

Composition : 18/8 steel contains 18% chromium and 8% nickel with the rest iron. Chromium contents vary between 8 – 25%

Uses : sinks, W/Cs, cutlery, wall tiles or panels, work surfaces, kitchenware, bowls, furniture, decorative finishes. (cutlery is usually 18/8 steel)

ALUMINIUM

It is resistant to corrosion. On the surface it forms a layer of aluminum oxide which resists attacks. It can be damaged by strong alkalis, stained by acids and scratches easily.

Uses: utensils, light fittings, venetian blinds, window/door frames and fittings, furniture, decorative finishes.

Protective coating: Anodising

For maintenance use hot synthetic detergent solution. Do not use soda or bleach. Use abrasives with care. Remove discolouration in saucepans by boiling a solution of water and lemon rind in it. Or add 15ml laundry borax to 500 ml washing solution.

To maintain gloss on showpieces, apply liquid wax polish.

ANODISED ALUMINIUM

A protective layer of aluminum is deposited on the surface during manufacture. If abrasives are used, the protective layer is removed and white powdery spots will appear.

PEWTER

It's an alloy of tin, copper and antimony. Tarnishes easily and has little resistance to alkalis, acids and abrasives.

Uses: ornaments, tableware.

Protective coating: lacquering

Maintenance: Wash in warm synthetic detergent solution and rub well when drying. Remove grease with methylated spirit before washing. Polish with a proprietary metal polish.

BRONZE

An alloy of tin and copper with properties similar to brass.

Uses: same as brass.

Protective coating: lacquering

GOLD

Can be used in solid form or as a plate or leaf. It is resistant to acid, alkalis and tarnishing. It corrodes if exposed to mercury.

Uses: ornaments, decorative finishes.

TIN

Used as a layer of plate on mild steel, brass or copper. It has good resistance to acids and alkalis.

Uses: food containers.

CHROMIUM

Used in a thin layer of plate on mild steel or brass. Surface oxidation can result in formation of white spots. Reacts with alkalis causing surface discoloration. Abrasives will wear away plate. These can become water spotted and greasy but will not tarnish. Washing and rubbing up is sufficient to keep up shine.

Uses: On taps, bath handles, shower fittings, furniture, etc.

ZINC

This is also used as a coating on steel and is commonly known as galvanized steel

Uses: buckets, furniture, dustbins.

PLASTICS

Plastics are a group of substances with similar though not identical properties. Their common properties are: -

1. Light in weight
2. Less noisy than any other material
3. Resistant to most chemicals
4. Non-conductor of electricity
5. Scratches with harsh abrasives and sharp articles
6. Easy to clean
7. Non-absorbent
8. Some are thermoplastic and absorb grease
9. Not liable to be attacked by moths and other pests

Various types

Polyvinyl chloride – This has many uses. Plastic floor finished in tile or sheet form are

generally based on PVC and it maybe incorporated with inert fillers, pigments and plasticisers, or it may form a surface layer on some suitable backing. It is also used as wall coverings as tiles or as a coating on wallpapers. It is used in soiled or waste pipes and translucent ceilings.

Polystyrene and some other forms – Polyurethane can be produced as a foam and this when set maybe used in tile or sheet form on walls and ceilings to give in heat and sound insulation, but there is a considerable fire risk.

Polyurethane and polythene are also produced as foams whish have resilience and can be cut into required sizes for mattresses and into different shapes for upholstered furniture. Polyurethane is also used as a clear seal on wooden floor and furniture.

Laminates – Melamine, phenols and other resins are used to produce plastics. They maybe stuck direct onto the wall, plywood or similar supporting material.

Synthetic fibers – polyamides, polyesters and acrylics, etc maybe produced as fibers or long filaments and woven into textiles. These synthetic fibers, owing to their great strength and poor absorbency, are durable, easy to clean and quick to dry.

Plastic can normally be maintained just by wiping, dusting or washing in hot water and synthetic detergent.

WALL COVERINGS

Wall coverings maybe purely decorative, in which case, ability to bring colour, pattern, texture, light or shade to the room maybe of the greatest importance. On the other hand the covering maybe required to give an easily cleaned and hygienic surface. The choice is very wide and the style should suit the purpose, furnishing and the architectural aspects of the room. The type of finish selected will depend largely on: -

1. Contribution to décor: - The colour, texture and pattern will influence the apparent warmth and dimension of the room and the level and type of illumination used. The type of room, it's existing size and decoration must be considered.
2. Ease of cleaning: - Smooth, hard, impervious surface, preferably light coloured can be cleaned easily; whereas textured surfaces tend to attract and hold dust.

3. State of existing surface: - textured and patterned finishes can be used to mask poor surfaces.
4. Resistance to abrasion and knocks: - Hard surfaces will be best for this purpose.
5. Stain resistance: - A non-porous surface has more resistance than porous ones.
6. Durability: - Surfaces subject to abuse, knocks, stains and abrasion require finishes that are resistant, can be cleaned easily, inexpensively restored or repaired whenever required.
7. Life expectancy: - Where décor of the room is intended to change relatively frequently, less expensive finishes are appropriate.
8. Insulation: - How-much-ever possible finishes with good sound insulation properties should be selected.
9. Cost: - While comparing cost of different finishes, not only should the cost of the material and its application be considered; but also the cost of it's damage restoration and expected frequency of complete redecoration should be borne in mind.

TYPES OF WALL COVERINGS

PAINTS AND LACQUERS

Paints can be applied to almost any surface providing it is free from water, grease or dust and is of sound construction. E.g. plaster must be smooth, hard and not flaking from the underlying plaster or brickwork. As wall covering paints offer a wide choice of types, colours, degrees of gloss and designs (murals can be painted). For window frames and sills, door and skirting boards, slightly glossy paint is required so that along with providing a contrast in colour and texture to the main wall finish, it acts as a protective coating, and thus contributing to décor of the room. It is relatively cheap, easily applied and cleaned and can give a textured and multicoloured effect. The only disadvantage is that it shows soils (especially for matt paints) and wall imperfections (in gloss paints) more readily than any other wall covering.

The main types of paints used are:- Emulsion
Alloyd
Multicoloured
Textured or Plastic
Microporous

Emulsion paints – They are water thinned but are based on dispersions of synthetic resins (e.g. polyvinyl acetate). They are tough, washable and wear resistant; and available in varying degrees of sheen, from matt, to semi–gloss, to silk finish. They are quick drying, low in odor and very suitable for redecoration of rooms, which cannot remain long out of use.

Alloyd paints – They are based on synthetic resins combined with vegetable oil such as linseed oil. The conventional types were natural resins, which are still used in primers and undercoat paints. Alloyed paints are generally easier to apply and have better durability and wearing properties than any other type. Polyutherene and silicone are sometimes included to give more scratch resistant surface. They are available in gloss, silk and flat finishes.

Multicoloured paints – They are usually dispersions of cellulose colours in water. Each colour is present in separate "blobs"or "spots". The resulting effect depends on number of different colours, degree of contrast between them and the size and distribution of spots. This paint should be applied by spraying. It is extremely hardwearing and the multicolour effect helps in hiding irregularities and imperfections. It is usually applied on walls of corridors, sanitary accommodations, and similar areas, to give a stain and abrasion resistant finish, which can be washed and cleaned regularly.

Textured or Plastic paints – They are usually plaster based and are intended to give a textured or relief effect on surface. The texture is obtained by working over the material after application and while it is still wet, using combs, palette, knives, strippers, etc. Some are self-coloured while others may require painting when they dry. The modern types are based on heavy-bodied synthetic resin emulsion and may be applied by spraying directly on the concrete or similar surfaces; thus eliminating the need of plaster.

Microporous paints – they have a rubberised base which gives little gloss but offers elasticity and allowing movement when the surface expands or contracts.

WALLPAPER

They may be smooth or have a textured surface effect. This may be done by superimposing or interlacing of other substance to give a rough surface, or by clever designing when visual effect gives an apparent depth (dimensional effect). Smooth finishes are more resistant to dust and dirt than rough ones, but generally stains show more in smooth finishes.

The pattern maybe floral, geometric, abstract, striped, etc. The choice depends on the room's aspect, height, size and use of room. Large patterned papers tend to overpower and tend to make the room appear smaller than it actually is. Wastage is also higher as patterns have to be cut to match each other. In addition to conventional wallpapers, now many paper-backed materials are also available, e.g. fabrics, wood, veneers, plastic, etc.

The main types are –

1. Surface printed paper – A pattern is applied to the surface of the paper by one of the following methods – hand printing
   Screen-printing A wide range of colours and designs are produced with usually a smooth surface finish. The cost is related to the design and the method of reproduction. The paper is not washable and damp wiping must be undertaken with great care. It can be easily soiled and stained.
2. Spongeable paper – They are specially treated during manufacturing to withstand water. They are similar in all other aspects to surface printed paper.
3. Washable papers – Similar to surface printed papers, but has a plastic coating giving it good stain resistance and enabling it to withstand washing.
4. Anaglypts – It's an embossed paper that is relatively inexpensive. Used to cover poor surfaces, it is normally painted after hanging. It's stain resistance and washability depends on the type of paint applied.
5. Lincrusts – A heavily embossed paper that may have a plastic coating, containing a paper backed textured composition and frequently stimulating wood paneling.

6. Oatmeal papers (wood chip) – Wooden floor or chips are sandwiched between two layers of paper. It's properties are similar to anaglypts paper.
7. Flock papers – A raised patterned pile is fixed by adhesive to a paper backing. The piles maybe cotton, silk, wool or synthetic. It attracts and holds dust and is expensive. The surface of the paper maybe damp wiped.
8. Metallic papers – Paper printed with gold or other metallic powder.
9. Food grain paper – Photographic reproduction of various food grains waxed during manufacture.
10. Paper backed hessains – Strands of hessiains fixed to a paper backing to give the appearance of a hessian coverings. It is not washable but surface can be damp wiped. It is easily stained and damaged by abrasion. It's available in large variety of colours.
11. Paper with felt backing.
12. Paper backed woven grasses – Pieces of grass are fixed by adhesives to a backing of paper or silk.
13. Paper backed wools – Fine or coarse strands of wool in natural colours or bright dyes are laid in a parallel fashion on a paper backing. They give a warm effect and provide good insulation.

Advantages of wallpaper
Contribution to décor
Ability to cover poor surfaces
Insulation
Disadvantages: -
Costly
Limited use
Not abrasive resistant
Stains easily
Difficult to clean
Cannot be easily restored
Not very durable

PVC Cloths – They are woven cotton finished with a layer of PVC, and are used to form decorative panels on walls or doors. It maybe plain or quilted, involving the use of a foam stuffing and fixed by adhesive or metal studs. It produces a luxurious effect, improves sound and thermal insulation but is expensive and difficult to repair satisfactorily.

Leather (hide) wall coverings – They are extremely expensive but very decorative. They maybe padded and studded with brass studs. They are usually not used to cover the whole wall. It's effect wherever required can be stimulated with plastics.

Plastic wall coverings – They are available in large variety. Owing to their abrasion resistance, they are more hard wearing and easily cleaned than any other covering. As they are non-porous, tendency for growth of moulds is higher. Therefore, adhesive should contain fungicides, or fungicidal wash should be applied on the wall prior to applying the wall covering.

The various types are: -

a) Paper backed vinyl – The vinyl may have the appearance of almost any material. E.g. silk, tweed, hessain, cork, grass paper, wood, stone or brick.
b) Fabric backed vinyl – Similar in appearance to the paper backed ones but is more durable.
c) Vinyl flock paper
d) Plastic wall tiles – Imitating ceramic tiles.
e) Laminated plastic – As a veneer or surface board, melamine is the resin frequently used during manufacture of these plastic laminates which may stimulate wood paneling. E.g. Formica.
f) Expanded polyutherene – It is used in sheets or tiles on walls and coiling to give heat and sound insulation, and helps eliminate condensation. It can be painted with emulsion paint or covered with paper. Spirits dissolves it and hence if oil paint is to be applied on it, it has to be lined with paper and given a coat of emulsion paint to act as a buffer. Polyutherene is inflammable, and hence it has to be treated to avoid fire risks.

Fabric wall coverings – it is possible to cover the wall surface with any fabric and it's durability will depend on the type of fiber and the weave used during it's manufacture. Fabrics used as wall coverings can be divided into two categories – Woven fabrics, e.g. hessian (used as wallpaper)

Hangings, e.g. tapestries, oriental carpets, drape.

Fabrics chosen should not be liable to sag, buckle or stretch when hung permanently on the wall and should not collect excessive dust or dirt.

Wild silk or other beautiful fabric maybe padded for heat and sound insulation but silks and tapestries are expensive, and thus found only in luxurious establishments only. Hessain, linen and some acetate viscose fabrics are cheaper and used more extensively. Fabrics are subject to attack by moths and mildew, hence proper proofing should be done.

WOOD PANELING

Wood used for paneling are usually hard, well seasoned and of a decorative appearance. Most commonly types used are oak, mahogany, teak, etc. it may cover the wall from corner to corner. It maybe solid or veneered and finished with wax polish, french polish or lacquer. It will last for years with little maintenance, providing precautions are taken in respect of dry rot and rot worm, though initial installing cost will be high. Wood paneling is usually found in enterance halls, staircases, assembly halls, boardrooms and restaurant.

GLASS WALL COVERING

Glass can be used in the form of decorative tiles, mosaics, bricks or full sheet. Glass bricks allow light to pass through the wall itself. Coloured opaque glass sheets or tiles maybe used in bathrooms. Mirror tiles are used to reflect light and to alter the apparent size of the room or corridor. Sometimes antique mirror tiles are used to give a duller surface with lesser reflection. Large uniform mirrors maybe used to cover the whole wall like over a vanity unit, or dressing table or on a corridor wall. A glassless mirror is also available which is lighter (almost 1/5th the weight of the conventional mirror), does not form mist and will not shatter if dropped. It consists of polyester film, vaccume coated with aluminium and mounted on a flat frame.

METAL WALL COVERING

Metals may be used as wall coverings for their hygienic qualities. Copper and annodised aluminium are decorative and maybe used in areas such as bars where metals in combination with rows of bottles and interesting lighting creates an impressive effect. Stainless sleet is used in tile form in kitchens where they present a durable, easily cleaned, hygienic surface. Metal skirting boards covers edges between wall and floor surfaces. Metal foil can be elegantly and sparingly used as a wall covering. Foil is available in variety if colours.

OTHER MATERIALS

Various flooring materials can also be used as wall coverings. They provide different colours, patterns and texture. Though expensive, they are hardwearing and abrasion resistant. The various types are: - Linoleum

Cork (in tiles or sheets)
Carpets
Marble
Terrazzo
Ceramic tiles
Granite
Bricks & stones (these can be used for exterior wall and left unplastered.
Also used in fireplaces and chimney breasts to give a
Decorative finish.)

CLEANING PROCEDURES

PAINTED SURFACE –

1) Remove light dust
2) Damp wipe or wash if necessary and permissible (when washing start from the bottom and work upwards)
3) Never apply wax polish or oil to gloss painted surface.
4) Do not use harsh abrasive, strong solvents, or strong soda solution.

WALL PAPERS

1) Remove surface dust (use low suction for flock papers)
2) Remove marks by rubbing or sponging
3) Attempt to remove grease.

FABRIC WALLCOVERINGS

1) Remove surface dust
2) For beautiful hangings dismantle and send to professional drycleaners.
3) Where hessains is stuck to the wall, scrub very lightly. If necessary use warm water and detergent.

WOOD PANELLINGS

1) Remove surface dust
2) Polish if necessary

3) Where paneling has become dirty or greasy, wipe with white spirit or vinegar and water. Then repolish.
4) Dark oak maybe wiped over with beer.

GLASS WALLCOVERING

1) Dust or wipe with a damp chamois leather or scrim.
2) Care should be taken while cleaning mirrors so that the damp does not go into the back.

METAL WALLCOVERINGS

1) Dust or wipe with damp cloth
2) Polish if necessary. (not required daily)

LEATHER WALLCOVERINGS

1) Remove surface dust
2) Apply polish sparingly and rub well.

PROTECTION

Life expectancy of a wall covering or finish can be increased and the cost of cleaning, maintenance and restoration reduced in several ways.

Selection of finish should be suitable fort he degree of soilage, abuse and damage expected.

Select a covering that does not hold and attract dust, can be easily cleaned and restored if damaged or stained.

Use a more durable and easy to clean and maintain surface for the lower part of the wall.

Use plastic sheets on less durable surfaces that are subjected to staining and knocks.

Fit fingerplates on doors, light switches and other places where hands will constantly come in contact with the surface.

Use doorstoppers to prevent damage to surfaces behind the door.

Use kick plates to protect the lower part of the door.

Treat porous surfaces with soil retardant finish.

WOOD

These hard surfaces are porous in nature and are used due to various reasons: -

Appearance

Resilience

Cost

Insulation

Porous materials absorb not only liquids but also dust. They scumb to fungal attack and pest infection. Regular inspection and maintenance are required for them to withstand regular wear and tear and to maintain it's appearance.

There are two types of wood in use – hard wood & soft wood

Hard wood is strong and is used for

- Floors (strips, board, block, parquet, mosaic)
- Furniture

- Wall (paneling)
- Incidental furniture (lampshades, picture frames)
- Kitchen and restaurant wares

It has more refined grains than softwood and the short fibers make it less likely to splinter, swell or dent. Hardwood is usually darker than softwood, and more expensive. They include teak, mahogany, oak walnut and beech.

Soft wood such as pine, dell and fir are used for construction of furniture, subfloor, joints, ceilings, broom handles, etc., where the wood is either covered up or out of public view.

WOOD PRODUCTS

These are less expensive as compared to solid wood items. The most commonly used ones include: -

- Plywood
- Chipboard
- Hardboard
- Blockboard

Plywood – It is made by bonding together a number of thin sheets (piles) of wood (usually hardwood) in such a way that the grain of one sheet lies at right angles to those on either side of it. It can be bent to any shape during manufacture and may have as many as nine piles. It's very strong and maybe covered with plastic laminate or a hardwood veneer.

Chipboard – It is used extensively for worktops, wardrobes, chests of drawers, etc. and nearly always has a wood veneer or plastic laminate. It is heavy and strong but flexible. It is made by mixing wood chips with a synthetic resin adhesive.

Hardboard – It is more flexible than chipboard and much thinner. Made from compressed brown fireboard, it is smooth on one side with a mesh texture on other. Hardboard is used as a backing for wardrobes, base of drawers, doorpanels, backing for pictures, base for floor tiles, etc.

Blockboards – This consists of strips of wood between veneers. The inner strips of wood are fairly thick (upto 30 mm) making it a strong material usually used for making shelves and table tops.

Wood products are nearly always faced with a plastic laminate, sunmica, formica or wood veneer. Hence they should be cleaned according to their outer surface. However all of them will deteriorate if excessive amount of water is allowed to penetrate.

CORK

It is used in the form of tiles or strips in varying width. It is extremely porous and will easily crumble, dent, burn and stain. Its high porous property also means that it has good insulating properties. It is ideal for notice boards and bathmats, but is also used as floors and walls. Various forms of cork are –

- Natural
- Resin sealed
- Waxed
- Vinyl coated

Cork floors are made from granulated cork moulded into blocks and then subjected to high pressure and temperature. Natural resin is used to bind the granules. The blocks are then cut into tiles of requires size and thickness (usually 0.5-1 cm)

Advantages – Give a warm and tasteful appearance

Very quite

Disadvantages – Very absorbent

Burnt easily by cigarette ends

Have little resistance to indentation when granules become loose.

Uses – in offices, corridors, bathrooms, etc.

CANE, WICKER AND BAMBOO

These are names given to items made from thick grasses (bamboo), palms (cane), willow sheets (wicker). They have similar characteristics to timber products but are usually woven or plaited into chairs, tables, headboards, etc. They are easily damaged and regular cleaning is necessary. Cleaning includes brushing or vacuuming everyday and wiping approximately once a week with a solution of warm water and washing soda or solution of 5ml borax in 50-ml water. Both methods should be followed by rinsing with cold water in strands. Oil or wax polish maybe applied to polished surfaces. Items used for food items should not be polished e.g. breadbaskets.

PROTECTING WOOD SURFACES

Unprotected wood surfaces will absorb moisture, which causes the grains to swell and so creates gap into which dirt and germs can fall and become trapped when it dries. Liquids such as coffee and wine leave a stain on the surface, which is difficult to remove, and scratching is difficult to avoid, particularly on floors. The following are the most commonly found methods of protection and maybe referred to as wood finishes.

Cellulose lacquer – this is a fairly durable matt applied to solid timber furniture during manufacture. It should be dusted and wiped with a damp cloth and then dried with a soft one. Cream or spray polish may be applied to give a gloss finish. Heat, water and solvents will cause damage.

French polish – This is also easily damaged by heat, water and solvents. Deterioration is caused by light and atmostphere in general. French polishing is produced by rubbing the solid wooden surface with a solution of Shellac (a dark red resin) and methylated spirits. It should be dusted daily and polished in the way of the grain. Occasionally cream, liquid or paste polish maybe applied to remove light soiling and improve the gloss.

Oil – Solid wooden furniture can be given a matt protective finish by rubbing the surface with a mixture of oil (usually linseed oil) and resin. This process gives very little protection although it will help to reduce the absorption of water. Daily dusting is essential. Marks can be removed by lightly rubbing with very fine steelwool. About twice a year the surface should be rubbed with a mixture of equal quantities of turpentine and raw linseed oil. Proprietary polishes should be avoided.

Paint – This is very widely used on furniture, window frames, doorframes, skirting, staircase railings, etc. Gloss paint is tougher than matt or silk and will withstand more frequent washings. All painted wood surfaces should be dusted daily and wiped with a synthetic detergent solution or solvent weekly. Spray or cream polishes can be used to retain the shine or gloss on surfaces. Heat, alkalis and abrasives easily damage paint.

Resin (varnish) – Natural and synthetic resins such as polyesters, melamine and polyurethane are used extensively on wooden furniture, window frames, skirting, floors and staircases. The finish maybe glossy or matt and is frequently applied to furniture made from chipboard. Resin is extremely tough and will resist heat, water, solvents and abrasives; but once damaged by scratching or chipping, it is very difficult to repair. Dusting should be done regularly. Cream or spray polish should be applied on glossy surface after damp wiping. Matt surface should be rubbed up occasionally using a mixture of 500ml turpentine, 100ml boiled linseed oil and 500ml vinegar.

Wax (bees wax) – This is applied on solid wood surfaces. It provides an attractive finish, exposing the pattern of the wood, but is easily damaged by heat, water and solvents. Waxed surfaces should be dusted daily and cleaned weekly with cream and liquid polish.

REMOVING STAIN FROM WOODEN SURFACES

Alcohol stain – Polish well. If the stain persists rub along the grain with a metal polish or a mixture of linseed oil and cigarette ash.

Burns (black marks) – Rub with metal polish. For wax or oil finishes, rub the mark hard with turpentine.

Heat marks (white rings) – Rub with turpentine in the direction of the grain.

Ink – Dab with vinegar, leave for 2-3 hrs, then wipe. If unsuccessful, use a matchstick or cotton wool and carefully dab with hypochlorite bleach, immediately wiping with a clean cloth or absorbent paper.

Scratches – Mask with similar coloured wax crayon, shoe polish or liquid polish dye.

Watermarks – Rub with turpentine in the direction of the grain. If the stain persists, rub with metal polish, followed with suitable furniture polish.

LEATHER

Leather is one of the toughest and most hard wearing natural substances known. It is made from the skin of animals, prepared and treated in such a manner that it does not decompose, and becomes supple (flexible) and resilient (resuming it's original shape after compression). Large skins are called 'Hide' and are derived from oxen and horses. Smaller skins are derived from goat, sheep, etc.

MAKING

- The skin is first washed with water to soften
- Then it is treated with lime to remove hair and loose skin
- They are often then treated to remove lime and then tanned
- Tanning process is carried out by the means of tannin from the bark of oak and other substances. It is very slow and takes several weeks
- After tanning leather is finished and dressed according to the kind of leather required and the purpose it is required for.

METHODS OF DRESSING

1. Currying – In this leather is smoothened and pared down on the flesh side, or is split if thick, into several layers. It is rendered soft and pliable and made water-proof. Waterproofing is done by allowing a mixture of tallow (animal fat) and cod liver oil (large sealfish) to penetrate the leather gradually.
2. Tawing – This is the treatment of skin by mineral salts and is employed for glove leather and soft leather for boots and shoes.
3. Shamoying – It is the process of making the leather very soft and pliable by soaking it with oil, and was originally used from deer and chamois skin. Most leather of this nature is obtained from split sheep and also known as wash leather.

MOROCCO LEATHER

Originally derived from goatskin, dyed and richly grained, this name is now applied to any leather (chiefly split calf and sheep skin) finished to resemble Morocco leather.

RUSSIAN LEATHER

This similarly is any leather with a smooth finish and treated with aromatic oils which gives it it's characteristic odor.

SYNTHETIC LEATHER

These are very tough and durable. Imitation leather was originally made by spreading a mixture of various substances, such as linseed oil, dyes and pigments on a canvas or other backing and finished to resemble leather.

CARE AND CLEANING

1. Leather upholstered furniture should be kept free from dust especially in folds or round buttons.
2. Good furniture creams help to keep it in good condition.
3. Oil and waxes make it supple and prevents cracking.
4. Dirty leather maybe wiped clean with damp cloth and liquid wax.

Polishes – This consists principally of a waxy substance or an oil, turpentine, a colouring matter and a preservative. For black polishes carbon is used in finely divided condition. For brown polish yellow ochre (earth used as yellow, brown and red pigments) and other pigments are used.

PATENT LEATHER

This requires grease of some kind to prevent cracking and hardening while not in use. Rub with vaselene or olive oil. Before using, all traces should be removed by rubbing with a soft cloth. Polish with commercial cream sold for this purpose.

SUEDE

Remove mud by brushing well with soft rubber brush. Clean with either a liquid suede cleaner or a cleaning block, which is rubbed on the leather to remove dirt and restore the nap (raised pile). If suede is shiny use old fine emery paper.

WHITE AND PALE COLOURED LEATHER

Sponge off marks with a damp soapy cloth. Apply cream, wipe with a clean damp cloth and polish with a soft duster.

Carbohydrates a nutrient
Sources – (carbohydrate content in food)
Food value in g/100g
Sugar 99.4
Rice 78.2
Jowar 72.6
Wheat 69
Rajma 60.6
Yam 26
Potato 22.4
Role of Dietary fiber

- Fibers are commonly known as roughages, bulk, and cellulose poly saccharides.
- Normally found in plant food
- This is not digested by humans for absence of an enzymes usually present in herbivorous animal.
- This acts as a laxative
- The contraction of digestive tract is stimulated by fibers.
- Fiber increased water absorption, forming a larger, softer stool that rapidly passes through the colon.
- Soluble fibers bind bile acids & cholesterol & are beneficial to people suffering from hart diseases.
- It reduced the triglyceride & blood sugar level in blood.
- It has no calories.
- It also beneficial to people on weight reduction regime.
- It helps in lowering blood sugar level.
- Regular intake of fiber may prevent cancers of the colon & rectum.
- The fiber contain in daily diet should be approximately 20 g/day is recommended by American Dietetic Association, National cancer institute suggested the upper limits as 35 g/day.(ref –study material IGNOU)

GLYCEMIC INDEX (GI)

The ability of carbohydrates to raise blood glucose is referred to as Glycemic Index (GI).

Factors affect the GI
Fiber in diet reduced the GI
High level of glucose increased GI level
High level of protein fat decreased GI level

The glycemic index, glycaemic index, or GI is the measurement of glucose (blood sugar) level increase from carbohydrate consumption. Foods raise glucose to varying levels. It estimates how much each gram of available carbohydrate in a food raises a person's blood glucose level following consumption of the food, relative to consumption of pure glucose.Glucose has a glycemic index of 100, by definition, and other foods have a lower glycemic index.

Glycemic index is defined for each type of food, independent of the amount of food consumed. Glycemic load accounts for the amount of food consumed and is calculated in terms of glycemic index

Classification

Examples

Low GI

most fruits and vegetables; legumes; some whole, intact grains; nuts fructose; kidney beans; beets;

Medium GI

whole wheat products, basmati rice, grapes, sucrose, raisins,cranberry juice, regular ice cream

High GI

white bread, most white rices, corn flakes ,glucose, maltose, maltodextrins, white potato, chapatti

As you can see from the figure above, meals containing carbohydrate-rich foods with a high glycemic index give a more rapid rise in blood glucose than meals with a low glycemic index. High GI foods are as known as "fast carbohydrates" while the term "slow carbohydrates" refers to foods with a low GI.

ENERGY

Food is digested, the complex nutrients i.e., carbohydrates, fats, protein are broken down into monosaccharides, fatty acids & glycerol, & amino acids, respectively. These simple forms are absorbed into the blood stream & supplied to the millions of cells in the body to be oxidized by series of complex steps to released energy.

Human being needs energy for the following:

- Basal metabolism
- Metabolic responses to food – thermo genesis / SDA
- Physical activities
- Growth
- For mothers in special conditions (pregnancy & lactation)

TEE = BMR (45 – 75percent) + Thermo genesis (10 percent) +
Physical activities (15 – 50 percent)

Factors affecting the BMR

BMR is the largest component of the daily energy demand representing 45 – 70 percent of daily total energy expenditure. It is highly variable & the cause of this variation include factors such as

- body size & composition ,
- age,
- gender,
- environmental condition,
- hormonal status,
- fever/illness/infection / injury,
- specific body conditions of mothers(pregnancy & lactation),
- other factors etc

Thermal effect of food (SDA)

Thermal effect of food (TEF) determined primarily by the amount of composition of food consumed .For example, is greater after consumption of carbohydrate & protein than after fat. It varies from 5-10 percent for carbohydrates, 0-5 percent for Fat, & 20 -30 percent for protein.

Physical Activity

Sedentary workers –persons taking, reading, watching TV, listening Radio, doing computer works specially sitting activities (teachers, office workers).

Moderate workers – with some activities servants, house cleaners, rural womans, students etc.

Heavy workers – Labour class.

Energy requirement

The amount of food needed to ensure good health will vary from one individual to another. All people do not requires the same amount of nutrients.Requirment vary depending upon age, gender, body size, activities, state of health etc.ICMR has prepared Recommended Dietary Allowances(RDA) for Indians.

[Xerox ,chart of RDA for Indians – 1989 was circulate in the class

Ref – Dietetics by Srilakshmi]

Energy balance: Energy out put – Energy input

Energy balance is a condition in which the energy provided by food is nearly equal to energy expenditure by the body resulting in a steady body weight.

Over weight & under weight both are the abnormalities

Both measured by BMI (body Mass Index)

BMI = Weight in kilograms / height in meters squares

PROTEIN

Definition – Protein come from a Greek word 'Proteo' means 'to take the first place.' are very complex nitrogenous organic compound. It is made up of carbon, hydrogen, oxygen, nitrogen. The present of nitrogen distinguished protein from carbohydrate& fats. Apart from nitrogen, elements like sulphur, phosphorous, copper, & iron are also found in some proteins. Lipid combined with protein formed lipo-protein.

The basic units from which protein are built are the amino acid. Each amino acid contains a carboxyl group (COOH) or acid group & an amino group or basic group.

Structure of amino acid given in class

Proteins consist of chains of amino acids that are linked to each other by a peptide linkage (-CO-NH-).

22 different amino acid are widely distributed in nature. The protein obtained from plants and animals are quite different both in amounts present & in quality. The protein contain of any food can be estimated by measuring the nitrogen contain of the food.

Essential Amino Acid – Those amino acids which cannot be synthesized in sufficient amounts by the body & must be provided by the diet are called essential amino acids. There are 10 essential amino acids. Among those 9 are essential for adults with it 1 for children.

Non essential amino acid – There are 12 non essential aminoacid.This Amino Acid can be synthesized in our body from other amino acid.(total – 22 amino acids)

Essential AminoAcid Non essential amino acid

Adults Additional for children Alanine

- Isoleucine Asparagine
- Leucine Arginine Aspartic acid
- Lysine Cystine
- Methionine Glutamine
- Phenylalanine Glutamic acid
- Threonine Trosine
- Tryptophan
- Valine
- Histidine

Classification of protein – (follow class note)

1. According to nature – plant & animal
2. According to quality - 1st class, 2nd class & incomplete
3. According to structure – Simple, compound& derived

Functions of protein - Protein performs three main functions

- Structural function
- Regulatory function
- Energy

Structural function –

Growth –

- Protein helps us in growth & development.
- All body fluid except urine & bile are made up of protein
- Proteins are the major constituent of muscles, organs, endocrine gland, & collagen.
- Collagen is the main structural protein of bone, ligament, skin etc.
- All enzymes, some hormones are like insulin are made up of proteins

Maintenance or wear & tear

It also helps to repair the dead cell.

Regulatory functions – Certain amino acid & protein have highly specialized functions in the regulation of body process & protection against disease.

Hemoglobin, an iron containing protein in the blood cells, performs an important role by transporting oxygen to the tissue cell.

Plasma protein maintains water balance & regulates the osmotic pressure in blood.

All enzymes & some hormones are made up of protein.

Energy – Like carbohydrate protein too provides 4kcal/gm.

Sources –

Food gm/100gm

Rice 6.4

Wheat 11.8

Lentil 25.1

Rajmah 22.9

Cheese 24.1

Cow's milk 3.2
Egg (hen) 13.3
Mutton 18.5
Effect of deficiency & excess

It is known as PCM (Protein calorie malnutrition) OR PEM (Protein energy Malnutrition)

Protein deficiency is more marked during periods when protein needs are more specially among pre – school children in developing country.

Leads with only protein deficiency known as Kwashiorkor symptom moon face, oedema,pot belly, irritated in nature, red colour hair etc.

Marasmus is a combined disease of calorie + protein deficiency. Symptoms skeleton like features, very eager to take food,etc.

Excess amount of protein causes kidney & cholesterol problem.

Fat

It belongs to lipids groups. We found as triglycerides in foods. It converts to Glycerid & fatty acid. It is made up of Carbone hydrogen & oxygen. Main source is providing energy i,e 9 kcal/gm. It is aster of fatty acid & glycerol.

The lipids are important to our health are fatty acid,fats,oils, phospholipids, sulpholipids& sterol.

Classification sources given in class

Saturated fatty acdis – These are found in animal food like meat, fish,eggyolk etc.No double bond, solid in nature.example- steric, palmitic,butyric etc.Maximum of 10 persent of our total calorie should come from our total calorie.

Unsaturated fatty acid – One, two or more double bonds, liquid in nature.

It is classified in 2 –

- MUFA- example Oleic acid & has one double bond .found in ground nut, olive oil; corn oiletc.they may help to lower the blood cholesterol level.
- PUFA – example- linoleic,lilonenic, arachidonic acid has two or more double bond. They help in lowering blood cholesterol levels & prevent atherosclerosis & coronary heart diseases.

Essential Fatty Acid: Poly unsaturated fatty acid cannot synthesized in our body. We have to take it through our diet. Example- linoleic, lilonenic, arachidonic acid.

Cholesterol - It is a fat like substance present in food. It is different in structure from triglycerids.It is present in all cell of the body & in large amount in brain & nervous tissue. The diseases related are cardiovascular disorder. The normal blood sugar level will be 200mg/100ml of blood.

Human get cholesterol from-

- Synthesis of liver
- Food rich in cholesterol

Functions of cholesterol are –

- It is precursor of all storied hormones
- A precursor of vit D, 7- dehydrochlosterol, is present in the skin which is irradiated by UV ray of sunlight to form vit D
- It is required for formation of bile
- It is an essential component of cell membrane.

WATER

An important nutrient .75 to 80 percent of our total body is water. The total body fluid is distributed among two major components

Extracellular fluid – contain sodium

Intercellular fluid – contain potassium

Water is made up of hydrogen & oxygen the ratio is 2:1

Sources visible & invisible water.

Visible water that we can see are- plain water, fruit juices, tea, milk, coffee etc

Invisible water that is inside the food s & metabolic water.

Function-

- Water quenched our thirst and is the most refreshing & cooling of all liquids.
- It is a structural component of all cell
- Water is a medium in which all chemical reaction takes place
- It is an essential components of all body fluid such as blood, ceribospinal fluid, bile,digestive fluid,urine.
- It acts like a lubricant & helps us to swallowed food or to digest food.
- It acts like a solvent for the products of digestion & help in transporting this product in different pare of body.
- It regulates the body temperature.
- It helps to throw the waste product from the body.

Water balance –

In a normal individual, the maintenance of water balance is archived by adjusting both water intake & excretion as needed. The major inputs of water are:-

- Fluids that we consume asbeverages, including water depending on climatic condition & habits.
- Different type of foods & fruits that we take as solid form.
- Metabolic water.

Output or loss of water from body

- Renal loss – Kidneys excrete about 1-2 liter of water daily
- Skin – The water loss from skin is through perspiration.
- Intestine – A small quantities of water is normally loss in faeces.
- Lungs – The air expired from the lungs also contains water.
- Sweat – It depends on the physical activity & environmental condition.

Daily intake & output of water

Intake ml/day Output ml/day

Fluid we take 2,200 Skin 350

From metabolism 200 Lungs 350 ——————— —- Sweat 100

2,400 Faeces 100

Urine 1,500

2,400

Dehydration – It is defined as an excessive loss of body water. It may occur because of inadequate intake of, or abnormal loss of body water or a combination of both.

The symptoms of dehydration are –

- Thirst
- Loss of appetite
- Decreased urination
- Nausea
- Impaired temperature regulation
- Muscular spasms
- Increased pulse rate

Symptoms of severe dehydration appear when Fluid level fall by more than 10 percent. A 20 percent loss of fluid from the body can be fatal.

A dehydrated person is usually managed by Oral Rehydration Therapy (ORT). The WHO recommended ORS (Oral Rehydration Salt) that are to be dissolved in 1 liter of water & make a Oral Rehydration Solution & have to be finished within 24 hours. He also can take HAF.(Home Available Fluid)

Home Available Fluid –

Normally we prepared in home 1 glass of water + 2 spoon full of sugar + a pinch of salt + few drops of lime juice (lime juice contained potassium & salt contain sodium which help to maintained the equilibriums among intra cellular & extra cellular fluid .)

ORS (WHO) for 1 liter

Content amount in gm

Glucose 20.0

Sodium Chloride (salt) 3.5

Sodium bicarbonate (baking soda) 1.5

Potassium chloride 1.5

A minimum +8 glass of water is recommended daily.

Excess amount of water causes oedema. (Swelling of the skin).

ANCILLARY DEPARTMENT

In any establishment a guest's first impression on entering the service area is of great importance. A guest can be won or lost on these impressions alone. There are many service areas behind the scene or what may be termed as back of the house which is required to be efficiently run, well organized, supervised and well stocked with appropriate equipments depending on the style of operation.

These service areas are usually between kitchen and the food service area. They are important areas in the make-up of the catering establishments acting as a link between kitchen and restaurants. These are also the meeting point for staffs of various sections as they carry out their duties and therefore there must be close liaison between the various members of staff and their respective departments.

In general, especially in large operations, five main back-of-the-house service areas can be identified:

1. Still room
2. Kitchen stewarding
3. Hot plate/ food pick up area
4. Linen room
5. Store

STILL ROOM/ PANTRY

The main function of the still room is to provide items of F&B required for the service of a meal and not created by any other major department like kitchen, patisserie, larder etc. Depending on the policy of the management and the volume of business at times it is supervised by a supervisor who may be a senior member of the f&b brigade.

When ordering goods from the main dry store, all requirements should be written on a requisition sheet in duplicate. The top copy goes to the store to be retained by the store-keeper after issuing the goods and the duplicate remains in the requisition book as a mean of checking the receipt of goods from the store by a member of the still room. The store keeper should not issue goods unless the still room supervisor or another person in authority has signed the requisition.

Equipments:

Following are the equipments required for proper storage, preparation and presentation of the food by the still room-

a. Refrigerator- storing butter, milk, fruit juice, cream and so on
b. Beverage vending machine- soft drink, tea, coffee etc.
c. Large double sink
d. Salamander or toaster
e. Bread slicing machine
f. Working table and cutting board
g. Ice maker
h. Storage cupboard for all dry goods held in stock and for such miscellaneous items as doilies, paper napkin, straw etc.
i. Gas range or induction plate

As a basic guide the following food items would normally be dispensed from the still room-

1. All non-alcoholic beverages including tea, coffee, soft drinks, chocolate drinks etc.
2. Preserves like jam, jelly, marmalade, honey, butter etc.
3. Various bread rolls like brioche, croissants
4. Various breakfast cereals like cornflakes, wheat flakes etc.
5. Pastries, gateaux, sandwich, boiled eggs are also dispensed

A proper control is very important for the items which are dispensed from the still room. Therefore all items should be issued either against a requisition from the service area or against a waiter's check.

KITCHEN STEWARDING

The kitchen stewarding is basically divided into two areas:

a) Wash up area-

It is an important service area and should be ideally situated so that the brigade can work speedily and efficiently while passing from the food service area to the kitchen. The waiter should stack the trays of dirties correctly at the side board with all the same sized plates together and all the tableware stacked on one of the plates with the blades of the knives running under the arch of the forks. All glassware should be stacked on separate trays and taken to a separate wash up area. Wash up section should be the first place when the waiter enters the back area.

Hygiene is of utmost importance at the wash up area, as all sorts of germs can originate from here and can contaminate the food. This section is normally in the charge of the stewarding supervisor who may in turn have number of wash up boys as per need.

Dishwashing Methods

There are two main methods used for dishwashing for foodservice operations-

Manual (tank) method

The dirty crockery is placed in a tank of hot water containing a soap detergent solution.

After washing, these are placed in wire racks and dipped into a second sterilizing tank containing clean hot water detergent at a temperature of approximately 75ÚC (179ÚF). The racks are left for two minutes and then lifted out and the crockery left to drain. If sterilized in water at this temperature the crockery will dry by itself without the use of drying up cloths. This is more hygienic. After drying the crockery is stacked into piles of the correct size and placed on shelves until required for further use.

Dishwashing machine-

Used in larger establishments. Debris should be removed from the crockery before it is placed into the wire racks. The racks are then passed through the machine, the crockery being washed, rinsed and sterilized. Having passed through the machine the crockery is left to drain for two or three minutes and is then stacked and placed on shelves until required for further use.

b) Silver room/ plate room-

In larger establishments the silver room or the plate room, as it is sometimes known, is a separate service area controlled by the kitchen stewarding supervisor. They take care of all the silverwares and the china wares stored in the silver room and are also responsible for silver polishing. The silver room should hold the complete stock of silverware required by the different department to meet the day to day requirements along with a surplus stock in case of emergency.

While stacking, large silver ware, like salver, flat platter etc. should be stored on shelves. When stacking heavier items should go on the shelves lower down and smaller and lighter items on the shelves higher up to prevent accidents. Flatware and cutlery should be kept in drawers lined with baize cloth to prevent them from moving about in the drawer and getting scratched or marked.

FOOD PICK UP AREA

This may be regarded as the meeting point between the food service staff and food preparation staff. It is very essential to ensure that there is an active cooperation and good relation between the staffs of these two areas. The aboyeur or the barker is in charge and controls the food pick up area during the service period. The aboyeur also controls the off board which tells the waiter immediately if any dish is off. It should be sited in a prominent position for all to see. The aboyeur receives the KOT from the waiter and places the order on the KOT to the respective kitchen area. He also helps the waiter to pick up the food.

Many a times all the crockery and hollowware are placed below the hot plate for easy meal service. The hot plate is operated electrically.

LINEN ROOM

It keeps a stock of various linen used in the restaurant/outlet. Example – table cloth, serviettes, guest napkin, slip cloth, baize etc.

Fresh linen is picked up by the restaurant staff in exchange of the soiled linen. Generally it is done once a day. But it might be more than once in case of coffee shop. A linen register is maintained on a daily basis for this purpose.

STORE

Store room is the area from where the F&B service staff requisite and receives items such as grocery and stationary that are required for smooth running of the day to day operation of the outlet.

CHAPTER 3

Food Production

INTRODUCTION

Cookery is defined as a chemical process involving the application and withdraws of heat; proper mixing of ingredients decision-making and technical knowledge and skill but with the changing definition cooking is defined as both an art as well as technology. In French the word 'cuisine' means the art of cooking and preparing dishes and the place kitchen where they are prepared. The art of cooking is ancient and generally originated when by chance a chunk of meat fell into fire and came out to be more tasty and tender and it was from this point only that cooking has evolved to reach the present level of sophistication.

There are 3 classes of professional cookery associated with the craftsmen and they are graded according to the quality of material used

CUISINE SIMPLE/PLAIN COOKERY

Here the basic necessities are used and the craftsmen prepare the dishes of highest standard with the minimum materials.

CUISINE BOURGEOISE

This is a type of cookery, which provides better raw materials to produce the dishes of better quality.

HAUTE CUISINE/HIGH CLASS COOKERY

In this cookery the best possible raw materials are used and the best quality dishes are prepared.

A. LEVEL OF SKILLS AND EXPERIENCES

SKILLS may be grouped into 3 general categories.

1) SUPERVISOR: The head of the food service, whether called Executive chef or head chef or kitchen director, must have management and supervisory skills as well as through knowledge of food production.

He should be able to:

- Organize and motivate people under him.
- Planning menus and production procedures.
- Controlling costs and managing budgets.

- Purchasing food supplies & equipment.
- Must be an experienced chef in order to schedule food production.
- Train and instruct workers.
- Control quality.

2) TECHNICALLY: The cooks are the backbone of the kitchen. These workers carry out the actual food production. They must have knowledge of and experience in cooking techniques. They must be able to function well with their fellow workers and co-ordinate with other departments. Food production is a team activity.

3) ENTRY LEVEL: This level of workers usually requires no particular skills & experience. The jobs assigned to them are stewarding or basic pre-preparation of vegetables. As their knowledge, skill & experience increases, they may be given more complex task which will eventually make them skilled chefs. Many ex-chefs begin their career as pot washers. Beginning in an entry level position and working one's way up has been the traditional way of advancing in a food service career. Today however, who are a graduate from hotel management start at entry level already possessing a general knowledge of food production practices, which would give them a head start over other beginners who have no knowledge.

B. ATTITUDES AND BEHAVIUR IN THE KITCHEN

'LA CUISINE' means the kitchen. Also 'Art Of Cooking'

C Care of equipment.

U Understanding the basic method (to achieve quality).

I Integrity in handling & serving food (would I eat the food prepared by me).

S Safety in handling equipments.

I Initiatives you will have to take.

N Neatness during work & presentation.

E Efficiency of yourself.

"BE POSITIVE AND THINK POSITIVE"

The emphasis of a food service education is on learning a set of skills. But ATTITUDES are more important because a good attitude will help you not only to learn skills but also to preserve and overcome many difficulties you will face in your career. The successful foodservice workers follow an unwritten code of behavior and set of attitudes, which may we call professionalism.

Set of qualities are:

1. Positive Attitude Towards The Job: In order to be a good professional chef you must like cooking and want to do it well. Satisfaction of doing your job well and making everything run smoothly will give you enjoyment, which you will always cherish. A chef with a positive work quickly, efficiently, neatly and safely. Professionalism has pride in their work and wants to make sure that the work is some thing to be proud of.
2. STAYING POWER: A food service personnel requires good health, physical and mental stamina and a willingness to work.
3. ABILITY TO WORK WITH PEOPLE: Works as a team & it is essential to be able to work well as a team and to co-operate with your colleagues.
4. COMMUNICATION:

- With your supervisors: let them know your difficulties.

- With your colleagues: share knowledge and learn from them. No body knows everything.
- With your subordinates: respect them & be courteous.
- With the food & beverage staff: control your temper.

5. EAGERNESS TO LEARN: There is more to learn about cooking than you will learn in a life time. The food service industry is changing so rapidly that it is vital to be open to new ideas. No matter how good your techniques are, you might learn an even better way.
6. MUST DEVELOP A FULL RANGE OF SKILLS: A chef must not only a good cook, but is also important to develop and maintain other skills that are necessary for the profession.

Must be able to understand and manage food cost and other financial matters

- Manage and maintain proper inventories.
- Deal with suppliers.
- Understand personnel management.

7. EXPERIENCE: There is no substitute for year of experience. Practice more & more to gain more experience.
8. AIMING FOR A QUALITY: What ever you do must have a distinctive sign of quality.
9. CREATIVITY: Sky is a limit "Nouvelle Cuisine".
10. RETURN TO BASIC: Experiments and innovation needs good understanding of basics.
11. CARE OF EQUIPMENT: Equipment has been put to your disposal to help you. TAKE CARE OF IT, treat it as your own, even if it does not belong to you, for others will also be using it.
12. SAFETY : Kitchens can be dangerous place injurious can occur by cuts, burns, handling of machines and equipment, falling etc. think about yours as well as others.

"NEVER RUN IN KITCHEN ALWAYS WALK"

C. PERSONAL HYGIENE.

A hygienic appearance of professional is indicated by high standards of personal cleanliness and is shown by cleanliness of hair, hands, face, clothing and shoes.Good personal hygiene helps prevent food borne disease; therefore these points must be put into practice.

- Shower or bath daily
- Wear clean clothes and uniform.
- Do not work if suffering from a communicable disease.
- Handle food as little as possible.
- Wash hands before and during work and after using the toilet.
- Keep hair clean and do not handle.
- Keep fingernails clean & shorter.
- Do not touch nose & mouth with hands.
- Do not cough or sneeze over food, use a tissue.
- Do not wear rings, earrings, jewellery & watches.
- Do not smoke in food areas.

- Taste food with a clean spoon.
- Do not sit on a work surface.
- Footwear should be clean and safe.
- Chef cap should always be worn when handling food.
- Open cuts, burns etc. must be covered with waterproof dressing.
- Persons suffering from diarrhea, sore throat, vomiting, cold etc. must not handle food.

If a person becomes aware that they are suffering from or are carrier of typhoid, paratyphoid, salmonella or staphylococcal infection, the parson responsible for the premises must be informed, who then must inform the Medical Officer of Health.

HYGIENE IN HANDLING FOOD

1. DRY FOOD STORAGE: Avoid moisture, air tight container, avoid insect & rodent.
2. FREEZER STORAGE: Well packed food with label store at -18° C, follow FIFO & thaw properly before use.
3. COLD ROOM STORAGE: Cooked items away from raw item. Store everything in container. Chill food before refrigeration. Keep temperature under 7° C.
4. HOT FOOD STORAGE: Do not reheat in Bain Marie. Cover all the food. Keep food above 65° C.
5. FOOD HANDLING:

- Work with fresh & safe food
- Use clean equipment & work table.
- Wash & wipe tools (knives, chopping board etc.) after every use.
- Wash ingredients.
- Re boil stocks, sauces, soups, milk before re use.
- Do not mix batches of cooked food.
- Use separate tools for vegetables & meats.
- Use separate tools for raw & cooked food.
- Quickly chill all high risk food for cold storage.
- Keep work area clean.

D. KITCHEN UNIFORMS & PROTECTIVE CLOTHING

CHEF CAP

- Should cover the hair.
- Retain sweat on the face.

SCARF

- Retaining sweat around the neck.
- Decreases risk of catching cold when going inside a walk in.
- Also brings neatness to uniform.

CHEF COAT

- Protect the chest from heat (double press, cotton).
- White colour (shows when dirty, less heat absorber)

APRON

- Protect chef coat & trouser.
- Not used to wipe hands.

TROUSER

- Generally black or black & white check.

SHOES

- Ankle high shoes.
- Low heal
- Leather with rubber or wooden sole.
- Always wear black socks.

E.SAFETY PROCEDURE IN HANDLING EQUIPMENT

Safety procedure in handling of equipment

- Do not wash equipment unless you understand the operation.
- Use all guards& safety devices on equipment.
- Do not touch or remove food, from any kind of equipment, while it is running.
- Remove particles of food with cloth, palette knife, needle or brush from cutting machine.
- Unplug electrical equipment before disassembling or cleaning.
- Make sure the switch is off before plugging in equipment.
- Do not touch or handle electrical equipment including switches, if your hands are wet or if you are standing in water.
- Test that it is properly assembled, plug in and switch on.
- Wear properly fitting clothing and tuck in apron string to avoid getting caught in machinery.
- Use equipment only for the purpose intended.
- Stack pots, pans and other equipment properly on racks so that they are stable and not likely to fall.

LARDER

DEFINITION & INTRODUCTION OF LARDER WORK

The larder or Garde Manger is a department set aside for the storage of perishable food, both raw and cooked and were food stuffs such as meat fish poultry and game are prepared and made ready for cooking.

In this department all cold food items found on the menu such as Hors d'oeuvre cold fish or meat dishes, cold sauces, salad dressings are prepared and dressed. One particular special duty of this department is the preparation and presentation of all types of cold buffet, which are nowadays a feature of so many functions.

For these functions to be carried out, it is **essential** that:

1. The larder be separated from the kitchen and located in a cool place. At the same time, it must be close to the kitchen to avoid undue running about between two departments which are closely interrelated.
2. It should be light, airy and well established and sufficiently spacious to allow the staff to carry out their duties in a clean and efficient manner. It must also be able to store prepared foods and buffets in a cool and hygienic manner.
3. It should be equipped with the necessary fitting, machinery and tools. In accordance with the volume and/or quality of the trade of the catering establishment in which it is situated.

BREAKDOWN OF WORK

Taking the above into consideration, it naturally follows that the work is broken down into various fields such as Hors d'oeuvre, Salads, Butchery, Poultry, Cold Buffet etc, and in effect, in large busy establishments each of these functions or duties are carried out by one or more men or sometimes women, who specialize in the work of that particular sub-department. As an example, the Butcher, Poulterer or Fishmonger may be an expert in that particular field without being a trained chef or cook, and it sometimes happens that the salads or Hors d'oeuvre are prepared by female staff trained in those particular duties only.

More frequently, these various duties are allocated by the Chef Grade Manager, who is in overall charge of the department, to commis or assistant chefs, and they are known as Commis Grade-Manager, whatever duties they re assigned to. Naturally, the busier the establishment, the more Larder work it entails, therefore more is required to man the department. The smaller the volume of trade the fewer commis required, and so on. In many establishments the Chef Grade-Manager is single handed and carries out all the various functions himself.

It should be mentioned at this stage that often quality rather than quantity, of trade is the determining factor in deciding the number of staff required in the Grade-Manager, or for that matter in the kitchen as a whole.

EQUIPMENTS FOUND IN THE LARDER

Heavy:

- Refrigeration equipment including refrigerators, walk-ins, reach-in, pull outs, traulsen, deep freezers, bottle coolers, ice machines, coolers and chillers.
- Food Processors with attachments for grinding, pureeing, kneading, mixing, Buffalo choppers, bone saws
- Gas range, boilers, heaters (if required)
- Weighing scales - Electronic and manual
- Steel tables, cupboards, storage racks and sinks

Light

Mixers, juicers, Butchers block, Storage bins and shelves, Slicers, Blow torch, Pots, pans, stockpots, larder tools such as serving spoons and ladles, sieves , Colanders , Conical strainers and Chinois, heat Presses , Pie moulds, whisks, egg slices, steel basins and graters

Miscellaneous

Frying and flat spoons - Assorted knives (Butchers Boning knives ,butcher's steak or cutting knives , Butchers saw(Tenon), Butchers saw(Bow), Butcher's choppers and cleavers, Butchers chopping Knives, Cook's 30 cms(12 inches)Knives, Cook's 20-24 cm (a/7 inches) knives, Cook's 6-8 cm (4 inches) knives, Cook's 14-20cm(7 inches) filleting Knives Tranchelard Knives, Palette Knives) - Butchers saw (Tenon and bow) - Butchers chopper - Filleting knives and palette knives - Piping bags and assorted nozzles – Peelers - fancy cutters - mandolin slicer - Wooden spoons and mushrooms (wooden mushrooms are used for pressing food stuffs through sieves) - Cutlet bat and steak hammers (for flattening cuts of meat) - Larding and trussing needles and pins(for larding and trussing joints of meat and poultry) - Lemon zesters & decorators (for scraping and channeling lemon peel) - decorating knives and vegetable scoops (for shaping vegetables & potatoes) – Skewers - butchers hooks (for hanging joints) - Brining syringe (for pumping brine solution into joints) - brinometer(for measuring density of brine solution) - assorted thermometers - Assorted trays for storage of food.

PLANNING THE GARDE MANGER

Layout : Planning the layout for a garde manger department can be a complex task. Unlike other departments that can depend on a basic menu and basic work load, the Garde Manger department is unique in its operation. On a daily basis the Garde Manger department may handle its own butchery, its own bakery, its own sauce making ,its own frying , smoking of fish and cold meats , all the decorating including tallow and ice sculpture , Plus a complete line on charcuterie products such as galantines and pates.

The Garde Manger department can relate to a food service facility in three ways:

- on a pick up Basis.
- on a distribution basis.
- on a combination of the two bases.

When a Garde Manger department Executes food order on an ala Carte basis, this is known as Pick up .This system operates in an unpredictable fashion ,Since the number and timing of orders is not known in advance. Work load is set depending upon the dishes listed on the menu.

When the Garde Manger department Executes food orders in advance for a known quantity, to be delivered at a certain time (Parties, banquets) this is known as the distribution basis. The main problem here is workloads will be different each day depending upon booking, functions etc., For this reason it is difficult to establish an appropriate mise-en-place on a daily basis as it is bound to vary

COMMON TERMS USED IN THE LARDER & LARDER CONTROL

Aging: Holding meats in coolers under controlled conditions to allow natural tenderizing to take place.

AP required: As-purchased amount necessary to yield the desired EP weight. AP required is computed as EP required divided by yield percentage.

Antipasto: Italian Hors d'oeuvre

Beginning inventory: The dollar value of all products on hand at the beginning of the accounting period. This amount is determined by completing a physical inventory.

Bin card: An index card with both additions to and deletions from inventory of a given product. To facilitate its use, the card is usually affixed to the shelf that holds the given item. Used in a perpetual inventory system.

Canapé: An hors d'oeuvre consisting of a small piece of bread or toast, often cut in decorative shape, garnished with savoury spread or topping.

Carpaccio: Very thin slices of meat or fish, served raw.

Carryover: A menu item prepared for sale during a meal period but carried over for use in a different meal period.

Casing: A synthetic or natural membrane used to enclose sausage forcemeat.

Caul: A fatty membrane that covers the stomach of a pig; used for wrapping meats for cooking and for lining terrines.

Chitterlings: Pork intestines.

Coulis: A vegetable or fruit puree, used as a sauce.

Crepinette: A sausage patty wrapped in caul.

Crudités: A raw vegetable served as a relish.

Daily inventory sheet: A form that lists the items in storage, the unit of purchase, and the par value. It also contains the following columns: on hand, special order, and order amount.

Edible portion (EP): This term refers to the weight or count of a product after it has been trimmed, cooked, and portioned.

Ending inventory: The dollar value of all products on hand at the end of the accounting period. This amount is determined by completing a physical inventory.

First-in, first-out (FIFO): Term used to describe a method of storage in which the operator intends to sell his or her oldest product before selling the most recently delivered product.

Forcemeat: A mixture of chopped or ground meat and other ingredients used for pates, sausages and other preparations.

Garniture: Garnish; the act or process of garnishing.

Inventory turnover: The number of times the total value of inventory has been purchased and replaced in an accounting period.

Lard: The rendered fat of hogs; to insert strips of fat into meats low in marbling.

Last-in, first-out (LIFO): Term used to describe a method of storage in which the operator intends to sell his or her most recently delivered product before selling the older product.

Par level: A system of determining the purchase point by using management-established minimum and maximum allowable inventory levels for a given inventory item.

Requisition: When a food or beverage product is requested from storage by an employee for use in an operation.

Shelf life: The period of time an ingredient or menu item maintains its freshness, flavor, and quality.

Tripe: The muscular stomach lining of beef or other meat animals.

Waste percentage: This formula is defined as product loss divided by AP weight and refers to product lost in the preparation process.

Working stock: The quantity of goods from inventory reasonably expected to be used between deliveries.

Yield percentage: This formula is defined as 1 minus waste percentage and refers to the amount of product available for use by the operator after all preparation-related losses have been taken into account.

Yield test: A procedure used to determine actual EP ingredient costs. It is used to help establish actual costs on a product that will experience weight or volume loss in preparation.

LARDER CONTROL

If the larder is to be run effectively, efficiently and economically, it is essential that the Chef Garde Manger exercise strict control over the foodstuff received and stored in the department.

This will involve:

1. Checking the quality and quantity of all food received in the department.
2. Ensuring that all food stuff is stored at the right temperature and that they can easily be checked
3. That the food is protected from contamination by vermin.
4. That portion control is ensured.
5. That stock is regularly turned over.
6. That food is not over stocked.
7. A simple daily stock sheet to be maintained by each sub department.
8. Every possible effort is made to ensure the highest standard of hygiene.
9. Pilferage is discouraged and controlled.

STOCK SHEET

The stock and order sheet should be as simple and easy to keep up to data as possible. A complicated stock sheet requiring too much writing will defect the whole purpose as it will be neglected during busy rush periods, the very time it is needed most. For some sub departments, devising an easy and simple system is reasonably easy. In some cases it is not so easy for example; also keeping of the stock of food sent in and returned by the cold buffet can be complicated and time wasting if one is to measure every ounce or inch. Therefore it is necessary to accept some rule of thumb providing it is well supervised. An experienced chef Garde Manger should be able to tell at a glance the weight, or number of Portion of a given joint or cold dish. The butchery department also presents some Problems and the stock sheet for this department needs careful consideration. Each establishment will devise its own system taking into account its own problems.

Department			Day and date		
Item	Unit	Stock	Unit Price	Cost	Order
Tomatoes	kg(lb)	2			12
Sardines	tins	4			8
Eggs	doz	1 1/2			4
Oil	1.(gal)	1/2			1
Vinegar	1.(qt)	1			2

YIELD TESTING

Most foodservice products are delivered in the **AP** or **As Purchased** state. This refers to the weight or count of a product, as delivered to the foodservice operator. **EP** or **Edible Portion** refers to the weight of a product after it has been cleaned, trimmed, cooked, and portioned. Thus, AP refers to food products as the operator receives them; EP refers to food products as the guest receives them.

Yield % is important in the area of recipe costing. This is true because a recipe cost must take into account the difference in price of products in their AP or EP state. In order to determine actual recipe costs, it may sometimes be necessary to conduct a yield test to determine actual EP ingredient costs. A yield test is a procedure used for computing your actual costs on a product that will experience weight or volume loss in preparation.

$$\text{Total Yield \%} = \frac{\text{Remaining Weight}}{\text{Original Weight}} \times 100$$

Waste % is the percentage of product lost due to cooking, trimming, portioning, or cleaning.

LIAISON WITH OTHER DEPARTMENTS

The Larder is both a storage department for most perishable foods and a preparation department for such foodstuffs. The Larder staff, under the supervision of the Chef Garde-Manger, are responsible for the ordering, storing and preserving of stores, keeping stocks up to date, and accounting for such items as meat, fish, poultry, game etc. which pass through the department on their way from the suppliers to the kitchen and eventually to the restaurant or banqueting rooms. The bulk of such foodstuff needs dissecting or cleaning, dressing, cutting into the required joints or portions, and generally preparing for cooking.

To function in an effective manner, the Larder department must operate in harmony with the Kitchen in particular, if confusion and wastage are to be avoided. A good layout of the Larder in relation to the Kitchen will avoid undue running from place to place. Lack of liaison between the departments could result in duplication of work, or sometimes in certain processes not being carried out to the best advantage.

For Instance:

- Certain foods intended for cold service are best cooked in the Kitchen where there are greater facilities for carrying out the operation
- Pastry for pies or puddings, and various savouries served from the Larder department, are best prepared by the Pastry staff, who will be more skilful in such work, and who are equipped with the necessary apparatus and tools for producing such items.
- Savoury fillings as are required by the Pastry chef for such items as sausage rolls, patties, or pasties, ravioli, etc., will be prepared in the Larder and transferred to the Pastry department as and when required.
- Another important function of the Garde-Manger is to process and utilize the 'leftover' which is transferred from the Kitchen to the Larder at the conclusion of every meal.
- A number of garnishes or accompaniments to dishes served from kitchen departments are prepared by the Garde-Manger. Such items as stuffings, forcemeats, lardons or bacon rashers, are naturally provided by the Larder, as well as cold sauces for the accompaniment of hot dishes.

RESPONSIBILITIES OF THE GARDE MANGER DEPARTMENT

1) Butchery (including the fish mongery & ecaillage)
2) Marinated Products
a Salads
b. Pickled Products – Vegetables, Fruit, Fish and Meats
c. Brines / Cures – Smoked Products.
3) Cold Soups and Sauces

4) Appetizers and Hors d'oeuvres
5) Forcemeat products
   Pâté, Galantine, Terrine, Sausage, Quenelle, etc.
6) Gelatin Products

Aspic, Mousse, Aspic jelly coating, Colle, Chaudfroid, etc.

7) Cold Fish and Meat – Roasted, Poached
8) Pièce Montée (Centerpiece)
   Ice-carving, Tallow/Butter Sculpture, Salt Dough, Vegetable & Fruit Carving
9) Specialty items – Cheeses, Caviar, Foie gras, etc.
10) Food Garnishes
11) Overseas pantry station

Menu Responsibilities of the Garde Manger Department

1- A la Carte : Hors d'oeuvres, Appetizer, Salad, Entrée
2- Buffet : Cocktail receptions, Dinners, Conference breaks, Salad bars.

RESPONSIBILITIES OF THE CHEF GARDE MANGER

1. He is responsible to the Executive chef for the smooth running and operation of his department.
2. He is also responsible for co ordination between his staff and has to make sure that they have understood the work required from them and the production schedule, either daily or weekly.
3. Training is another important function he has to carry out. The work of the larder is of a highly skilled nature and involves a lot of expensive ingredients, procedures and equipment It is therefore imperative that the staff is well trained.
4. The larder Chef is also responsible for staff scheduling and duty rotas.
5. He is also required to co ordinate with the other departments like the kitchen and the bakery. A lot of pre preparation is done in the larder for the other departments and satellite kitchens. Their requirements must be made available well in advance.
6. He also has to maintain registers to record the receipts and dispatch of the foodstuff.
7. He is also responsible for maintaining hygiene and sanitation standards in the department. A lot of the foodstuff being processed here is in the raw sate and susceptible to contamination and possible food poisoning.

Le Garde - Manager

FUNCTIONS OF THE LARDER DEPARTMENT

The Cold Larder or Grade Manger is the department set aside for the storage of perishable foods, both raw and cooked, and where food stuffs such as Meat, Fish, Poultry and Game are prepared and made ready for cooking. In this department, too, all 'cold' items found on the menu, such as Horsdoeuvres, cold fish or meat dishes, cold sauces, salads, salad dressings, etc., are prepared and 'dressed'.

For these functions to be effectively carried out, it is essential that:

1) The room is separate from the kitchen, and located in a cold place. At the same time it must be close to the kitchen to avoid undue running about between the two departments, which are closely inter related.

2) it should be light, airy and well ventilated and sufficiently spacious to allow the staff to carry out their duties in a clean and efficient manner.
3) It must be equipped with the necessary fittings, plant, machinery and tools, in accordance with the volume and quality of the trade of the catering establishment in which it is situated.

BREAKDOWN OF WORK

Taking the above into consideration, it naturally follows that the work is broken into various fields such as Horsdoeuvres, Salad, Butchery, Poultry, Cold Buffet etc and in effect large busy establishments each of these functions or duties are carried out by one or more men or sometimes women, who specialize in the work of that particular sub department. As an example, the Butcher , Poulterer, or Fish manger may be an expert in that particular field without being a trained chef or cook, and it sometimes happens that the salads or Horsd Euvre are prepared by female staff in those particular duties only.

More frequently those various duties are allocated by the Chef Grade Manger, who is in over all chare of the department, to Commis or assistant chef, and they are known as Commis Grade Manger, whatever duties they are assigned to. Naturally, the busier the establishment, the more Larder-work it entails, therefore more commis required, and so on. In many establishments the Chef Grade Manger is single handed and carries out all the various functions himself.

It should be mentioned at this stage that often quality, rather than quantity, of trade is the determining factor in deciding the number of staff required Grade-Manger, or for that matter in the kitchen as whole.

RESPONSIBILITIES OF THE CHEF DE GRADE MANGER

The responsibilities of the Chef Grade Manger, therefore, are many and aried. He is responsible to the Chef for the efficient running of his department and the coordination of the work of his staff, for the foodstuff In the department, some of which may be stored in refrigerators or even in deep freeze, or preserved by other means. The responsibility is his keeping a record of such food stuff and a day by day record of issues to kitchen or other departments.

He must study the menus in advance, so as to be able to order meat, fish, etc., in time for the foodstuff to be prepared and cleaned and made ready for the kitchen in time for it to be cooked; and also all necessary stores for the various larder productions such as salads, Hord d'Euvre , sauces, buffets, etc.

He is responsible for the efficient storage of food to avoid deterioration and wastage for the cleanliness and hygiene in the department , to avoid any danger of contamination and possible food poisoning, he should also advice The Head Chef as to what items of foodstuffs require using to prevent eventual wastage.

LARDER CONTROL

If this department is to be run efficiently and economically, it is essential that the Chef Grade Manger should exercise the strictest possible control over the foodstuffs received and stored in the department.

1) Checking the quantity and quality of all goods delivered to the larder.
2) Ensuring that all foodstuff are stored at the right temperature and that they can

be easily checked.

3) That the food is protected from contamination by vermin etc.
4) That portion control is rigidly carried out eg. A given weight of meat , or fish, or vegetable etc., should always produced the required number of portions of steak, fish, fillets, salads, or Horsd'/'Euvre.
5) That stocks of food are regularly turned over.
6) That food is not over stocked.
7) That a simple daily stock sheet be kept by each sub department and handed to the Chef Garde-Manger at the end of each days business to enable him to write out his order for the following day.
8) Obviously, every effort must be made to maintain the highest possible standard of hygiene, to revent any deterioration in the foodstuff under his control and every precaution should be taken to discourage pilfering

The stock and order sheets should be made as simple and easy to keep up to date as possible. A complicated stock sheet requiring too much writing, will defeat the whole object of the exercise, as it will be neglected during busy rush periods, the very time it is most needed.

For some sub department stocks, the devicing of a simple but effective list reasonable easy. With others it is not quite as easy. For eg: the keeping of the stock of food send in and returned by the cold buffet an be complicated and time wasting, if one is to measure every ounce or inch. Therefore, it is necessary to accept some rules of thump, providing this is well supervised. Note that an experienced chef de froid or chef grade manger should be able to tell at a glance the weight, number of portions of a given joint or cold dish, with in very narrow margins.

The butchery department also presents some problems and the stock sheet for this department need careful consideration. Fish, Salad vegetables, canned foods, and dairy products on the other hand, are comparatively easy to control. Naturally, each catering establishment will produce its own system, taking its own problem into account, but the stcok/order sheet given here should meet the requirements of most larder departments.

LIAISON WITH KITCHEN AND PASTRY DEPARTMENT

The larder or "Grade Manger" is both a storage department for most perishable goods, and preparation department for such foodstuffs (fig-1). The Larder staff, under the supervision of the chef Grade Manger, are responsible for the ordering storing and preserving of stores, keeping stocks up to date, and accounting for such items as meat, fish, poultry, game, etc., which pass through the department on their way from the suppliers to the kitchen and eventually to the restaurant or banqueting rooms. The bulk of such foodstuff needs dissecting or cleaning dressing, cutting into the required joints or portions, and generally preparing for cooking.

To function in an effective manner, the larder department must operate in harmony with the kitchen in particular, and in many cases with the pastry departments, too if confusion and wastage are to be avoided.

Lack of liaison between the departments could result in duplication of work, or sometimes in certain processes not being carried out to the best advantage. As an example, certain foods intended for cold service are best cooked in the kitchen where there are greater facilities for carrying out the operation, as well as being more closely supervised, thus obtaining the best results.

Likewise, pastry for pies or puddings, and various savouries served from the larder department are best prepared by the pastry staff who will be more skill full in such work, who are equipped with the necessary apparitus and tools for producing such items for used by the larder department. Such tasks as the lining of pudding basins or the covering of meat pies, prior or after filling, by the larder staff in readiness for cooking in the kitchen are examples of such cooperation between the departments.

On the other hand, such savoury fillings as a required by the pastry chef for such items as sauages rolls, patties, or pastles, ravioli, etc, will be prepared in the larder and trabnsfered to the pastry as and when required.

Another important function of the Grade Manger to process dna utilize the 'leftover' element of any meal, and consequently paries of cooked joints. Poultry, fish or even eggs , vegetables and potatoes will be transferred from the kitchen to the larder at the conclusion of every meal. Naturally, the Head Chef will seek to keep the left over to a minimum by careful ordering but, in a busy establishment with a varied menu, a certain amount of leftovers are un avoidable.

It is the task of the chef Grade Manger in consultation with the head chef to make the best possible use of these. Some will go to the preparation of horsdeuvre or salads ; others, suitably trimmed and dressed, to the preparation of cold dishes; and some will be used in 'made up' dishes. All these factors should be , and usually are, taken into account by the Head Chef when planning his menus and the close cooperation of the Chef Grade Manger can be of the utmost importance.

A number of garnishes or accompaniments to dishes served from kitchen departments are prepared by the Grade Manger and a list is given at the end of the chapter. Such items are stuffing , force meats, lardoons or Bacon Rashes, are Naturally Provided By the Larder as well as cold sauces for the accompaniment of hot dishes, such as tartar or remoulade for fried or grilled fish, sauce menthe for roast lamp, sauce raifort for roast beef, sauce ravigote or vinaigrette for calf's head, And many others which are delt with in another section.

In some instances, savoury butters too are prepared by the Larder department for use by the kitchen. But such preparations as dumplings and some savoury patties used by the kitchen for garnishes are prepared by the pastry department, with the savoury ingredients, chopped suet or fillets provided by the larder.

It will be seen from the above the Chef Grade Manger must be familiar with the Garnishes and accompaniments of all dishes on the menu, in particular the classical fish dishes and entrée and soups. Close liaison, therefore, is essentials; between these various departments if delays and complication are to be avoided at the time of serving these dishes

It is advisable, therefore, for the student to make himself familiar with the more commonly used classical garnishes. There are some very good books on this subject, notably the Escoffier's Guide of Modern cookery, or Le Repertoire de la cuisine.

Use and care of equipment, machinery and utensils

REFRIGIRATORS

These play a very important part in the function of the Grade Manger as the enable perishable foods to be stoared at a low temperature and thus prevent deterioration in the food and particularly the growth of harmful bacteria. It should be clearly understood that the refrigirators are not deep freeze compartments and the temperature should be set at a little freezing point or 0-1°C (320 f). a temperature of around 2-3°C (34-36 f) is desirable and, as too great a variation in temperature can be harmful to the food in store, an effort must be made to keep the temperature as constant, or as near constant as possible. The following principles must be observed.

a) Ensure that the refrigerator is in good working order; check the thermostat to make sure it is function; have the refrigerator or serviced regularly and the level of the refrigerant ' topped up' if necessary;

b) Defrosted regularly to enable the evaporator to function efficiently. This is done by switching off the motor and opening the doors too allow the warm air to melt snow, frost and ice which is clinging to the veins of the evaporator and the coils. Never in any circumstance should on use an ice pick or a knife to dislodge the ice as there is the danger of perforating the coils, thus allowing the refrigerant to escape.

c) Use the door as little as possible and never leave it open longer than is necessary for depositing or withdrawing foodstuffs from the refrigerator. The atmosphere outside the refrigerator will be at a much higher temperature normally and will, therefore, be attracted into the colder temperature causing it to raise rapidly.

d) Never place hot food into the refrigerator as this will raise the temperature and is harmful to the other foods in cold store.

When the refrigerator is being defrosted, it should be thoroughly cleaned. The racks and bars are removed and scrubbed with hot water containing grease solvent, rinsed and allowed to dry. The walls, floor and doors should be through sponged down likewise, with hot water containing grease solvent, then rinsed and dried. During this cleaning and defrosting operation the foodstuff will naturally have been removed and transferred to alternative storage.

MINCING MACHINE AND BOWL CUTTER

This is a combination machine and is used for a number if functions in the Grade Manger eg: mincing of meat for sausages, meat loaf, Gelatin Farce etc, mincing of fat prior to rendering for dripping, mincing or chopping of cooked foodstuff, as well as raw for various larder preparations .

The bowl cutter will mix as well as chop the foodstuff and is particularly useful for sausage meat. The mincer can also be used for breaking down bread and crusts, which have been thoroughly dried first, in brown bread crumbs and the bowl cutter can be used for crumbing fresh crust less bread into white bread crumbs, it can also be used for chopping vegetables if required. Care must be taken to ensure that meat and fats are free from any bones or sinews, which would cause damage to the knifes, and that fresh bread is not put through the mincer as this becomes packed tight in the barrel and can cause the motor to seize up. Seizing up can also be caused by overloading the machine, which must be avoided. While every precaution is taken by the manufactures to make the machine safe to use, it must be used with care to avoid accidents. Metal spoons or spatulas must not be used to push or stir the foodstuffs while the machine is in motion, as they are likely to get caught up in the blades with serious results.

Both the mincing and bowl cutting attachments can be dismantled for cleaning , which should be done with hot water containing grease solvent, then rinced and dried before reassembling. The bowl itself is not removable and must be cleaned on the machine. Some of the parts are of cast iron and care must be taken not to drop them on to hard surfaces as they will cracker break.]

Finally, the machine must be lubricated at regular intervals with lubricating oil provided. The operator should study the instruction chart so that he becomes familier with the ceiling points.

Slicing maching

This machine is used for cutting slices of cooked meats such as ham, tounge, or any other joint of meat which must, naturally, be boneless. It is also used for cutting bacon or gammon rasher which will of course be uncooked. A calibrate scale is fitted to determinr the thickness of the slice or rasher and one must ensure that this is returned to zero prior to placing one's hands in the vicinity of the blade to remove or adjust the joint of meat or to clean the machine.

The slicer is the gravity feed type but other makes and types are available example horizontal feed. They may be hand operated, semi automatic or fully automatic, the latter having both blade and carriage mechanically operated.

For cleaning, the machine should be dismantled in accordance with the instructions chart provided by the manufactures and all parts washed in hot water containing a grease solvent. They should then be rinced and dried prior to reassembling. The parts not removable should be cleaned on the machine and care must be taken to ensure that no foodstuffs are left clinging to any part of it as this could be the ideal breading rounds for bacteria. Cotton waste and wooden pallet are used for cleaning the edge of the blade.

Remember, the .scale must be set at zero before undertaking any of these operations.

The blade should be kept sharp by using the grained stone attachment provided, when necessary but care must be taken not to do this too often or for too long as it will cost wear to the blade.

The machine should be kept lubricated with the oil provided, in accordance with the instruction book.

SCALES AND WEIGHING MACHINES

There are several types, the uses of which are ovious. Large platform scales, for weighing large joints of meat or other heavy weights are obtainable. For lesser weights there are smallest scales such as graduated scales fitted with a price chart showing at a glance the prices of the odd grands (ounces) and / or the price per kilogram (lb). The Inspector Of Weights and Measures should inspect and set these periodically .

No maintenance is necessary other than keeping them in a scrupulously clean condition. This is done by sponging them over with a cloth soaked in hot water and then drying thoroughly. The pans of the small scale and the tray of the graduated scale are remove able and should be washed in a sink of hot water. Foodstuff will not be placed directly on to the platform or pans of the scale but should always be on a clean dish or tray or on a sheet of grease proof paper when being weighed. Naturally, the weight of the container must be taken into account when reckoning the weight of the food.

ELECTRIC GRINDING MACHINE

This machine is used for grinding and edge on knives and choppers, or cleavers, as and when required. It should not be abused and should be brought into use only when the steel or the hand carborundum stone fails to set a sufficiently keen edge to the cutting tools. The too frequent use of grinding machine not only unduely wears the steel of the knives etc, but has a detrimental effect on the steel itself, causing it eventually to loose its temper. The following instruction should be carefully observed:

a) Make sure there is sufficient water in the well and that the water is being pumped on to the grind stone, before using. Never use the stone dry.
b) Use the guides fitted to the machines for either knives or choppers, as this ensures the correctly set edge.
c) Hold the handle of the knife or chopper, in the right hand and draw the edge along the stone from the heal of the knife to the tip, with the stone revolving tin the forward position. Now switch to reverse and reverse your drill; knife handle in the left hand, edge of knife from heal to tip, from right to left. Do not over grind. Set the edge with a steel.

Keep the machine in a clean condition by sponging the stove enameled part with a damp cloth, then dry. Change the water frequently to prevent sediment from clogging the pump.

For lubricating, follow the instruction on the chart and learn the lubricating points.

Boiling plate or gas rings

They are used to heat or cook food stuff as required, eg principally for cooking vegetables for horsdoeuvres, for rendering fats, and for the making of aspic jelly, sauces, pickles and other larder preparation. The flame must at all times be controlled to avoid the risk of burning the food and the taps are adjustable to a range of settings to sit all purposes.

Spilling, over boil avers,,, should be wiped down immediately to prevent then from baking hard on the hot surfaces. When bars are cooled, remove any crusted matter, then wash in hot water containing a grease solvent. Periodically, the burner will require the same treatment and must carefully dried before replacing. The enamel surround should be sponged down with water. Abrasives should not be used as they damage as scratch the eamel.

GRILLER/TOASTER(SALAMANDER GRILL)

As the name implies, this is used for either grilling or toasting foodstuff. It is used principally for toasting bread for making savoury and canapé, and for grilling sausages, chipolatas or other food stuff for savoury.

For cleaning the burners should be carefully wiped clean as they are easily damaged. The fat drip tray must be emptied and cleaned daily. A little water in the tray will prevent the grease from baking on. Do not allow crumbs to burn in the tray. The stove enamel part should be sponged with a damp cloth and wiped dry.

GAS BOILER

Used for cooking large joints such as hams, gammons, tongues, etc, and also for cooking lobsters or crabs. The pan interior must be emptied and cleaned, washed and dried each time is used.

BUTCHER'S BLOCK

These are used for all butchery work: desetting, jointing and cutting meat, as well as cutting fats, breaking and chopping bones, etc. they are composed of a number of sections of timber in block form, joint together and framed around with a stout wooden frame the whole secured together, they have the advantage of being reversible, so that when one surface becomes badly worn, the block can be reversed. They can also be resurfaced when badly worn by having the surfaces cut by the large saw at a timber yard.

The block usually rests on a stout deal frame, into which may be fitted drawers to contain the butchers tools. A good general rule is to keep the surface as clean as dry as possible. the top should never be scrubbed. It should be scraped or brushed with the scrapper of wire brusher provided and left to dry. Wet meat should not be allowed to lied on the block longer then is necessary, as brine or water can soften the joints or produce the wet rot between the blocks. Never wash the tools on the block, as this can add considerably to the moisture content.

STEEL TABLE These are used as work benches but foodstuff s must not be cut on them. Apart from scratching the surface of the table,such mal practice can also blund the edge of the knife or tool being used. Boards are provided for such a purpose. The tables should be cleaned by sponging with a cloth soaked in hot soapy water, rinced with clean water and dried. The chopping boards should be well scrubbed and dried after used. In particular, care should be taken not to leave any fish scales clinging to the surfaces. Formica top tables can be sponged down as for the steel tables, but the wooden frame work must be scrubbed and dried.

SAUCEPANS AND LIDS These are mostly aluminum and require utmost care to keep clean. Certain foods cause bad discolouration of aluminum and the sauce pan should be washed in hot soapy water, polished to a bright shine with wire wool and soap, thoroughly rinsed, and dried each time after use. Soda must not be used, as this causes pitting and discolouring. The same treatment is given to aluminum trays and other cointainers. Enamel trays are washed in hot soapy water, rinsed and dried as also are China and earthenware bowls and basins and plastic horsdoeuvres dishes.

FRYING KETTLES AND FRYING PAN The frying kettles are used for deep frying and for rendering fats into dripping. The frying pans are used for a variety of shallow frying or sautéing operations. Both are made of wrought steel and are best cleaned, while it Is still hot, with a heavy dry cloth.

POLYTHENE BINS – HYGIENE Three is the minimum quantity required for daily use in the larder; 1) for bringing meat (usually kept in refrigerator), 2)for swill (all waste foodstuffs, suitable for feeding pigs), 3) for refuse (all waste unsuitable for pig feed ; paper, tin, glass, floor sweaping etc).

The swill and refuse bins should be emptied daily and washed out with warm water. They must not be exposed to excess heat, otherwise they will loose their shape or even melt. In particular, no disinfectant must be used in the swill bin, as this could poison theee pigs. The bin for bringing meat must not be Interchange with the either of the other two.

Finally, at the end of each section the sinks, counters and floor must be left in a clean condition, together with all the other items mentioned above. Porcelain sinks should be cleansed with scouring powder and rinsed out. Drains should be cleard, clothes washed and hung up to dry. Counter should be scrubbed, window skills spomged clean, and finally the floor well swept.

If these operations are carried out, the department will always be clean and fresh for the commencement of each section.

OTHER LARDER TOOLS

The following tools are made of steel or tined steel and are cleaned by wahing in hot water containg grease solvent, then rinsed and dried:

Serving Spoons and Ladle	:	for spooning or ladling foods
Sieves	:	for sieving various foods
Colanders	:	for draining food stuffs
Conical Strainers and 'Chinois'	:	for straing sauces
Meat Pressers	:	for pressing joints etc
Pie Moulds	:	for pork or veal and ham pies
Whisks	:	for whisking and stirring food
Egg Slicers	:	for slicing hard boiled eggs
Steel Basins	:	containers
Graters	:	for grating fruits

KNIVES, CHOPPER, SAWS, ETC

All these tools are made of tempered steel and should be cleaned with scouring powder, prior to washing in hot soapy water rinsing and drying.

Butchers and Boning Knife	:	for joining and boning
Butcher's Steak or Cutting Knives	:	for cutting meats
Butchers Saw (Tenon)	:	for surface bones
Butcher's Saw (Bow)	:	for deep seated bones
Butcher Chopper and Clivers	:	for chopping bones
Butcher Chopping Knives	:	for chining joints
Cook's 30cm (12in.) Knives	:	for poultry
Cook's 20-24cm (9/7in.) Knives	:	for vegetables
Cook's 6-8cm (4in.) Knives	:	for turning
Cook's 14-20cm (7in.) Knives	:	for fish fillet knife
Tranche lard Knives	:	for carving or bacon rashers
Pallet Knives	:	for lifting and turning food
Potato Peelers French or English	:	for peeling vegetables
Mandoline Vegetable Slicer	:	for slicing vegetables

WOODEN UTENSIL

Wooden spatulas and spoons are used for stirring food stuff to prevent burning. Wooden Mushrooms are used for pressing foodstuff through sieves. These wooden utensils should be well scrubbed, washed, rinsed and dried after use.

MISCELLANEOUS

The following tools are kept clean by washing in hot water, rinsing and drying. Care should be taken to prevent them from rusting or deteriorating.\

Cutlet Bat	:	for flattening cuts of meat
Trussing Needles	:	for poultry trussing
Larding Needles	:	for larding cuts of meat, poultry, etc
Larding Pin	:	for larding joints, etc
Lemon Zesters	:	for scrapping of lemon peal
Lemon Decorators	:	for channeling lemon skin
Vegetable Scoops	:	for shaping vegetables and potatoes
Butcher's Hooks	:	for hanging joints etc
Skewers	:	for skewering meat, etc
Brining Syringe	:	for pumping brine into joints
Brino Meter	:	for measuring density of brine]

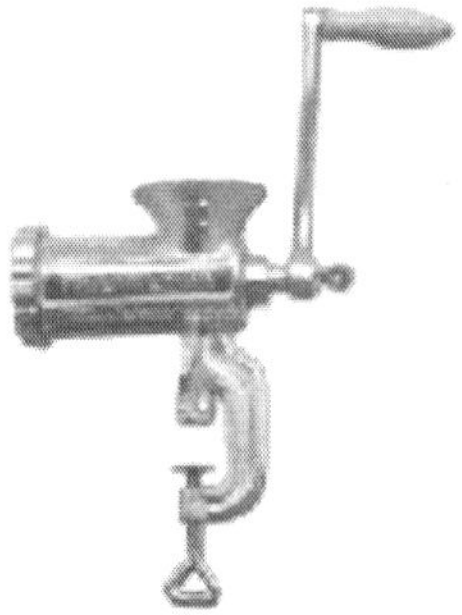

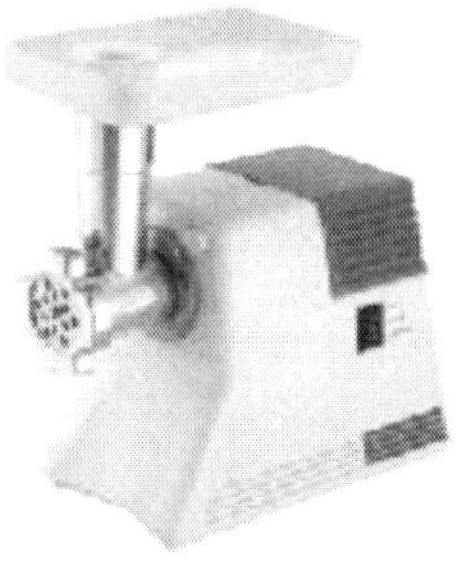

MECHANICAL EQUIPMENT

Mincers

Mincers are used for chopping vegetables or meat. Mincers are compact, hygienically designed machines capable of providing a cool, efficient mincing action without squashing or pulping the product.

Mixers

A mixer is a kitchen appliance intended for mixing, folding, beating, and whipping food ingredients. Mixers come in two major variations, hand mixers and stand mixers. A hand mixer, as the name implies, is a hand-held mixing device. It typically consists of a handle mounted over a large enclosure containing the motor, which drives one or two beaters. The beaters are immersed in the food to be mixed. Mixer A stand mixer is essentially the same as a hand mixer, but is mounted on a stand which bears the weight of the device. Stand mixers are larger and have more powerful motors than their handheld counterparts. They generally have a special bowl that is locked in place while the mixer is operating. Heavy duty commercial models can have bowl capacities in excess of 100 quarts (95 L). Typical home and commercial models are equipped with bowls of around 4 quarts (4 L). A typical home dick stand mixer will include a wire whip for whipping creams and egg whites; a flat beater for mixing batters; and a dough hook for kneading.

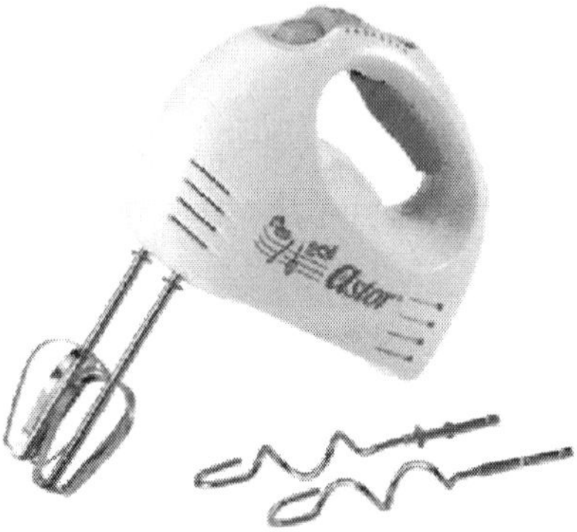

Blender

A blender or liquidiser is a kitchen appliance used to mix ingredients or puree food. The blending container can be made of glass, plastic, or stainless steel, and often has graduated markings for approximate measuring purposes. At the top of the container is a lid to prevent ingredients from escaping during operation. At the bottom is a serrated blade assembly, sometimes removable for cleaning purposes.

Refrigerators A refrigerator (often called a "fridge" for short) is a coolingappliance comprising a thermally insulated compartment and amechanism to transfer heat from it to the external environment,cooling the contents to a temperature below ambient.

Kitchen Equipments and Cooking Fuel Refrigerators are extensively used to store foods which deteriorate at ambient temperatures; spoilage from bacterial growth and other processes is much slower at low temperatures. A device described as a "refrigerator" maintains a temperature a few degrees above the freezing point of water; a similar device which maintains a temperature below the freezing point of water is called a "freezer". Freezers keep their contents frozen. They are used both in households and for commercial use. Most freezers operate at around -18°C (0°F).

KITCHEN ORGANISATION

Kitchen Brigade
Duties and Responsibilities of Kitchen Staffs

INTRODUCTION

The staff in kitchen needs to be able to prepare, at any given moment, a wide number of items. The size of the kitchen staff can range from one person to a large group, classically known as the brigade. The size of the kitchen staff is determined equally by the number of meals the restaurant commonly serves and how extensive the menu is. The number of people actually employed in a kitchen will vary greatly from one operation to the next such as breakfast, lunch, dinner, bonquet, etc. Georges Auguste Escoffier, a French chef, restaurateur and culinary writer popularized and updated traditional French cooking methods. He organized his kitchens by the brigade system, with each section run by a chef de partie. In this system everybody had a distinct task, which meant that no one duplicated anyone else's work. This system provided efficiency, economy, safety and an esprit de corps.

Many establishments today are far from modest in scope, and the lack of skilled workers in all of these distinct areas, along with technological advances that call for a certain consolidation, has modified the brigade system substantially. It is important, however, to understand the hierarchy that Escoffier formulated, because that will give you a good overview of just about every task that might be faced in the universe we call "the kitchen".

KITCHEN BRIGADE Brigade de cuisine is a system of hierarchy found in restaurants and hotels in France that employ extensive staff and are commonly referred to as kitchen staff in English speaking countries. This structured team system delegates responsibilities to different individuals that specialize in certain tasks.

Note: The lead person in each kitchen section was called the chef de partie and had commis (cooks or helpers): premier commis (station cook), deuxieme commis (cook's helper) and troisiem commis (cook's helper assistant).

Kitchen Brigade

Chef
(Executive Chef)
Sous Chef
(Asst. Executive)
Chef)
Saucier (Sauce, Stock,
Preparation)

Potager
(Soup Preparation)
Poissoner
(Fish Preparation)
Entremetier (Vegetable
Preparation)
Rotisseur
(Roasted Meals)
Grillardin
(Broiled Meats)
Garde Manger
(Cold Foods)
Pattisier
(Desserts)
Baker
(Breads)
Tournant
(Swing Cook)

Note: The lead person in each kitchen section was called the chef de partie and had commis (cooks or helpers): premier commis (station cook), deuxieme commis (cook's helper) and troisiem commis (cook's helper assistant).

Below is an exhaustive list of different members of the kitchen brigade system. Only the largest of establishments would have an extensive staff of this size. As noted under certain titles, certain positions are combined into other positions when such a large staff is unnecessary.

Food Types and Recipes Force meat: Meaning uses types and recipes.

Panada: Meaning, uses, types and recipes.

Compound butters: Meaning, uses, types and recipes and examples.

Marinade: Different types and uses.

Brine: Types and uses.

Aspic jelly: Uses and preparation.

Chaud Froid: Uses and preparation.

Sauces: Types and preparation.

ASPIC Aspic is a jelly derived from by boiling the meat and bones of most animals, straining to get a clean stock and cooling to gelatinous solid. This gelatinous solid is called Aspic jelly. When the stock does not congeal sufficiently, it becomes necessary to use commercial jelly, in the form of sheets or powder. Aspic or jelly plays an important role in the preparation of innumerable garde manger delicacies by highlighting the ingredients being presented. It also provides special protection for cold dishes, enabling them to retain their original flavour and freshness for a long period.

Aspic jelly must always be odour – free, crystal clear and of a light golden colour. Though easy to treat, Aspic requires carefull handling; foremost it is easily affected by temperature. When the temperature is too high, jelly will melt. On the other hand, if it is low it will become like rubber and not melt in the mouth. When set, aspic should be neither too firm, nor too soft. The room temperature and the length of time the dish must retain its shape have considerable bearing on setting setting jelly. In summer months it is advisable to make the aspic a little more stiff. To test it out, a ladle a couple of tablespoons on to a plate, refrigerator for 10-15 mins, remove and check the consistency and the flavour.

Aspic has shown itself to be extremely vulnerable to bacteria – and it spoils within hours of being touched by hand. As such it should never be touched and to taste and test a spoon should be used. When set, use a ladle or a knife to remove the required quantity

If treated with care, aspic jelly can be stored in the cooler – not freezer- for more than two weeks. Under no circumstances should it be allowed to freeze.

The colour always depends upon the raw materials. Aspic derived from meat is dark, from poultry medium and from fish is light in colour. The use of aspic corresponds with the ingredient: meat aspic with a meat delicacy, a chicken aspic with chicken dish, etc. there is never any mixing of the two. However, if the colour is too light, add a few drops of strained caramel colouring to correct.

Aspic can also be used for decorating dishes which are not moulded. For example, it can be used to garnish any cold roast. In fact, it is a must on the cold buffet, where it can easily enhance eye appeal.

HOW TO PREPARE ASPIC

In the past, the base for aspic was prepared from stock, prepared form the head and feet of calves. Today this method is considered complicated and cumbersome. Indeed, meat broth or consommé are used.

The process for preparing aspic is the same as that of consommé expect for the addition of gelatine. The gelatine must be stirred constantly-but lightly-to prevent sticking and burning until it reaches boiling point. Thereafter simmer over very low heat for an hour. For best results, add all the ingredients while the aspic is being cooked. The addition of salt or wine at a later stage is likely to make the aspic cloudy.

Once prepared, aspic has to be stirred carefully to ensure that it is crystal clear. A greasy cloth or an improperly washed napkin can ruin the aspic. Equally important is the use of appropriate utensils thoroughly washed and dried stainless steel or stone bowls are best suited for the purpose.

TERRINE DE VIANDE

A cold meat mince preparation, cooked blind(without dough covering or fat caoating) in a bread mould, is called a meat loaf in culinary terms. The mould is covered with foil (to prevent the mince from becoming dry or browned on the top during cooking), then placed in a double boiler. The double boiler is then placed in a pre-heated oven (375°f) and the meat cooked for 40-45 mins. Thereafter, the meat is cooled, wiped and refrigerated. Meat loaves can be prepared from chicken, veal, pork, steak and mutton or a combination of any or all.

RECIPE:Veal 2kgRed wine 45 mlBlack peppercorns 5gPork fat 300g
Seasoning:10g pate spice180 ml heavy cream4 eggs120 ml brandy
Garnish:20g pistachio100g pork fat60g pimentos

PREPARATION:

- The veal: clean, debone, and cut into 1" chunks.
- The pepper: crush in a pepper mill.

- The marination: mix pepper with veal in a bowl, pour wine and marinate for 4 hours.
- The mince: cut pork fat into ¾" chunks, put in a mincer, add veal along with the marinade and make a fine mince. Remove, transfer to a large bowl and refrigerate for 1 hour.
- The Eggs: beat in a bowl.
- The Garnish: blanch pistachio and peel the skin. Cut pork fat and pimentos into ¼" dices.
- The paste: mix seasoning, pate spice, cream, eggs, and brandy with the mince and make a fine and smooth paste in a buffalo chopper. Remaove to a large bowl, add the garnish and mix well refrigerate.
- The oven: pre-heat to 375 °f.

COOKING

Grease a paste mould, transfer the paste, spread evenly compress and thump the mould on the table or the floor to remove any air pockets. Place in a double boiler and bake in the pre-heated oven for 45 m ins. Remove, cool and refrigerate overnight. Demould, wipe with a warm, wet cloth, wrap in foil and refrigerate again.

GALANTINE

The term is derived from galine, old French name for chicken. In the days of yore, galantines were made only from chicken and game birds. Today a variety of meats and fish is used. In culinary terms, the word has come to mean a delicate filling in the centre of raw, boned meat, rolled and enveloped in muslin, tied and poached in a rich stock.

The filling, which must be seasoned carefully, is the centerpiece- literally and figuratively and the preparation requires great skill while deboning. Under no circumstances can the skin be allowed to be lacerated. The cooking process is just as important. It has to be done to perfection, never over cooked, which would make the galantine dry and hard. The choice of meat can make or mar the delicacy – it must always be young.

Very often galantines are confused with ballotines, which too are prepared from similar basic ingredients. How ever and this is a big difference – ballotines are baked or braised, shaped into ballots and served hot as entrees. Galantines, on the other hand, are always served cold as starter.

The best base for galantines is large capons. Turkey and pheasant are the two other commonly used poultry. Among meats, veal and lamb are excellent base for galantines, as is fish.

RECIPE:Chicken 1.8 kgWhite pepper corns 5gWhite wine 45mlPork fat 200gChicken mince 1.6 kgEgg white 5

Seasoning:10g pate spice120 ml heavy cream5 L chicken stock75g gelatine powder120 ml brandy

Garnish:40g pistachio20g black olives or truffles100g carrots4 eggs

A good garnish is important as the galantine itself, without it there is no eye-appeal. A combination of several of the following ingredients can be used for garnish: canned mushrooms, pistachio, port fat, liver, fillet of chicken, cooked ham, black olives, stuffed olives, hard boiled egg whites, prunes, boiled carrots, and if splurging, truffles and foie gras.

PREPARATIONS

- THE Chicken: clean debone, starting from the spine, carefully without lacerating the skin. Spread, flatten and place the birds on sepearte rectangular pieces of aluminium foil (enough to wrap the chicken roll)
- The pepper: crush in a pepper mill
- The marination: sprinkle pepper and wine on the chicken and keep aside for atleast 30minutes.
- The egg whites: beat in a bowl.
- The garnish: remove pits from olives and cut into ¼" dices. Peel, wash, boil, cool and cut carrots into ¼" dices. Blanch pistachio and remove the skin. Hard boil eggs, cool, shell, cut into halves, discard yolks and cut into ¼" dices
- The paste: mix pork fat, egg whites, seasoning, pate spice, brandy, and cream with chicken mince and make a fine and smooth paste in a buffalo chopper. Remove to a bowl, add the garnish and mix well. Divide into 4 equal portions.

PATE

Pate is French for "paste" and in the world of cooking it means a pie of fine and smooth meat, fish or poultry paste. It is also the oldest among garde manger delicacies – there are innumerable references in ancient recipe books. To the connoisseur, it is pate that sets the standard of dishes to come.

The most commonly used ingredients in the making of pate are: chicken liver (goose liver is the most sought after ingredient but its rarity and price necessitate the use of substitute and chicken liver soaked in milk for 24 hours as the usual substitute), truffles and a combination of forcemeats accompanied by garnishes.

The art of making pate involves four important and distinct procedures.

1. Preparation of dough
2. Preparation of farce or filling
3. Baking
4. Preparation of jelly

Once pate is ready, it is important to allow it to mature. Refrigerate or store it in a cool place for atleast 2-3 days to allow fermentation, which permits the spices to really permeate the paste, improving the taste and aroma. Never cut freshly baked pate.

Ingredients

15g cloves
15g dry ginger
15g nut meg
15g paprika powder
10g basil powder
10g black pepper powder
10g white pepper powder
2 bay leaves
15g thyme
5g marjoram

PREPARATION

- The pate spice: pound all these spices together and sieve.
- To store: store in a sterlised, dry and air tight container.

MOUSSE A versatile delicacy, a mousse can be served cold or hot and can be made with just about everything meats, vegetables, fruits, cheeses and leftovers. In garde manger terms, a mousse is a mixture of cooked ingredients, turned ito a heavy puree, bound with aspic gelatine or veloute mixed with cream and then flavoured. A mousse is used either as a filling (ham mousse for ham cornets) or a topping (fish mousse on a poached fillet or on a canapé). Mousse can be set in moulds. Upon demoulding, a mousse is decorated and napped with aspic to give it eye appeal.

MOUSSE DE POISSON (FISH MOUSSE)

INGREDIENTS:
1 kg pomfret
150 ml liquid aspic
SEASONING:
Worcester sauce (a few drop)
15g parsley
100g mayonnaise
200ml whipped cream
120 ml white wine
45ml lemon juice

PREPARATION

- The fish: clean, debone, remove the skin and poach. Remove, cool and make a fine paste. Transfer to a large bowl.
- The parsley: clean, wash and finely chop.
- The mousse: add all the ingredients to the fish paste and mix thoroughly. Refrigerate.
- Yield: 1.6 kg
- Preparation time: 30 minutes.

GARNISHERS: Garnishers – Importance, names of garnishes used with – Soup, beef, poultry and game. Cold Preparation – Galantine, Balloting, Terrine, pate quenelles, mouse, Mousselines, suffles- recipes of above.

During a week, with a daily changing menu, the different chefs de partie need numerous garnishes. The following garnishes, or fillings, as used in different departments of the kitchen, are a few examples in each case of this large subject. They will serve to emphasize their importance and the need for detailed study of this branch of cold Larder work. Only by being familiar with most of these will the chef Garde - Menger be able to order all items of food needed, thus promoting a smooth liaison between departments.

POTAGER:

GARNISHING FOR SOUPS

A simple dish can be transformed by feasting the eyes firstwith even the most casual of garnishing – a sprig of mint, basil orparsley can add colour and aroma which looks attractive anddemonstrate a caring attitude to a meal.

1) One of the simplest garnishes for soup is a tablespoon of salted whipped cream sprinkled with a dash of paprika or a little parsley chopped very fine.
2) Eggs are used as garnishes of soups in the form of a baked custard cut in fancy shapes, or as egg balls. The whole yolks poached in salted water just below the boiling-point may be used; one yolk is served with each plate of soup
3) Noodles, tapioca, spaghetti or macaroni cut in fancy shapes or quenelles make simple and attractive garnishes for soup.
4) Cooked vegetables cut in thin strips or in Julienne style or in fancy shapes or slices, are often used to add color flavor and nutritive value to a soup.
5) Soups may be garnished also with cubes of bread or puff paste buttered and browned in the oven or fried in deep fat. Garnishes for soups needn't be complicated or time consuming, but they should meet two objectives:

They should be pleasing to the eye, adding to the visual impact of the bowl; and

They should be edible, complimenting rather than competing with the main flavours of the soup.

METHOD OF SERVING SOUP

1) Soup dishes are always deep.
2) Soup plates are used for dinner soup.
3) Soup bowls and cups are used for luncheon soups.
4) Set soup dishes on a plate slightly larger than the soup dish.
5) A soup spoon is smaller that a tablespoon and larger that a teaspoon.
6) Bouillon spoons are small round-bowled spoons.
7) In using a soup spoon, dip the spoon away from you. Take the soup silently with the lips from the side of the spoon and not the tip.
8) Do not leave spoon in soup dish. When not using it, place on the plate.
9) When soup is served in a bouillon cup it is customary to take a few spoonfuls and then it is permissible to set the spoon on the plate, and drink the remainder of the soup from the cup.
10) It is permissible to put two or three pieces of crackers or toast on top of soup.

Small quenelles of meats – Brunoise of chicken, ham & tongue.

Small quenelles of Poultry – Julienne of chicken, ham & tongue

Small quenelles of Fish – Clarification for Consomme

Small quenelles of bone – Marrow – Giblets for consommé

Slices of bone – Marrow croutons

POISSONNIER: Quenelles de brochet (Fish or main course) – Prawns soft rose, Plain or Pane.

Small quenelles de poisson – slices of truffles or dice.

Slice or dice of crawfish & lobster – Oyster & Mussels.

Tails of crayfish & scampis – Fish croquettes, cutlets & cakes stoned Oliver & grapes (Fish or main course) Shrimps.

SAUCE: Sulphicons of varying compositions Chicken livers.

Ragouts and fillings for vol an vent Dice of pork fat.

Sliced, diced or chopped truffles Lardons.

Champignons – Brunoye of meats, Poultry and vegetables.

Stoned Olives – Julienne of Meats, Poulrty and vegetables.

Cocks Kidneys – Slices of beef – bone Marrow.

ROTISSEUR/GRILLADIN: Various compound butter – Missbeau, anchovy butter, anchovy olives.

Various cold sauces – Holstein garnish

Various Mayonneise derivatives – vienne Garnish.

ESITREMENTTIETR:

Diced cooked ham (omlettes)- Lamb kidneys (Egg dishes Meyerben) Chicken livers (crousavouries)-Crayfish tails (Egg dishes Rothschild)

Oyster (Croutons – Savouries).

PATISSIER:

The patissier need is not so much for garnishes as for fillings.

Sausage Meat (Sausage rolls)

Diced Meat (Cornish Pas ties)

Salpicon of different compositions (Dartois)

Anchovy (Dartois)

Sardires (+Dartois)

Meat, Poultry and game forces (Pies – pate en croute)

Chopped shet (Shet pastry)

Ravioli filling (Ravioli)

CLASSICAL GARNISHES:

1. Americains (Fish) : Slices of lobster & truffles.
2. Dieppoise (Fish) : Shrimps, bearded mussels, mushrooms.
3. Fiananciere : Chicken quenelles or prawns, bearded mussels.
4. Mariniere (Fish): Shrimps or prawns, bearded mussels.
5. Milenaise : julienne of ham, mushrooms, tongue, truffles, tomato.
6. Mirabean (Grills) : Anchovy butter, Fillets of anchovy, stuffed olives.
7. Normande (Fish) : Bearded systers and mussels, mushroom heads, crayfish tails, gaujon of sole, slices of truffles, croutons.
8. Regence:
   a. Fish – Fish quenelles, Cray fish tails, mushrooms, bearded oysters, soft roes, slicens of truffles.
   b. Chicken Sweet-bread: Chicken quenelles, cockscombs, triangles of foegras, mushroom heads.
   c. Game: Game quenelles, Cockscombs, triangle of foiegras, Mushroom heads, and croutons.
9. Re'forme : julienne of ham, tongue, beetroom, whites of egg, gherkins.
10. Stresbourgeoise: Lardons of boiled bacon, slices of foie gres, chipolatas.
11. Tortue : Quenelles, mushroom heads, gherkins, round slices of tongue, calves brain, deep fried egg. Crayfishtails, truffles, croutons.
12. Toulousaine : Chicken quenelles, sweet bread, cockscombs, mushrooms, slices or dice of truffles.
13. Viennioise (Entrée): Slices of lemon, snchovy, sieved whites abd yolk of eggs,

S.No.	Garnish	Composition of Garnish	Menu term (example)
1.	Bercy	Poached with chopped shallot parsely, Fish stock and white wine, Finished with W. wine sauce and glazed.	Fillets de sole Bercy
2.	Bonne – femme	As for Bercy, with the addition of sliced mushrooms, glezed	Supreme de turbot bonnefemme
3.	Braval or d' antin	As for bonne-femme, with the addition of chopped tomatoes, glazed	Supreme de barbue Breval
4.	Veronique	Poached with white and fish stock coated with W. wine sauces glazed and garnished with grape.	Sole Veronique
5.	Dieppoise	Poached, coated with white wine sauce, garnished with mussels, shrimp tail & mushroom	Supreme de carrelet dieppoise
6.	Duglere	Poached with chopped shallots, parsely, tomatoes Fish stock, coated with a sauce made from liquor.	Filet d' algrefin Duglere
7.	Mornay	Poached, coated with cheese sauce and glazed.	C equille de cabillaund Mornay
8.	Florintine	Poached, dressed on a bed of leaf, spinach, coated with Mornay sauce and glazed.	Supreme de tin both Florentine.
9.	Hollandaise	Plain boiled, service with hollandaise sauce and plain boiled potatoes.	Troncon de turbot hollandaise
10	Meuniere	Shallow-fried on both side garnished with slice of lemon, coated with nut brown butter, lemon juice, parsely.	Truit de riviere Meuinere
11	Bell-Meuniere	As meuniere, with the addition of grilled mushroom, a slice of peeled tomato and a soft herring – reo.	Sole bellemeuniere
12	Doria	As for Meuniere with a sprinkling of small, turced cooked pieces of cucumber.	Supereme de fletan Doira
13	Grenogloise	As for mouniere, with the lemon in peeled segments and capers.	Rouget grenobloise
14	Bretonne	As for menuiere with picked shrimps and sliced mushrooms	Filet d'aigretin bretonne.
15	Princesse	Poached, coated with W.wine sauce garnished with asparagus heads and alice truffle	Delices de sole princesse.
16	Saint Germain	Filleted whitefish dipped in butter, breadcumbled, Grilled, served with be arnaise sauce and noisette potatoes	Fillets de pile st. GErmain
17	Orly	Deep fried and served with tomato sauce	Fillet de cabillandal' orly.
18	Boulangere	Onions & potatoes	Gigot d' agrean baulangere
19	Bouquetiere	Artichoke bottoms, carrots, turnips, lpeas, French benas, cauliflower, chatcan potatoes.	Filet de bocuf bouquetiere
20	Bourgeoise	Carrots, onions, dice of bacon.	Bocuf braise bourgeoise
21	Bruzelloise	Braised chicory, brussol sprouts chatern potatoes	Noix de ven bruxelloise.
22	Clamotrt	Arthicoke bottoms filled with peas ala francise or puree of peas and chateau potatoes	Carre d' agrean clamart
23	Dubbary	Small balls of cauliflower mornay , chatean potatoes	Contrefielet de boeuf dubarry
24	Fermiere	Paysanne of carrots, tyrnips, onions, celery	Poulet en basserole feruriste
25	Fleuriste	Tomatoes filled with carrots, turnips, peas, French beans & chatean potatoes	Neisette d' agneau fleuriste
26	Henri. IV	Pont-neuf potatoes and water cress	Tournedos Henri IV
27	Julie	Stuffed tomatoes, braised lettuce, chatean potatoes	Longe d'agrean judic
28	Mascotte	Quarters of artichoke bottome, cocotte potatoes	Poulet sauce Mascotte
29	Mercedes	Grilled tomatoes, grilled mushrooms, braised lettuce and croquette potatoes	Sclle de veau Mercedes

30	Parmentier	1 cm dice of fried potatoes	Poulet sauté parmentier
31	Portugaise	Small stuffed tomatoes, chatean potatoes	Tournedos a la portugaise
32	Pritainer	Turned carrots and turnips, peas, dice of French beans	Navariv d'agnean printainer
33	Reforme	Short batorns of beetroot white of egg, gherkin, mushroom, truffle and tongue.	Cotelette d' agneau reforme
34	Sevigne	Braised lettuce, grilled mushrooms, chateau potatoes	Carre de veau Sevigne
35	Tyrolienne	French fried onions, tolato concasse	Noisette d'agneau Tyrolienne
36	Vert pre vichy	Straw potatoes and watercress with vichy carrots	Blanquette do veau vichy
37	Washington	Sweet com	Polarde poele Washington
38	Duxelle	Finely chopped shallots & chopped mushrooms	-
39	Glaze	With cream	Meringue glaze Chantilly
40	Moka	Coffee flavor	Glace moka
41	Praline	With chooped almondand hazel-nut toffee	Goteau pratine
42	Melba	With vanilla ice-cream & raspberry puree or sauce	Pache mlba
43	Helena	Vanilla, ice-cream hot chocolate sauce	Poire Helene.

parsely.

14. Walewska (Fish): Slices of lobster tails, slices of truffles.
15. Zingara : Julienne of ham, mushrooms, tongue & truffles.

COLD PREPARATIONS

GALANTINE

It is deboned poultry and game, stuffed with forcemeats rolled tightly and cooked. Poultry and game selected for galantine preparation should be loss tender than for other uses.

Recipe

Claned chickem -1 No. (2kgs) I
Salted Ox-tongue, cooked – 150gms.
Porkfat-150gms
Truffles cut in small size-50gms II
Pistachios, skinned – 30gms
Brandy – 150ml.
Vealfish – 750 gms.
Grated nutmeg – a pinch III
Double cream – 300ml.
Porkfat cut in very thin slices – 400gms. IV
Fonds de volaille – 10liter V
Sauce chaud – froid Blanche ....2liter VI
Gelee de volalle 2 liter
Groutons of chicken jelly for decoration VII

METHOD

1. Single carefully and cutoff the winglets and the legs at the first joints. Cut the skin along the back & carefully remove the skin with the point of a small shape

knife. Make sure that the skin is not punctured. Clean the skin of all fat and flesh and soak in cold water for 30mts to whiten.

2. Remove the flesh completely from the chicken. Cut the breast, tongue and porkfat (lard) into a basin of long stripes, approx ½ x ½ cm. thick. Place into a basin with the pistachis, truffle and brandy. Season lightly with little salt & pepper and allow to Marinate until required.
3. Removing the tendons from the boned chicken legs. Pass the chicken flesh and veal twice through the fine mincer together with any trimming from the chicken breasts. Place into a basin & season. Mix in the cream and finely add the brandy from Marintion together with truffles and pistachios. Check the seasonings and adjust if necessary.
4. Drain and dry the chicken skin, spread it on a damp cloth and cover the skin completely with the slices of the porkfat. Place a layer of 1/3 rd of the mixture along the centre of the skin and arrange half of the marinated strips on top. Finish with the remainder of the mixture. Envelope the mixture completely with the chiken skin, roll it up in the cloth in the shape of a thick sausage and tie up at both ends and in the middle.
5. Poach the ga;antine with carefully in the Chicken stock for approximately ½ hrs. Remove re-tie lightly and allow to cool on a tray under slight pressure.
6. Coat the galantine with chaud-froid, decorate, glaze with the Chicken aspic & arrange on a silver dish previously set with a layer of jelly. Garnish with croutons of jelly.

BALLOTINE

The Ballotine is made of a piece of meat fowl, game or fish which is boned, stuffed and rolled into the shape of a bundle. The term Ballotine should strictly apply only to meat, boned and roll. But not stuffed. However, it is also applied to dishes which are actually galantine

Chicken legs	-	10 Nos. I
Farce de volaille	-	250gms II
Butter	-	75 gms. III
Sliced carrots	-	150gms. IV
Slicesed celery	-	100 gs.
Bacon triings	-	75 gms
Bayteaf	-	½ No.s
Thyme	_	1 Spring
Espagnole	-	¼ liter V
Fonds biren	-	½ liter
Chopped parsely	-	for garnish VI

METHOD

1. Bone pout completel without opening the flash of the drumstick.
2. Stuff the legs with the farce and i.e. carefull with this string.
3. Heat in a shollow brasing pan, season the Ballotine and fry quickly to brown on all sides. Remove the Ballotine to one side.
4. Cover te bottom of braising pan with those ingredients then place the Ballotines

on top. Cover and place in a hot oven for 10 ts. To set.

5. Add the espagnole and sufficient stock to cover a good 2/3 rd of the Ballotines. Bring to the boil & season remove cook till tender for 35-45 mts. Remove the Ballotines and discard their strings. Arrange the Ballotines in earthenware dishes cover & sauce through a fire strainer into a clean pan. Reduce to a light coating consistency and adjust the seasoning as necessary.
6. Pour the sauce over arranged Ballotines and garnish with chopped parsley.

Note: Chicken Ballotine may be served with suitable accompaniments and garnishes. Eg. Navilles an b eurres, Riz pilall, Jar diniere, Paysanne etc.

TERRINE

Terrines are onl made without a pastry crust. Bone but medium-size duck. Remove the breasts & cut each beast in four lengthways. Bone out legs keep all these pieces in a tray and matinate with brandy. Use the remainder of the game to prepare gae forcemenat as per the recipe given already.

Line a 2 liter capacity terrine with the pork for leaving the ends to overhang the terrine Place a first layer of the forcemeat in the bottom of the terine then strips of the flesh of duck. Strips of salt pork, truffle and the finishing off with the remainder of the mixture when filled fold over the porkfat fro the sides and cover the top with hot water. Cook in the oven at 165^0-170^0 for approx $2^1/_2$ hrs. A trussing needle may be used to ascerain if the terrine is cooked.

When cooked remove the lid. Cover with a dish or board and keep a weight on top to press it down slightly while it is cooling. Then remove the weight and cover & drain off any fat.

Fill the terrine with sufficient duck jelle to cover the surfaces. Allow to cool in the refrigertor to set. Serve from the terrine accompanied with hot toast.

PATE

Pates are made in many shapes and forms, including pafe on croute, pate ala maison terrines. Galantines and mousses. Among the large variety of ingredients and garnished used in pates the most common are liver, truffles various forcemeats, and seasonings. Pates can be prepared in adcance kept refrigeated and serviced as appetizers over buffets. A description of the major typers of pates follows:

PATE de VEAN et JAMBON En CROUTE

STAGE 1 :	INGREDIENTS	QUANTITY
	Lard	15g
	Hot water paste	750gms.

METHOD

Lightl grease a 22-23 cm. Hinged ovel pie mould with the lard. Remove a quarter of the paste, cover and keep warm, roughly roll out the reainder to the size of the mould then place I the mould. Work it up with the fingers firly fro the centre of the bottom to cover the side. Aim to give an equal thickness over the bottom and sides and to make it stand proud for appox ½ cm. At the top edge of the mould. Take care to press it firmly into the shaped designs of the ould to prevent air packets forming. Be careful not to crack the paste.

STAGE 2:	**INGREDIENTS**	**QUANTITY**
	Veal, lean	600 gms.
	Raw ham or gamon, lean	600 gms.
	Pork back fat	750 gms.
	.Ground mace	a pinch
	Fresh thyme leaves finely chopped	½ thsp.
	Fresh age leaves, finely chopped	½ thsp.

METHOD:

Coarsely mince the at and fat. Place in a bowl. Season with salt and pepper and add the ace & herbs, mix well together.

STAGE 3:	**INGREDIENTS**	**QUANTITY**
	Pork fat, thin slices	400 gms.

METHOD

Line the party slices of pork fat leaving the ends to overhang the top edge of the mould. Place the mixture into the prepared mould. Make sure that it goes well into the corners & edges at the bottom. Turn over the fat slices & moulds the whole into an even shape, higher than the mould.

STAGE 4

METHOD

Egg wash the top edge of the paste in the mould and over with the reaining paste rolled out to approximately 3mm thick. Tri the edges togther and decortate the surface with party shape. Egg wash the surface and make a hole in the centre. Allow to sent for 20 minuter.

STAGE 5

METOD

Place I the over at 200c for 20 minutes to set the surface colour. The temperature at 165-170C and continue baking for a further $1^1/_2 - 1^3/_4$ hours. Cover with grease proof paper or foil it necessary to prevent over browning. Remove from the over and allow to cool.

QUENELLES

Theses are prepared from various forcemeat in various shapes & size as follows.

1. By prepared from various forcemeat in various shapes & size as folloes.
2. By piping the mixture into a buttered tray.
3. By moulding with spoon.
4. By moulding with the finger in the shape of a cook's comb.

Quenelles for ordinary garnish should be moulded with tablespoons or piped out using a plain or star tube. The average weight of these quenelles would be between 12-15 gms. Each.

Quenelles used for decoration should be moulded in round, ovel or elongated ovel shapes. Approximate weight of these quenelles is 40-50 gms. These quenelles are often decorated with truffle and red salted ox-tongue.

All quenelles should be poached except for quenelles of Godivean which should be cooked dry. Quenelles should be poached in salt water using 10gm. Of salt per liter of water. This water should be boiling and poured gently into the pass containing quenelles and then kept at just below boiling point unitil they are cooked.

COLE OUSSES, MOUSSELINES AND SOUFFLES:

Mousses, Mousselines and souffles are prepared from the same basic mixtures. Te nature are given based on their sizes and the ways of moulding.

Recipe:

Cooked puree of Principle ingredients	1 liter
Melted Aspic jelly	250 ml
Veloute	400 ml
Cream	400 ml

The proportions of the above ingredients may be slightly adjusted according to the nature of the main ingredient.

METHOD

Add the cool jelly and veloute to the basic puree and mix together on ice. When cold & thicken in consistency, add and fold in the cream. Cream should not be more then half whipped, if fully whipped, the quality of the mousse will be less delicate and of a dryer texture.

A mousse is made in a large mould which is sufficient for more than one person. The moussaeline are moulded either with spoon, piping bag or in special moulds having the shapes of large quenelles, this size is suitable for only one person. Soufflés are small mousses moulded in a cassolattes or other utensils of this type of a size suitable for one person only.

Kitchen Organization: Kitchen organization allocation of work job description, duty roasters, production planning, production scheduling and production quality control forecasting and budgeting.Kitchen stewarding – importance of kitchen stewarding, organization of kitchen stewarding, department workflow in kitchen stewarding garbage disposal.

The Organization of kitchen will vary mainly due to the size and the type of the establishment. Even when there are two kitchens of similar nature, the internal organization may vary as each chef de cuisine will have his own way of running the kitchen.

Basically the principle of kitchen organization represents a standard practice though there are no set rules for deciding how many sections and how many staff a particular kitchen require. The number of staff in a section is determined by the amount of work to be done. Now a day some of the traditional job titles are no longer used. What is common is grouping the operation and organizing the kitchen.

- According to main area of activities.
- According to the destination of the final product.
- According to the kitchen hierarchy.

This means levels of each section or parties as shown below:-

- Chef de partie
- Demi chef de partie

- First commis (senior cook)
- Second commis
- Third commis
- Apprentice

In the organization charts of the modern kitchen, the following are observed:

- In large kitchen a generalist second in command is designated executive sous chef.
- Pastry is kept on a higher level than the chef de partie.
- In very large kitchen a generalist third in command is designated sous chef. This means he/ she act for the chef de partie during their off day.

Organizational chart

A CDP of a restaurant in similar to a production manager of a particular brand and the restaurant manager is similar to a product manager. In most hotels the executive chefs uses the food and beverage secretary or the banquet secretary or the pool secretary shared by the other departments heads.

Traditional Kitchen Brigade Titles

Main Area	French Titles
• Administration	Chef de cuisine (Ex.chef)
• Pastry	Patisserie (head pastry chef)
	Torner (pastry man)
	Confisseur (confectioner)
	Glacier (ice cream cook)
	Boulanger (baker)
• Larder	Chef garde-manger (larder cook)
	Boucher (butcher)
	Hors-d'ouere
	Saladier
• Sauce	Chef Saucier (sauce cook)
• Others	Chef poissoneir (fish cook)
	Chef de nuite (night chef)
	Chef rotisseur (roast cook)
	Entre meteur (vegetable cook)
	Chef tourant (relief cook)
	Break fast cook

Allocation of work: The objective is to make work easier and this can be achieved by simplifying the operation, eliminating unnecessary movements, combining two operations into one or improving methods. The work in the kitchen is normally broken down into various other segments in the kitchen such as,

- Larder section
- Sauce section
- Roast section
- Fish section
- Vegetable section
- Soup section

- Indian section
- Pastry section

In each of these sections, specialists head the parties and with their assistants help produce complete dishes with great speed and efficiency.

Job Description:

1. Chef de cuisine
- The chef carries the full responsibility for the kitchen
- He must have a strict sense of control and efficiency.
- He should prepare a pre- determined percentage of profit and works in accordance with the policy of the establishment.
- The chef is responsible for the staffing of the kitchen and the organization of duty roasters.
2. Sous chef
- Assistant to the head chef.
- He has to the call up the order from the kitchen and supervises the service.
- He is responsible for the efficient day-to-day function of the kitchen
3. Chef Saucier
- The chef saucier is in charge of preparation of the sauces required for the necessary dishes.
4. Chef Rotisserie
- Responsible for the production of all roasts and grills of meat, poultry and game.
5. Chef Potage
- The soup cook prepares all types of soup and is responsible for the garnishes accompanying soups.
6. Patisserie
- This chef is responsible for the pastry section.
- His work is specialized, and he produces all breads, pastries and other confectionaries and desert.

Duty Rotas:

Duty rotas are like schedule for the employees working at the kitchen in any organization the duty rotas will specify the timings based on a shift basis for each employee. The duty rotas serve as a guide for the employee to work in the organization.

While framing the duty rotas, the various shifts which an employee may get are,

- Straight shift for eg: some say 6 am to 4 pm / 4 pm to 11 pm
- Break shift for eg: 6 am to 10 am / 7 pm to 11 pm

Based on these timings, the duty rotas is planned out for each and every employee and it ensures that the department is operational through the it's working hours.

Day	A	B	C	D	E	F
Mon	I	II	III	OFF	II	III
Tues	II	I	OFF	III	I	II
Wed	III	OFF	I	II	III	I
Thurs	I	III	OFF	I	II	III
Fri	III	II	II	OFF	II	III

Sat	II	III	I	III	OFF	II
Sun	I	II	III	I	II	III

In the above duty rota, for a bakery, the working hour for a bakery is 24 hours. So there fore the allotment of the schedule of the timings should be planned in a way that the working hour is justified with each employee. In this way out only the operational timings are covered for the department but also the timings for the each employee is divided accordingly with 9 hrs each.

Fore casting: Before making planning it is necessary to look ahead, to forever possible and probable outcomes and to allow for them. While forecasting future is divided into two parts.

- Immediate future or "tactical" forecast from today into the future, as for as the trading peculiarities of the enterprises will permit such forecasts to be accurate predictions.
- Long-term or strategic forecasts based on projection of tactical forecasts for the future. Last come the policy decisions on matter of day-to-day policy and action. Particularly regarding the investment of future capital in long-term projects.

Budgeting

Budgeting control is now generally regarded as an important management tool-required for a critical instrument of planning and control. The budgeting is an integral part of the overall budgetary process, and has three principle aims.

1. First and foremost it is a planning instrument. The budgets are detailed plans of action, which shows what should be achieved, the spending power and profit margins.
2. The budget provides a basis for evaluating current results and in therefore an important mean of performance evaluation.
3. Finally it involves a detailed review of anticipated trends in levels of activity. This should enable the budget committee identify any periods and decide how to take advantage of any period.

The actual determination of the budgeted figures in carried out as follows.

1. The first step is to ascertain the figure for the current year, where the budget year runs from January to December.
2. The second step in to take into account.
- The most recent trends
- Prospects for the following year.
3. The decision on appropriate percentage changes between the current year and the following year.
4. Finally, we take the current figures, adjust them by appropriate percentage and arrive at the figures for the following budget year.

Kitchen Stewarding

The kitchen stewarding section provides a very useful service to both the kitchen and to food and beverage service. The main duties of an executive kitchen steward and his/her team will be as follows:

- Handling stocks of small operating equipment (cutlery, crockery, glassware, kitchen equipment).
- Cleaning, washing of all such operating equipment.
- Washing and cleaning of entire kitchen & "back of the house" area.
- Co-ordinating the servicing of the kitchen equipment with the maintenance department.
- Planning the requirements list and purchasing orders for all small operating equipment and helping the food and beverage manager with the budget in this area.
- Garbage clearance operation from all food and beverage outlets or areas.
- Ordering chemicals, washing liquid, polishing liquids, etc.
- Handling polishing and buffing of silverware.
- Minimum the breakage and loss of all small operating equipment.
- Kitchen pot – washing operation.

Importance

This is often a neglected and under rated area. However, poor attention paid to this section often causes operational delays (eg: In banquets owing to wet plates), which brings down the entire efficiency of the entire food and beverage department. This may lead to guest dissatisfaction, decrease of sales and a lowering of departmental profits. Some hotel corporations believe that all trainee food and beverage manager should gain a few months experience in handling kitchen stewarding.

Equipment cleaning schedule

Equipment	Location	Standard Time
Main kitchen	hot range	1 ½ hr
Hood	hot range	1 hr
Filters	hot range	½ hr
Salamander	hot range	½ hr
Chinese kitchen		
Hood	the fish kitchen	1 hr
Filters	the fish kitchen	1 hr
Tilting pan	production	1 hr
Soup Area		
Hood	production	1 hr
Filters	production	1 hr
Steam kettles	production	½ hr
Steamers	production	½ hr
Oven	production	½ hr
Baking oven	production	½ hr
Cold Kitchen		
Espresso machine	pantry	½ hr
Deep freezer	pantry	1 hr
Coffee urn	pantry	1 hr

Butchers shop		
Potato peeler	butcher	daily
Mixing machine	butcher	½ hr
Vegetable washer	staff cafeteria	15 min
Dish Washing Area		
Glass washing	main kitchen	½ hr
Dish- washing machine	main kitchen	½ hr
Machine curtain	dish washer	½ hr
Scrap trays	dish washer	½ hr
Spray arms	dish washer	½ hr

Production quality and quantity control

Quantity control

The control of the quantity consumed ensures that everything consumed should be of accounted for. It does not ensure profitability, but provides a useful supplementary check and is simple to operate. For simple dishes, this method is good, but not for complex dishes.

Quality control: Whatever the size of the establishment that is operated, the basic management is essential from the cost control point. View is to know how many has been received and second how much it has received and second how much it has cost to take that many. In order to control quality of the products, certain quality checks are carried out at the time of the delivery of the goods. Any faulty or under quality goods should be immediately returned back to the supplier. The product entering various sections should be the highest possible quality to ensure proper guest satisfaction.

Production planning: Along with the restaurant, the kitchen determines the number of customers to be dealt with during service periods. Kitchen area varies according to the type and number of meals provided. As the number of customers' increases, the area of the kitchen relating to the seating capacity tends to be reduced. The floor is subjected too much traffic, so durability must meet the demand of the particular premises. The floor must be impervious to moisture and should not be affected by grease, salt, vegetable or fruit acid. The walls should be tiled to the ceiling or at least to a height of one meter. Above eye level, can be painted the ceiling should not harbour dirt and must be cleaned regularly to prevent dirt and considerations dropping on to the supplier and food items below. The window and mechanical inlets using ducts and fans should be carefully planned and sited. Over cookery ducts to exhaust fans should connect equipment and range.

Garbage disposal: Garbage disposal is of utmost importance and the basic guidelines should always be displayed in the kitchen. Every number of staff should be aware of the importance of the guidelines such as,

1. Know the various types of garbage, eg toxic, dry or wet. Biodegradable etc.
2. Label the container in which the garbage is stored to avoid contamination.
3. Ensure that the garbage is place in the right garbage bin allotted for each spe-

cific type of garbage.

4. Removal and clearance of the garbage bags should be carried out on daily basis.
5. Use the leg muscles rather than the back muscles when lifting heavy objects.
6. Ensure that the garbage is segregated and stored properly until it is transported to the waste disposable site, where the disposal of the garbage carried out properly based on the substance and chemical composition.

Question:

1. How will you prepare duty roasters?
2. What are the points to be considered in quality control?
3. Write the importance of kitchen stewarding?
4. Write about equipment find in kitchen stewarding department?
5. Give a note on garbage disposal?

Kitchen Management

The objective of Kitchen Management id to lead organize and control the means of production and service of food.

To manage the kitchen Manager/Chef de Cuisine should have a sound practical knowledge and should have the ability to organize labour, delegate the responsibility. To appropriate staff who communicate well. The maintenance and cleaning of the machine is his responsibility.

A good management will see that food cost is controlled and the people working in the kitchen are content in their jobs and the work given is comparable with their ability. Staff should be trained on the job and if the performance is good, incentives, increment or promotions should be given, if need be.

Certain factors such as budgetary control, portion control, cost control, proper purchasing, control of production and service, control of waste, etc., play an important part in managing the kitchen.

Proper layout of work areas in the kitchen contribute to a successful catering establishment which will not only satisfy customers but also the staff will be contented.

Cramped and lack or proper kitchens delay food preparation and service. Certain points have to kept in view before planning such as the types of meals to be served, forecast of peak period, ventilation, proper drainage. Etc., it is important that the kitchen should be close to the restaurant to facilitate efficient service.

Meal production

Food preparation is the term employed to denote cooking. Meal production follows a flow pattern which commences with the purchasing and selection of materials, their handling and processing and the ultimate presentation of the dishes to the purchasing of 'food service' takes over. It is therefore obvious that we should at the beginning and see that the purchasing of food in done property.

The budget committee is formed for the purchasing of preparation, coordination, review and revision of budgets. The various departmental budgets and master budget represent a coordinated effort. The budget is made period wise or annually. The seasonal character of the business is taken into consideration. The first step in preparation is giving management objectives for the forthcoming year and giving a proforma to be used in preparation of budgets. The accounts section prepared their budget in duplicate and sends one copy to the Head of the Unit who is responsible for the budget if the establishment and the budget committee reviews it.

PURCHASING

Buying quality and freshness of supplies and portion control are of the utmost importance for the operation of a successful business.

Large establishment will often employ a purchase manager, as the can concentrate and get the best supplies. Requisition for supplies are placed with the Stores/Kitchen Stewarding Department at specified time in advance by the Chef de Cusine for hughly perishable supplies. The storekeeper will forward his requisitions for "Day Stores" and cleaning materials in the same manner. Supplies should be changed from time to time.

Knowledge of baying is very essential. The buyer should have a reasonable technical knowledge in catering, as he will be able to follow the requisitions properly and understand the importance of delivery times, size, quality and specification, etc, the purchaser should assimilate information, new ideas and techniques, gathered from trade journals, visit to exhibitions and food processing plants. The comparison of competitive price lists from must be done occasionally.

When selecting the suppliers, following points should be considered.

- The prince are competitive for the goods specified in relation to quality.
- The goods offered should meet specification by looks and other related factors factors. Samples should be taken for checking.
- Financial terms offered relating to credit facilities and discount for settlement. Selection will then be made of at least two suppliers for each "group" of suppliers required in certain "groups" which include many commodities such as groceries. Three or even more suppliers should taken for checking.
- Financial terms offered relating to credit facilities and discount for settlement.

Selection will then be made of at least two suppliers for each "group" of suppliers required in certain "groups" which include many commodities such as groceries. Three or even more suppliers may be selected. Where supplies are obtained by contract, obviously this will not apply.

Specialized supplies such as pao bhaji masala, Amristsari papad, Paparika, avocado pears, capers, artichokes, etc., may be obtained from a single supplier.

Instructions to suppliers

After the selection has been made of various supplies, written instructions on the following points should be made:

- Delivery times and any special requirements of delivery.
- The person or persons authorized to accept and sign for supplies.
- That goods supplied are as ordered, including special instructions relating to "brands and sizes".
- No alteration will be accepted between quoted and invoice prices.
- The names of people authorized to order supplies.

If there is a contract, it will operate for a given period often for one year. The purpose of "Contract" buying is to obtain the best supplies possible at a fixed price over a stated period.

Ordering of Supplies

Orders for supplies, generally fall in 3 categories: (a) Daily orders (b) Weekly orders, (c) Standing orders: Daily orders are usually placed for perishable items such as meat, poultry, game, fish, fruit vegetables, milk and cream, etc., the orders can be placed by telephone, confirmed by a written order.

Weekly orders consist mainly of dry stores, i.e. groceris etc.,

Standing orders –Certain types of supplies such as milk, eggs, bacon, etc., ordered for a specified quantity. The quantity stated is the minimum requirement. If more is needed, supplementary order is given.

STORE CONTROL AND FOOD CONTROL

Food control begins when the orders are placed; it ends when the ultimate cash takings are banked.

The stored should be close to the preparation area. Basic aim smooth flow from stores to preparation, to cooking, to server space appropriate to the size of the kitchen.

The functions of the stores is to receive, check, store correctly, issue gods as required against requisition properly authorized. Strict control should be exercised as it provides cost figures and assist in future budgeting. It is essential to check all incoming supplies for quantity, Weight and price. Supplies received should be promptly taken into stock, non-perishables should go into dry stores. Perishable items be stored in cold rooms, freezers. Etc., The ideal dry store temperature range is 15^{0}C to 18^0 C.

Refrigerators for penrishable foods are maintained at 1^{0}C to 4^{0}C.

Records should be kept show the stock of each commodity received, issued and on hand with dates of receipt and issue. So that at any time the management can check the accuracy.

The stock should be taken at least once a month. The best system of accounting is a card index comprising a separate card of each commodity and all issues supported by relevant documents. The system is amenable to periodic spot checks as required.

COST CONTROL

Whatever the size of the establishment that is operated, the basic management essential from the cost control point of view is to know first how money has been received and second how much it has cost to take money. The caterer must learn how to understand this and be able to interpret the results so that adjustments can be made where and when necessary. Theis is very important for the financial success of a catering establishment.

The cost of all naturally into three distinct sections, the first being the cost of the food and second the cost of the overheads which include fuel, light, heat, water, staff uniforms and laundry, social security payments, superannuation contributions, printing and stationary, cleaning materials, advertising, telephones and postage, power, etc., linceces, maintenance, contracts, replacement of crockery and cutlery, linen, utensils, repairs in general insurance and finally rent rates and interest on capital outlay outlay. The third seetion is labour, the salaries and wages, the relationship between these classes of costs is always a matter of interest. Which varies considerably from one type of catering establishment or another, the overheads, etc, usually being greater than the bare cost of food.

The problem of any management control system is to make sure that a pre-determines food and wage cost percentage has been decided. This figure will take in all aspects of expenses. The final trading results will show that a correct return has been made. To obtain this the following information should be studies.

- All purchases must be controlled
- Details of all merchandise received must be recorded, as and when issued.
- Any over-production of food must be checked and of course reused in the best and most economical way.
- Production-ingredients and amounts.
- Check of sales with direct numbers catered for.
- An efficient system of cash control.
- Sales of any kind checked with cash receipts.
- A record of costs for each section (wine, cigars, flowers, meals room) must be made and recorded. These must be compared.
- Total daily wage costs must be recorded.
- A weekly summary of all the relevant details must be prepared.
- The trading profit and loss account should be prepared.

Material costing

There are three basic methods of cost control

- Quantity
- Selling Price
- Cost Price

An effective system will disclose shortfalls in receipts which may be due tone or more of the following.

- Faulty buying
- Inefficient storing
- Bad and wasteful cooking
- Petty theft and leakage.

Once it becomes known that the receipts from sales are less than could have expected from the amount of food consumed. It becomes worth while to exam more closely where the loss is occurring and to take corrective action before it becomes disastrous. Costing and control must be regular and continuous.

PORTION CONTROL

"Portion Control" means the amount of size of a portion of food to be served to a customer. Food costing and portion are complementary and the need for this form of control comes from both sides of the business-from the caterer and his customers. There is a natural tendency for clients to eye one another's portion when they are served and if one is thought to be slightly larger than the others, there is apt to be resentment and a reaction detrimental to the good name of the establishment. Only exact portion control can eliminate this. It is not something that can be introduced at the service point, it must start when orders are placed for supplies.

Monitoring portion control could be done by direct supervision by sales analysis and by comparing Purpose of Portion Control.

- To ensure fair portions for each customer
- To see that each department utilizes purchase to the full
- To control waste
- To ensure that standard costing is as accurate as possible.

Method of Monitoring Portion Control

- Ordering the right quantity and supervising when receiving it.
- Even preparing the food in the production area, under direct supervision.
- Bys proper checking of the service of food.
- Comparing the requisitions of each department with issues
- By sales analysis

1. Aids to Portion Control

Portion control is done by using equipment and utensils as for example a scoop)Ladle) use mainly for ice-cream, can also be used for mashed potatoes as a portioner for mixture.

- Automatic Portion Control Equipments include

Tea dispensers
Butter pat machines
Bread slicking and uttering machines
Gravity Feed clickers
Coffee making e.g. cona mashines
Mint steak moulding machined
Milk dispensers

- **Utensils used in portion control include**

Ladles	
Serving spoons and scoops	Dariole moulds
Woven wire service	Pie dishes
Scales	baking tins
Measures	

- **Serving ishes that help in portion control**

Glasses	casseroles
Coupes	tureens
Sundae glasses	sauce-boats
Souffle cases	Vegetable dishes
Cocotted	entrée dishes

2. Portion Sizes

As portion size vary from one establishment to another between table f'hote and a la carte services.

It is difficult to give definite average portion sizes,

A few examples are being given to act as a guide-line

Hors d'ieuver	Fruit juices	75ml to 110ml
	Fruit cocktail	120 gms

	Cavier	30 gms to 40gms
	Salarni	45gms.
Farinaceous dishes	Spaghetti/macaroni	60gms
	Rice	120gms
Egg dishes	Boile/poached/ Fry for a la carte	2 large ones
	Omellette	3 eggs
Meat	Steaks	120gms. To 150gms.
	Chops	30gms. To 150gmd.
	Stews	100 gms. Raw weight
	Hamburger	120gms.

Losses in Preparation

The Percentage of the waste of vegetables in preparation will be according to the kind and the qualit. The compute portion control and cost, the waste from peeling and triming and also the shrinkage in coking be trained to judge quality merchandise in order to be able to apperециate its value.

3. VisualAids Sheets

A portion control sheet can be used for costing various items of food or complete dishes. The object is to ascertain the total ield of a given commodity after preparation and processing. Such a sheet can be used in the experimental or research kitchen of a catering group or in the food preparation area when compiling standardized recipes.

4. Standardized Recipes

They assist in food costing and portion control by taking the guest work away and substituting more exact approach, b listing the ingredients and methods in a readil-understood from as the results will be unifor every time it its featured. The food cost can also be up to date with any price changes. The stsndard recipe will give a warning when the price charged becomes uneconormical and an inrease becomes necessary.

The effects of Irregular of Badly Administrated Portion Control

Following effects will emerge:

- Dissatisfied customers resulting in decrease of business
- Food costing will be inaccurate, affecting profits.
- A lack of sense of responsibility among personnel leading to a loss of standand.

Portion control in the catering industry is one of the greatest factors that contributes to a successful business. The general rule should be "a fair portion for a fair price".

YIELD TESTS

Coputing the cost of recipe ingredients is a simple matter if the food are used the way they are received and there in no waste or tri. This is rarel the case, however. The aount of a food ite as purchased (AP) and the aount of the edible portion(E.P) of that the same item ay vary considerabl, particularly with meats and fresh produce. In this context, yield is the usable or edible quantity reaining after processing the as-purchased quaantit of the food ite. That is, yield refers the amount of usable lettuce after the case of iceberg is cleaned, or the amount of meat that is served after timing. The yield factor or percentage is the radio of usable quantity to the purchase quantity. It is always less than 100% and may be calculated in dollars or weight by volum amounts.

Because purchase specifications and fabrication techniques vary from operation to operation, there are no precise, standard yield amounts. Each kitchens must determine its own yield factor. Yield test ust be conducted on A.P.items as they are received from purveyors. To be effective several must be conducted and the results average to arrive at a specific operations yield factors for that item.

The method of calculating yield depending on whether the items trim is all waste (for example, vegetable peelings) or whether the trim creates usable or salable by products (for exaple meat and popultry).

RAW YIELD TEST WITH OUT BY PRODUCTS

The simplest yield test producer is for items that have no usable or salable byproducts. These items include most produce as well as some fish and sell fish. Unless these ites are ready to serve as received from the purveyo, trimming is requires and all trim is waste. For example one pound of apples may yield only 13 ouncess of flesh after peeling and coring. If the recipe requires one pound of peeled, cored apples, for such ites, the chef must start with slightly more the one pound of A.P.apples. In order to detemine accuate costs or such item loss must be taken into account. Even seedless grapes do not havea 100% yield factor. The weight of the steams and bad grapes must be calculated and deducted from the A.P.weight to deterine the correct price per pound of servable fruit.

There are 3 steps for calculating yield when trim is waste.

STEP : 1 Calculation the total weight of the trim produced from the specified A.P.quantity this is know as trim loss.

STEP : 2 Subtract the trim loss from the A.P.weight to arrive at the total yield weight.

STEP : 3 divid the ield weight by the A.P.weight to deterine the yield factor.

Comon Produce Yield Factor

Produce	Yield factors(%)	Produce	Yield Factors(%)
Apples	75	Mushrooms	90
Apricots	94	Nectarines	86
Aritichokes	48	Okra	82
Avocados	75	Onion	90
Banana	70	Oranges	60
Berries	95	Papayas	65
Broccoli	70	Parsley	85
Cabbage	79	Peaches	75
Carrots	78	Pears	75
Cauliflower	55	Oea Ponds	90
Celery	75	Peppers	82
Cherries	82	Pineapple	50
Corn-Cob	28	Plums	75
Cucumbers	95	Potatoes	80
Eggplant	85	Radishes	90

Garlic	88	Rhubard	85
Grapefruit	45	Scallions	65
Grapes	90	Spinash	60
Liwi	80	Squash,Summer	90
Leeks	50	Squash winter	70
Lemons	45	Tomatoes	90
Lettuce	75	Turnips	75
Limes	45	Watercress	90
Melons	55	Water melons	45

Beause each operation has its own standards for cleaning and trimming raw products, yield factors should be personalized, list of cormon yield dactors are available, how ever, as an indication of industry norms. Some are include in table.

Applying Yield Factors

Now that you understand what yield factors are and how to calculate the, we look at how they are used in costing recipes. First, yield factors are used for accurate recipe costing.

Example:

Carrots cost \$6.50 per 25 pound bag and have yield factor of 75%. In other words 22% of that 25 pound bag is wate. The price should be recalculated to account for that waste. That is the A.P (as purchased) unit cost must be convert to an E.P.(edible portion) unit cost. This is done by dividing A.P.cost by ield percentage.

A.P. Cost(\$) Yield Percentage = E.P.(\$)

26 pound (6.50/25)/78 = 33/ pound

Thus, carrots have an E.P.unit cost of \$ 0.33 per pound (as compared with an A.P price of \$ 0.26 per pound) Note that E.P.cost is always greater than A.P.cost. When costing recipe, you should use the \$ 0.33 per pound price as the accurate ingredient cost.

Second, yield factors are necessary for accurate purchasing. Most recipes list ingredients in E.P. quantities. Therefore the chef must considered waste of trim amounts when ordering these otems. If only the amounts listed in the recipe are ordered and them the ite requires triming, the number of portions (or recipe yield) will be less then the desired amount.

Example

A recipe requires 20 pounds of shredded cabbage. The yield factor for cabbage is 77%. Therefoe, 20 pounds is 79% of the A.P. quantity. Divided the amount need by the yield factors to determine the minimum A.P.quantity.

E.P.Quantity / yield percentage = A.P.Quantity

20 pounds / 079 = 25.3 pounds

It will take 25-1/3 pounds of cabbage to provide the 20 pounds of shredded cabbage. (This figure will be increased to an even aount for purchasing because ield factors are, at best, only an estimate). Note that the A.P.Figure must be always being greater than the E.P. Figure in this formula.

Exercise Question:

1. Write a note on purchasing
2. Give the important points on cost control
3. Write about portion control
4. Draw a standard recipe format
5. What are the advantage and disadvantage of standard recipe?

Larder, Garde Manger, Cold kitchen

The term Garde Manger originally identified a storage area. Preserved foods such as: Hams, sausages, bacon, cheese, etc. were held in this area, cold foods for Banquets and Buffets are arranged here. Over the years this term evolved to mean more than just a storage area. It now, also indicates a station in the professional kitchen, responsible for preparing Cold foods, Buffets, Decorative pieces, etc. and it s Chefs who prepare them.

Definition: The Larder is a department set aside for the storage of all perishable foods both rawand cooked and is also used for processing and preparation of all cold items served to the.

Functions: The Larder or Garde Manger or Cold Kitchen is a department in the professionalkitchen for:

The storage of all perishable raw food items which needs a storage temperature of minus-18 degree C.

2.The storage of all prepared and cooked items like cold appetizers, cold meats, cold sauces, salads etc. and all cold items found on the Menu.

In order for the Larder to function properly it is essential that the Larder is separate from the hot Kitchen and is located in a cool place but not very far. It must be well lit, airy and well ventilated; it must be sufficiently spacious for staff to carry out their duties in a hygienic and efficient manner. And it must be equipped with the necessary fittings, plant and machinery, tools, etc. in accordance with the and / or quality of work.

Sub-Sections of the Larder Kitchen

Its main responsibility is to cater to the requirements of the Hot Kitchen for raw materials such as fish fillets, steaks, etc, and to supply the finished products as required by the Room Service, Buffets, Banquets, etc, for all cold dishes.

The Sections of the Larder can be divided depending on the volume of work into:-

BUTCHERY.

FISH MONGERY.

HORS D OEUVRE / COLD SAUCES.

SALADS.

COLD BUFFETS.

And MASALAS in the Indian context.

The Area which processes raw materials like meat, fish, etc, is the Butchery and the Fish Mongery. Basic cuts are produced, marinated, roasted, smoked, or poached over here. The portion or cuts or joints are prepared according to the demands from the different outlets with- in the hotel.

The following products are produced:-

Gelatine products:

Aspic

Mouses, Mousseline

Colees

Chaufroid sauces

Cold soups

Marinated Products:

Salads

Brines and Cures

Pickled products

Smoked Products

Forcemeats for Galantines, Pâtés, Sausages, Terrines, Quenelles, Timbales, Roulades,etc.

Piece Montee or Centerpieces or Non-Edible Displays:

Ice carvings

Tallow sculpture

Salt dough sculpture

Fruit and vegetable displays

Pastillage

Jelly logos

Thermocol displays

Cold Hors d'oeuvres

Sandwiches

Specialty items such as, Caviar, Oysters, Snails, Foi gras, cheese, etc.

LARDER EQUIPMENT

Large or heavy duty equipment

Buffalo Chopper or bowl chopper

Mincing machine

Bone saw machine

Gravity slicer or meat slicer

Vegetable processor

Dough mixer

Vacuum packing machine

Sandwich counter

Hanging rail system.

Sausage stuffer

Smoking machines

Grinding machine

Refrigerator

Walk in

Steel work tables

Weighing scale

Salamander
Butcher s blocks
Fish kettle
Steam kettle

Tools and small equipment

Zester
Channeller
Can and bottle openers
Corer
Pitters
Egg slicer
Mandolin slicer
Butcher s chopper and cleavers
Boning knife
Filleting knife
Oyster knife
Buntz knife or wavy knife
Cheese knife
Mezzaluna or mincing knife
Sieves
Chinois
Pie moulds
Terrine moulds
Trauchelard
Larding needles
Trussing needles
Perissienne scoops
Steak hammer
Meat thermometers
Brining syringe & pump

Duties and responsibilities of the Chef Garde Manger

He is responsible directly to the Chef de Cuisine.

He is responsible for all perishable and frozen foods stored in the Larder.

He is responsible for all cold foods that are issued from the Larder.

He is responsible for supplying different cuts, joints, etc. of meat and fish as required by the outlets.

He is responsible for all the staff in the Larder and their Training.

He is responsible for Hygiene in the larder as per H.A.C.C.P. standards.

He is responsible for maintaining Larder control, like checking for quality and quantity, storing, keeping records of issues, daily stock sheets, etc.

He is responsible for controlling pilferage.

Essentials of Larder Control

All invoices to be checked for quality and quantity against goods delivered to the

Larder.

To ensure that all goods received must be stored at the right place and at the right temperature.

Portion control while pre-preparation must be carried out to ensure „yield and required number of portions.

Stock of food both raw and cooked must be regularly turned over. (FIFO).

Do not over stock.

Food items stored must be protected from vermin and pest.

Proper record of issues from the Larder both raw and cooked.

A daily stock / consumption sheet to be maintained.

Ensure complete hygienic standards are followed as per H.A.C.C.P.

Precautions must be taken to avoid pilferage

BRINES, CURES AND MARINADES

Brines and cures or salting is a method of preserving food and has been practiced since antiquity. Probably the first preserved foods may have come about by accident-fish drying on the seashore, either dried for future use or became rotten, unfit for eating.

INGREDIENTUSED FOR PRESERVING

SALTThe salt most commonly used the World over is the common salt or Sodium Chloride. Salt changes foods, by drawing out water, blood and other impurities. In doing so, it preserves them, making them less susceptible to spoilage and rot.

The important role played by salt is:-

OSMOSIS- is the movement of water through a semi-permeable membrane, such asthe cell walls of plant and animal, in order to equalize the concentrations of a solute (typically salt) on both sides of the membrane. This is known as osmotic pressure. Plant and animal cells contain relatively weak solutions of natural salts. Bacteria and other micro nutrients thrive in such solutions, drawing in nutrients through the cellwalls. If however these cell walls are exposed to a strong salt solution the outward osmotic pressure created by the strong solution prevents them from feeding and thus from reproduction, there by their activity is inhibited and decay is prevented.

DEHYDRATION: The presence of „free water is one of the indicators of a food srelative susceptibility to spoilage through microbial action. In order to increase the shelf life it is important to remove as much excess water as possible. Salt has a dehydrating effect on foods by attracting the free water and making it unavailable to microbes. Exposure to air or heat for controlled periods allows the water to evaporate, reducing the overall volume and weight of the food.

FERMENTATION: Decay in foods is also caused by enzymes naturally present infoodstuff as well as by living micro-organisms. Salt stops all enzymatic action by upsetting the electrical balance of the liquid in which they act. The strength of the salt solution is important. Some micro-organism can tolerate strong solutions of salt. Among these are certain lactic acid producing bacteria, which, rather causing decay, bring about beneficial fermentations. For this reason just the right amount of salt is used so as to kill all harmful pathogens and allowing these to grow. The lactic acid produced by these bacteria, itself safeguards it from bad bacteria. Eventually the acid becomes so concentrated that even these bacteria die and fermentation stops ant the food keeps, however the foods flavour is changed.

DENATURING PROTIENS: salt inevitably changes the structure of proteins in food.Smooth foods become grainy and firm foods may soften.

CURING SALTS

For thousands of years humans have been eating meat cured with unrefined salt. Those meats took on a reddish colour. However the reason for this colour change was discovered, only in the 20th century by German scientists who proved how nitrates and nitrites compounds already present in unrefined salts cause cured meats to redden.

Sodium nitrate or NaNO2 gradually break down inside the cured foods, but by the time they lose their effectiveness the curing and in some cases smoking procedures are finished, the food is then cooked or refrigerated and the food remains safe. However in the case of Prosciutto and some Salamis a stronger chemical Sodium Nitrate (NaNO3) is used as they breakdown more slowly than Nitrites and therefore are effective for a longer time. Potassium Nitrate or saltpetre is sometimes used, but it is not safe and since 1975 has been banned as a curing agent in commercially prepared cured meats. Nitrites and nitrates are the subject of controversy regarding their safety as substances known as „nitrosamines are formed when they are subjected to high heat, and are known to cause Cancer, but their use makes foods safe from Botulism infection.

Two special mixtures are generally used for curing purposes:

Tinted Cure Mix (T.C.M.) or Pink Cure or Prague Powder

Prague Powder is a commercially-sold salt mixture used in preserving meat. It is a generic term, not a trademarked name. The mixture is sold dyed pink to avoid confusion in homes with table salt.

The mixture contains nitrites to give meat its pink colour, and prevent botulism. The nitrites break down into nitric oxide and then dissipate. Ultimately, what is produced in the meat is nitric oxide, which combines with myoglobin protein to give a pleasing red or pink colour to the meat. As appealing as that benefit is, it's a minor one compared to the prevention of botulism.

Two versions of Prague Powder are sold; you cannot swap one for the other.

Prague powder #1

Prague powder #1 is 1 part (6.25%) sodium nitrite to 15 parts (93.75%) salt, plus anti-caking elements.

It is used for all curing other than dry cure. You use 1 teaspoon for 5 pounds (2 kg) of meat, or 100g per 100 pounds (45 kg), and mix it with cold water to use.

Prague powder #2

Per pound (16 oz) (450g) of Prague powder #2, there is 1 oz (6.25%) sodium nitrite, .64 oz (4%) sodium nitrate, 14.36 oz (89.75 %) salt, and anti-caking elements. It is mostly for dry curing (e.g. products that require no cooking, refrigeration or smoking.) These meat products typically take a longer time to cure. You mix with cold water to use, using 1 teaspoon for 5 pounds (2 kg) of meat, or 100g per 100 pounds (45 kg.)Certain strains of micrococcus bacteria ferment the nitrate in Prague Powder #2, converting it to nitrite. Prague Powder #2 lasts longer in food, because while the nitrite turns into nitric oxide anddissipates, the nitrate instead has to first break down into nitrites before it can dissipate as nitric oxide, thus you have a preservative present for longer.

SUGARSOrdinary white sugar and other forms of sugar, including corn syrup, honey, and maple sugar is used in some cures. Using less sweet forms of sugar, such as corn syrup and dextrose, provides the advantage of sugar without adding too much sweetness. Sweeteners are used for:-

Overcoming the harshness of salt in the cure.

Balance the overall flavour.

Counteract bitterness.

Help stabilize colour in cured meats.

Increase water retention in the finished product.

Provide a good nutrient source for fermentation.

HERBS, SPICES AND OTHER FLAVOURINGS

Nearly any spice or flavourings that are used in cooking may be used in curing. Some traditional herbs and spices used are garlic, pepper, coriander, caraway, nutmeg, mace, dry mustard, cinnamon, all spice, cardamom, etc. in addition, ingredients such as dry and fresh chillies, infusions and essences, wines and vinegars may also be incorporated to give a contemporary appeal.

FUNCTOINS OF CURING

Curing is done for the following reasons:-

For fixing of colour so as to give meat a nice colour. The nitrous oxide obtained from reduction of nitrite reacts with haemoglobin and myoglobin to form nitric oxide haemo or myoglobin, which upon heating or maturing is converted to the bright pink nitrosylmyochromogen.

To alter and improve flavour.

Provides antioxidant function.

Provides protection from Clostridium Botulism.

To retard the development of rancidity.

To make the texture rougher.

To improve shelf life.

CURING METHODS

The two basic methods of cures are DRY CURES and WET CURES or BRINES.

DRY CURES Probably the oldest method still used. In a dry cure the cure ingredients are mixed together and packed or rubbed over the food product to coat it completely. The length of time required for dry curing meats depends on their thickness. Whole Joints may take as long as 45 days, in such long cures the food is repeatedly turned and rubbed with the cure mixture in order to maintain uniform contact.

WET CURES or BRINES When salt and other curing agents are dissolved in water you get brine. To make brine you may use hot water or even bring the brine to simmer to infuse the spices or other aromatics. However the brine must be thoroughly chilled before you use it to cure foods. The simplest way to use brine is to immerse the food in brine, may be by using weights and let it soak until the cure is complete. However, brine may take a long time to penetrate to the center of large items such as ham. To hasten the process brine may be pumped or injected into the meats to make sure it penetrates evenly. After injecting the Joint may then be soaked in brine as well. Commercial operations use multiple needle injection method. The length of time required for wet curing depends on the size and thickness of the item. Fresh brine should be made for each batch of cured items, do not reuse brines.

PELLICLEBefore cured foods are smoked, they should be allowed to air dry long enough to form a tacky skin, known as pellicle. The pellicle plays a key role in producing excellent smoked items. It acts as a protective barrier for the food and also plays a role in capturing the smoke s flavour and colour. The exterior of the item must be sufficiently dry if smoke is to adhere.

SMOKINGSmoking has been used as a way of drying and preserving food since prehistoric times. Smoking does have some preservative effects, but for modern cooking, it is more important for the flavours that it gives to meats, poultry and seafood. Even smoked chesses and vegetable are relished for their special flavours.

Basic rules for smoking:-Do not smoke meats, poultry and fish that have not been cured, without the preservative effects of curing, smoking could be unsafe.

Foods must be air dried after curing and before smoking.

In order to smoke foods a "Smoker" is necessary. The basic feature shared by each type of smoker is a smoke source, a smoke chamber where the food is exposed, circulation and ventilation.

The wood used for smoking could be Hickory, Oak, Walnut, Chestnut, apple, wood from citrus trees, etc. In order to produce a rich, aromatic smoke soft woods must be avoided.

In addition to various hardwoods other flammable materials like teas, herbs, stems, whole spices, corn husks, fruit peels and peanut shells, may be added. Wood must be free from oil or charcoal.

TYPES OF SMOKING There are two types of smoking; they are Cold smoking and Hot smoking. In cold smoking the temperature inside the smoke house is kept at or below 30 degree Celsius. At these temperatures, the food take on the flavour of the smoke but are not cooked.

In hot smoking the temperature in the smoke house may be as high as 90 degree C, for fish and poultry. These temperatures are high enough to cook the foods being smoked. Higher temperatures tend to cause excessive shrinkage. Foods may be hot smoked until they reach an internal temperature of 150 to 163 degree C, to ensure that they are fully cooked.

To summarize, the smoking process consists of the following steps:-

Curing (dry or wet)

Air drying

Smoking (hot or cold).

MARINADES

To marinade means to soak a food product in a seasoned liquid in order to:-

Flavour the product.

Tenderize the product.

Lessen the cooking time.

To increase the shelf life.

The tenderizing effect of acids in the marinade is relatively small but essential. The marinade can also serve as the cooking medium and become part of the sauce.

Marinades must have the following 3 categories of ingredients:-

OIL helps to preserve the meats moisture besides providing flavour.

ACIDS from vinegar, lemon juice or wines helps to tenderize protein foods bybreaking them down, however employing strong acids may partially coagulate the protein of meat making it seem partially cooked. It also carries flavours into the product.

FLAVOURINGS a wide choice is available from a range of herbs and spicesdepending on the purpose.

TYPES or KINDS of MARINADES

Cooked used when long keeping quality is important. Modern refrigerations have made cooked marinades less widely used. An advantage of cooked marinades is that spices release more flavour into the marinade.

RAW most widely used for long Mari nation under refrigeration.

INSTANT marinade may be used within a few minutes.

DRY marinade also called dry rub or a spice rub is a mixture of salt, spices and herbsmade into a paste using oil or garlic. This mixture is rubbed onto the surface of the meat, poultry or fish. The item is then refrigerated to allow it time to absorb its flavours. The rub may be left on the item or scraped off before cooking.The word is derived from Latin "marinus" referring to the brine that was used in ancient times.

Carbonade marinades use beer instead of wine.

History of Chacuterie

Charcuterie: French from chair „flesh and cuit „cooked is the branch of cooking devoted to prepared meat products such as bacon, ham, sausages, terrines, galantines, pàté and confit primarily from pork. Charcuterie is part of Garde Manger chef s repertoire. Originally intended as a way to preserve meats before the advent of refrigeration, they are prepared today for their flavours derived from the preservation processes.In prehistoric times, probably sea fish was the first to come to the notice because brined by the sea they either, fermented and became rotten, when left to dry on the shore or they dried, thereby preserving them.

Meats were hung off the ground and near the fire to keep it out of reach from scavengers and insects, in the process it dried and got smoked there by preserving them.

As communities settled down into herdsmen and farmers, they developed skills necessary to ensure a relatively steady food supply, for example they not only developed skills for domestication of animals and crops, but also to preserve them. There are records of *Sumerians* as far back as 3000 B.C. used a similar method for preserving meats after saltingthem. Records also show that Chinese and Greeks produced salted fish. Greek writer *„Strabo'* was the first to record a detailed process of fish salting centres in Spain; some of them are still prepared in the same way even today.

The Gauls were successful in domestication of Hog, and became experts in preserving them as Ham and Bacon. Food preservation skills and the necessary ingredients like salt, sugar and spices were greatly in demand.

The starting point of the Garde Manger commenced with the growth of guilds in the 12th century. The right to slaughter and preserve foods which was one of the most important activity occurring in Fall when cows, sheep and other animals were butchered before the onset of winter, was a visible symbol of power, wealth and rank. This privilege belonged to the Kings, Lords, Dukes and other nobility as well as to Monasteries and convents of the Catholic Church.

As trade grew between countries the demand for specialty skills grew and the formation of guilds came into being. Rules were established so as to prevent abuse of monopoly and unfair pricing. These rules governed how merchants prepared and sold goods and services. The guilds that prepared and sold cooked items made from pork were known as

Charcuterie meaning cooked flesh in French. These guilds kept the practical work ofpreserving meats alive and thriving, making Ham, Bacon, Pâtés, etc.

With the advent restaurants, eating houses and hotels these skilled people found employment, however till the great "*Auguste Escoffier*" came on the scene, there was no organized structure in the Kitchens. It was only after him that Garde Manger was incorporated into the Kitchen Brigade and it retained the traditions of preparing a variety of preserved and cold foods. The Garde Manger, now, has expanded its scope to include appetizers, salads, sandwiches and accompanying cold sauces and condiments.

Skills required by the Chef Garde Manger The techniques required for preparing pâtés, terrines, sausage and cheeses are the particular domain of the Garde Manger. A skilled Chef must possess a broad base of culinary skills, those directly related to handling basic cold food preparation as well as those required to handle / prepare hot food items, like roasting, poaching, simmering, etc., of meat, poultry, fish, game, vegetables, grains, legumes, etc,.

Because the skills are so broad and varied, this is a highly specialized job and lucrative too.

The Chef Garde Manger besides being an excellent cook is also an artist.

SAUSAGETypically a chopped meat mixture stuffed into tubular casing. It is derived from the Latin word "Salsus" meaning salted. The concept originated in antiquity when it was desirable to find some way of preserving the blood and minor bits and pieces of a pig after slaughter. The first recorded sausages makers were Roman. North American Indians made "PEMMICAN" sundried lean buffalo or Venison meat, pounded with fat, mixed with vegetables, stuffed in hide skins and sealed with tallow.

This method of preserving meat has proved to be so adaptable and successful that sausages have come to take many forms and question of definition and classification are complex.

Although meat, especially pork, is most commonly used, it is not the defining character, for it is a known fact that fish sausages were also made. Glamorgan sausages in fact, contain only vegetables, cheese & leeks. As regards shape, the Lorne sausages from Scotland are square in shape without casing.

The evolution of sausages its hybrids are as vast as to make its classification difficult.

TYPES OF SAUSAGES

Sausages may be classified into 3 basic groups:-

Fresh sausages

Cured sausages

Smoked sausages

FRESH sausages is one that contains no nitrates or nitrites. It is basically a mixture ofground meat, seasonings and flavourings. Although they are often raw, fresh sausages may contain cooked ingredient, or they even be fully cooked before being sold. Any fresh raw sausages containing pork, of course, must be fully cooked before being served/ eaten.

CURED sausages is one that contains nitrates and nitrites of sodium. These chemicalshelp prevent spoilage and food borne disease and also keep the meat red or pink, even when cooked. Cured sausages may be sold raw or cooked like soft and most fresh sausages, semidried and firm, or dried and hard like salami. Some dried sausages may be eaten raw as the curing, aging and drying process renders them safe to eat.

SMOKED Sausages may be hot smoked, and therefore cooked, or cold smoked. Smokingmay be light or heavy, depending on the sausages. Sausages are cured before being smoked and that cure mixture is mixed directly with sausages meat.

The Basic sausages ingredients are as follows:-

Lean pork or other lean meat

Pork fat

Salt

Spices, herbs, other seasonings and flavourings.

In case of cured sausages, curing mixes are added to the above list.

Lean pork or other lean meat

Pork is the most commonly used meat in sausages making. Beef, veal lamb, chicken, turkey, Duck, liver, rabbit, and venison are also used in combination with pork

Pork fat.

Pork fat or other fat constitute an important part of a sausage. Juiciness in any cooked meat is largely due to the meat fat content. Without it the texture of the cooked sausages would be very dry.

Fat makes up 25 to 50% of the total weight with 33% fat being the norm. Hard fatback is preferred over other fats for pork sausages. Softer fats are more likely to melt out of thesausages during cooking.

Cereal ingredients and fillers (rice, barley, bread crumbs etc.) can be used to help reduce fat content. Because, these starches absorb and retain moisture, they enhance the total moisture content of low fat sausages.

SEASONINGS:-Herbs, spices and other flavouring account for the primary difference among sausages. It is the seasonings that give them their characteristic flavour. Some of the major spices and herbs used in sausages making are :- Allspice, Mace, Cayenne pepper, tarragon, cinnamon, caraway seeds, ginger, basil, nutmeg, cumin, mustard, thyme, parsley, black pepper, paprika, sage, etc.

OTHER FLAVOUR ENHANCERS

Monosodium glutamate

Mono-ammonium glutamate

Nucleotides

Bacterial cultures

Enzymes

Phosphates.

Acidulates: They are used for softening of tissue, juice retention etc.

STABILITY ENHANCERS

They are used to protect flavour, slow down mould growth, extend and bind the product.

There are 3 classes of extenders and binders.

Animal based, are Gelatine and non fat dry milkfermentation based is done by introducing specific type of micro organism

Cereal based are flour, eat, wheat barley corn and rye.

They extend the products volume by acting as fillers.

Garlic	Shallots	Wine	eggs
Onions	Chives	Vinegar	

CASINGS

From the earliest time people discovered that parts of the slaughtered animal such as intestines, stomach, caul and bladder made practical stuffing bags for the seasoned meat, these casing are at the very heart of the sausages making process.

After the seasoned and or cured meats is stuffed into the casings, it dries for a specified time in an environment of controlled temperature and humidity. As the casings hold the ingredients in close proximity, complex chemical reactions take place and transform the meat into sausage. Flavours mature, enzymes modify the textures and the meat is preserved, this activity continues for days, weeks, and even months.

This curing period may be followed by smoking, where the permeability of the casings allows the smoked to penetrate and create a distinctive flavour, colour and an outer protective layer.

The casings give each sausage its identity either by its shape and colour.

Natural casing

Natural casings are made from the intestines of animals. Soon after they are slaughtered the intestines must be cleaned.

The steps taken to process the intestines are as follows:-

Empty the intestines by flushing thoroughly with cold water

Remove all the external sinew, blood vessel and fat.

Wash again in running cold water.

Drain all the water by pressing the intestine between two fingers and run them from one end of the intestine to the other.

Soak the drained intestine in a disinfecting solution of potassium permanganate at 10^0C for 2 hours

Drain and rinse the intestines

Sort according to size and use.

Casings are packed in dry salt for storage, when used they must be systematically washed and rinsed in cold water before use.

Sheep casings are the smallest ranging from 3/4 inch (18mm) to 1 inch (25 mm) in diameter

16-18 mm	Cocktail Sausages
18-20 mm	Chipolata Sausages
20-22 mm	Frankfurters, Chipolata
22-24 mm	Strasbourg, frankfurters

Hog casing are medium sized about 26-50 mm diameter. They are used for many popular fresh sausages

e.g. 26-30mm Small Toulouse

Beef casings range in size from around 45 mm in diameter to more than 100 mm.

e.g.	34-37 mm	Bloodwurst (dry)
	37-40 mm	Spanish Chorizo
	40-42 mm	Leberwurst
	50-55 mm	Large Salami
	90-150 mm	Mastadella

Natural casing are often sold packed is salt. Because of the preservative effect of salt the casings keep indefinitely as long as they are refrigerated. They are easy to use. Before they are stuffed casing must be untangled, rinsed and flushed and examined for holes.

Manufactured Casings :-Manmade casing are made from animal products such as collagen, while other are manufactured from approved plastic materials. The advantages of manufactured casings are:-

Economical

Practical

They require very little preparations before use.

They come on easy to handle rolls

they come in various colours

In various lengths

Their uniform dimension makes accurate portion control easier.

Disadvantages:

Not easily available

Quite expensive

Casings may be reinforced with natural fibres or nylon, some can shrink into the sausage to create a pleasing appearance. Both plastic and collagen casings offer the same control of smoking as the natural ones.

TYPES of casings Collagen casings can be made very thin and are delicate enough to be completely edible. The collagen is made from the inside or corium layer of cattle hides. The casing is available in size range of 14 to 45 mm. They hold up especially well on today high speed stuffing and linking machines. They can be linked quite short Shrinkage loss is less with collagen casing because the uptake of colour is very rapid, resulting in faster processing. These casings are both sanitary and clean, thus saving time and labour. They are also available in a curved style. Collagen casing require refrigerated storage at 10°C. They do not need nor can tolerate prolonged soaking.

The Hukki Knitted collagen casing is formed around a nylon web which creates a verystrong casing. It is highly recommended for dry and semidried sausages that will not be exposed to high smoking temperatures, the limit for this casing is 76.°C,they are available in popular size and can be stored indefinitely at room temps. A 10 minute soaking is required before use.

PLASTIC OR CELLULOSE CASINGS They can be tailor made to any size and are very strong. They do not need refrigeration, cleaning them before use is not necessary. They can be coloured and imprinted with labels and logos, for e.g. red suggests Bologna, white indicates Liverwurst etc. These casings are universally used in the manufacture of skinless hot dogs and frankfurters.

FIBROUS- CELLULOSE CASINGS. These are by products of the food processing industry, Cellulose and fibre is extracted from the husks, skin, peels, pips and seed of the fruit and vegetable during the processing stage, which are them processed further to make casings. These types of casing are also referred to as peel able cellulose. The fibre adds to the strength of the casings and enables them to handle high temp especially during smoking.

PROTEIN LINED FIBROUS Cellulose Casing A protein lining is often added to the inside of the above type of casings. The protein lining caused the casing to shrink as the meat is cooked or dried so that it retains the shape of the sausage. Used mainly for dried or semidried sausages. They need to be left soaking in water before stuffing as the protein tends to stiffen during storage.

CAUL FAT (NATURAL CASSING)A membrane lining of the stomach is used as casing to make flat sausages e.g. Crepenette. The membrane is networked like a spider s web with streak of fat. Caul fat is ideal to wrap items of uneven size like the „Joukanika which are patty like Greek sausage and the crepinette.

METHOD OF PRODUCTION

There are two methods of production:-

Basic grind.

Emulsion grind

BASIC GRIND

This method used for the following types of sausage

Fresh sausages which are raw sausages that are typically pan fried, grilled, baked or braised before serving.

Cooked sausages: are poached or steamed after shaping, they may be sliced and served cold or prepared by grilling baking or pan trying.

Smoked & Dried sausages are cold or hot smoked, then allowed to air dry in a curing room to the desired texture, they may be prepared for service in the same manner as cooked during smoking or are not fully dried must be fully cooked before serving.

Procedure

Grind chilled and diced meats, as well as other ingredients as required by the receipt to the desired texture.

Mix the around sausage meats until they become homogenous

The sausage mixture is now ready to test, garnish and shape.

EMULSION GRID SAUSAGES Emulsion sausages, such as frankfurters and mortadella are made from basic mixture known as 5-4-3 forcemeat- 5 part trimmed raw meat to 4 part pork jowl fat to 3 part water in the form of ice. Many emulsion style sausages are poached before smoking. The procedure is as follows:-

Cut the meat and then grind through the fine grinder die.

Grind the chilled fat through the fine grinder die keep aside.Add crushed ice and process until temp. drops to below 30F

Add the ground fat to the meat when the temp reach 40^0F

Add remaining ingredients including non fat dry milk and seasoning when the temp reach 50^0F

Now ready for testing, shaping and finishing the sausage.

TESTING

No matter how many times you have used a particular receipt, it is important to make a test each and every time. The quantity of your ingredients the temperature of the sausage mixture and the conditions of your equipment all play a big role in the final quality.Test the sausage by making a small sample that has been cooked in the way that you intend the entire batch to be prepared the temperature of the forcemeat must be the same as you would intend to serve.

Sausages may be

Baked

Pan-fried

Oven baked or roasted

Poached in water

Braised or stewed

served cold

GARNISHES Sausages maybe garnished after the forcemeat has been tested cheese, vegetable cured or smoked meats, nuts and dried fruits are examples of garnish used.

Non Meat ingredients These are food additives which can be legally added to sausages or other processed meats. They enhance Flavour, Colour, they slow or prevent bacteria growth, act as preservative and extend the volume of the sausage.

There are six types of additive

Water is added during the blending stag. It improves the mixing and helps to extractthe proteins from the meat.

Curing Agents: - They are necessary to inhibit the growth of clostridium botulinuman anaerobic bacteria and improve shelf life.

Curing accelerators speed up the curing process. The accelerators should not bedirectly mixed with curing agents some e.g. ascorbic acid, enythorbic acid, citric acid.

Sensory enhancers also used to enhance the flavour, smell colour and feel of theSausage. They are: - Salt including MSE, sweeteners both nutritive and non-nutritive are used.

Nutritive sweetness is cane or beet sugar, dextrose & corn syrup. Non-Nutritive are saccharin, sorbitol, etc,.

Flavourings used are spices, hydrolyzed plant, vegetable and milk protein autolyzed yeast extract and mustard flour :- adds to flavour increases volume act as binders and improve peeling

Colouring both natural and artificial- if artificial they must be certified food colours. Natural colourings may be obtained from paprika, saffron, turmeric caramel etc.

TYPES OF FOCEMEATS used in SAUSAGES

Cured minced forcemeats

Cutter pulverized forcemeats

Combination forcemeat

SAUSAGES OF SPIAN-PORTUGAL

CHORIZO made from small piece or chopped or mixed park with some fat, peppers to givecolour garlic ginger and other spices may be soft or hard cured goes with caldo verde cabbage pot soup.

MORCILLA. black pudding or blood sausage seasoned with clove, cinnamon nutmeganiseed fennel pine nuts etc.

BOTIFARRA DOLÇA: - Sweet venison cured with sugar flavoured with cinnamon and

lemon juice eaten as dessert.

SAUSAGES OF BRITAIN

Cambridge –sage cayenne and nutmeg.

Oxford- pork + veal +beef suet, sage, nutmeg+ herbs

Wiltshire: ginger & seasonings.

Yorkshire nutmeg+cloves&cayenne

Glamorgan: cheese and leek sausage skinless coated with egg white

SAUSAGES OF FRANCE

Fresh sausages are known as SAUCISSE

e.g. Saucisse de Toulouse

saucisse de Strasbourg

Large sausages are known as Succession e.g. succession à curie

Andoville and and Andouillette tripe based, they are make in the Normandy region e.g. Andoville de Vire cerealsare short stumpy fresh sausage made with pork, beef, coriander, allspice nutmeg+ garlic.

SAUSAGES OF GERMANY

Three major categories

BRÜHWURST –which means parboiled sausage made from finely chopped raw meat maybe smoked red in coloure.g.

Frankfurter

Bierwurst coarse pork and beef sausage – garlic flavour.

Westphalian Schinkenwurst – smoked over a fire of Birchwood and juniper berries.

ROHWURST

Raw Sausage intended for keeping,-cured dried and sometimes smoked eg. Teewurst smooth

fine textured spiced

Mttwurst Raw smoked

Cervelatwurst. Not cured

KOCH WURST

Fully cooked sausages not intended for keeping
E.g. Leberwurst liver sausage
Rotwurst blood red sausage
Bhitwurst
Zungenwurst Tongue sausage.

SAUSAGES OF ITALY

Casalingo: homemade coarse black pepper flavoured.
Milanese also known as crespone mild garlic flavoured.
Salami Largest sausages
Pepperoni- long narrow highly spiced
MORTADELLA- largest
LOMBARDY-cloves and Cinnamon.

LARDER-TERMS

Al dente:

Firm not soft or mushy, to the bite, refers mainly to vegetables and pasta. Italian expression "to the tooth". Correct degree of cooking pasta and vegetables.

Antioxidants:

Fats can be protected against the rapid development of rancidity by the addition of antioxidants and has become an important commercial practice..Some of the important antioxidants are:

B.H.A.- Butylated hydroxyanisole.
B.H.T.- Butylated hydroxytolune.
T.B.H.Q.-

Antipasta:

Italian hors d oeuvres.

Attereau:

a hot hors d oeuvre consisting of various raw or cooked ingredients that are threaded on to a skewer, dipped in a reduced sauce, coated with bread crumbs and fried.

*The name attereau is also given to Burgundian specialty consisting of minced meat and ground liver and neck of pork, wrapped in a caul, shaped like large balls, they are baked in an earthenware dish and served cold.

*May also be a hot dessert made with fruit and pastry, dipped in custard mixture, coated with breadcrumbs and deep- fried.

Avgolemono:

Greek soup made from chicken stock, egg and lemon juice.

Aspic:

Many authors believe this word was derived from "ASP" a serpent who s icycoldness recalls that of a jelly or from the Greek word "Aspis" which means a shield. It is reduced clarified stock to the point of a jelly so that it solidifies when cold.

Bagna cauda:

A hot dip, which is a specialty of Piedmont, in northern Italy. It is a festival dish dating back to the 16th century. A puree is made using olive oil with a little butter, pounded garlic and anchovy fillets heated for some time and served like a fondue- not as a meal but as a snack.

B.H.A.- Butylated Hydroxyanisole.

Used as an antioxidant and preservative in many foods containing fat or oil. The foods in which it is used may be, potato chips processed meats, cereal products, biscuits, ice-creams and shortenings.

Baked Alaska:A classical dessert consisting of ice-cream on a sponge cake base, covered with meringue and browned in an oven

Balsamic Vinegar: It takes its name from "balsamic" meaning health giving. It is a traditional product of the province of Modena in Italy and is the authentic standard authorizer.

The Must from specially cultivated grapes is fermented and acidificated for a year, then it is reduced by slow simmering to half or one third its volume.This sets off on its long slow journey from youthful zest to sumptuous maturity – siphoned from one container into another in a "batteria" of barrels of decreasing size, each made from different woods which add its own aromas to slowly concentrating liquid.This traditionally takes place under the roof tops of homes in the region from the "Este"palace in the centre of Modena where the ducal acetia flourished in the 18th century to the attics of ordinary families. Here the extremes of temperatures and climate contribute to the maturing process as the Aceto Balsamico concentrates by evaporation during the stifling summer heat and matures during the cold clammy winters. The densely perfumed brew needs to be used with respect for its qualities. A small dose in a liqueur glass makes a fine after dinner digestive, reminding us of its medicinal use in the past, and hence its name.

Barding: Thin slices of pork or bacon fat which are placed around Joints of meat, some game birds & poultry, before roasting to prevent them from drying out in the heat of the oven. Bards are alsoused as a lining for Pates, and lining the inside of a pie crust. The bards are usually removed before serving.

Ballonttine:A hot or cold dish based on meat, poultry, game birds or fish in aspic. The flesh is boned, stuffed, rolled and tied up with a string, usually wrapped in muslin cloth then braised or poached.

Barquette:A small boat shaped tart made of short crust pastry or puff pastry baked blind and then filled with savoury or sweet filling.

Baste: The term for lightly moistening of food like meat/fish, that is being cooked in an oven or in a pot or under a grill. It also denotes spooning melted fat or cooking juices over the joint, it may be repeated several times till the food is cooked.

Beurre Manie: Equal parts of raw butter and refined flour mixed to a smooth paste.

Beurre Noir:

Butter heated till dark brown and flavoured with vinegar.

Beurre Noisette:

Butter heated till light brown and flavoured with vinegar.

Birds' Nest (Nids d'hirondelle) Nest built by the salangane, a type of Chinese Swallow which produce edible nests. Just before the breeding season the birs feed on gelatinous seaweed, which makes their salivary glands secrete a thick glutinous saliva with which they construct their nests. Used in traditional Vietnamese and Chinese cookery. This preparation is very nutritious.

BitokeA dish made with minced lean beef moulded into a flat, oval or round shape. Introduced into French cookery by Russian emigrants.

Black PuddingA savoury sausage consisting of seasoned pig s blood and fat stuffed in a casing. The black pudding is said to have been invented by Aphtonite, acook of ancient Greek. Fried or grilled it is traditionally served with apples or mashed potatoes.

BliniA small thick savoury pancake made with leavened batter that contains both wheat flour and buckwheat flour. In Russian cookery bilinis are served with soured cream and melted butter as an accompaniment to caviar and smoked fish.

Bombe glacéeA frozen dessert made from a bombe mixture consisting of 32egg yolks: 1 ltr, of milk: 1ltr, of cream; often enriched with various ingredients and frozen in a mould. The dessert was named after the spherical mould in which it is used to be made. Traditionally bombe moulds are filled with two different mixtures, the bottom and sides of the mould are lined with a layer of plain ice-cream, a fruit ice or sorbet, the inside then filled with the chosen bombe mixture. The mould is clamped and frozen. To serve the bombe, it is turned on a serving dish and may be decorated with crystallised fruits, jam, nuts, whipped cream, etc.

BotvinyaA cold sweet and sour soup from Russia made from beetroot leaves, spinach and sorrel. It is garnished with cucumber and small pieces of fish.

Bouquet GarniA selection of aromatic plants used to flavour a sauce or stock. They are usually tied together in a small bundle in muslin cloth, to prevent them from dispersing in the liquid and are removed before serving. A bouquet garni usually consists of parsley, thyme, bay leaf, celery, leek, cloves, pepper corns, sage, etc,.

BraisingBrowning joints of meat, poultry, game or fish by sauting in hot fat and then cooking them in liquid as in stewing.

BrainFrench for brain is Cervelle.

BratwurstA fine German uncured sausage.

BrochetteA large slightly flattened skewer made from cast iron or Stainless steel on which pieces of meat, vegetables, etc., are threaded for cooking over charcoal or under a grill. Preparations cooked in this way are also known as brochette.

CailletteA small flat sausage made of minced pork meat and green vegetable baked in an oven and eaten hot or cold, is a speciality of South France.

Caldo VerdeA Portuguese national soup made with olive oil, potatoes and curly cabbage. It is garnished with slices of garlic, sausage and is served with maize bread and red wine.

CarbonadeA Flemish speciality made of slices of beef that are browned and then cooked with onions and beer. The word comes from Latin "carbonata". The name is also given to broiled pork chops as well as to certain beef stews with red wine prepared in south of France.

CaroteneOrange pigment found in orange/yellow coloured fruits and vegetables.

Caul also known as **crépine** in French.

A thin membrane veined with fat that encloses the stomach of animals, e.g. Pig. The caul is soaked in water to soften it and make it easier to handle, it is used to wrap around sausage meat to produce a type of sausage known as **Crépinettes**.

Chapelure

Dried breadcrumbs.

Chaudfroid

A dish that is prepared as a hot dish, but served cold. They may be pieces of meat, poultry, fish or game, coated with chaudfroid sauce and glazed with aspic. Part of a cold Buffet or entree.

Choucroute or Sauerkraut

Cabbage preserved in brine and vinegar, German cuisine, has a sour flavour.

Chtchi or tschy or stschy Russian soup consisting of sauerkraut, brisket of beef,duck or chicken, bacon and smoked sausage topped with sour cream.

ChemiseA French culinary term meaning to coat or line the bottom and sides of a mould with something to prevent the food from adhering to the container and enabling it to be turned out easily.

ClouteTo stud with cloves, etc.

ChorizoA long dry Spanish sausage flavoured with red pepper and garlic. The best known chorizo is from Jabugo in Andalusia. Used in stews, cocido or paella.

ChowderA term first used in North America in the 1730 s and represents a hearty American cream soup made from fish/shellfish and vegetables usually containing milk and mashed potatoes and served with cream crackers and cheese, the most famous being „clam chowder .

ChipolotaA small, fresh sausage about 2 cm. in diameter made with medium or coarsely chopped sausage meat enclosed in natural sheep s intestine. It may be eaten fried or grilled.

Chiplota garnish The garnish used for game, poultry, meat or eggs, consisting of braised chestnuts, pearl onions, glazed carrot, sautéed mushrooms, bacon and fried chipolata sausages.

ChiodnikAn iced soup of Polish origin, common in several Slavonic countries. The word means refreshment. This soup is made with sorrel, beetroot leaves and cucumber puree, thickened with wheat semolina flavoured with fennel and tarragon, and garnished with various ingredients such as hard boiled eggs, crayfish and freshly diced cucumber.

ChinoiseA conical strainer with a handle, also known as china cap.

ChoronBéarnaise sauce + concentrated tomato sauce.

ClamartAny of the various dishes that include green peas either whole or in a purée, named after a district in theHauts-de-Siene. The garnish comprises of tartlets or artichoke bottoms filled with green peas.

Clear meatA mixture of ground meat, egg white, vinegar and flavouring ingredients used to clarify consommé.

ColleA French term for gelatine, that has been softened in water, ready to dissolve, — also applied to melted aspic.

ConcordeA garnish for large joints of meat, consisting of creamed potatoes, trimmed and glazed new carrots and peas sautéed in butter.

ConfitA piece of pork, goose, duck or turkey cooked in its own fat to preserve it.

Contre fillet or faux fillet of tenderloin Part of beef sirloin which has been deboned and trimmed.

CoppaItalian or Corsican charcuterie made by deboning and trimming loin of pork, seasoning and marinating it with garlic and red wine. It is then rolled out and tied in a section of gut. The Coppa is first braised and eaten before it dries out and becomes hard. The word means "nape of the neck".

Cornicho A variety of cucumber with small elongenated fruits are picked when still unripe and pickled in vinegar as a condiment. It is used as an accompaniment for cold meats, boiled dishes, pastrami, pâtés, terrines and dishes using aspic.

CoulisA thick puree made of cooked and seasoned.shellfish, vegetables or fruits. It may be used to enhance the flavour of a sauce, it may, itself, be used as a sauce or it may be used as an ingredient in a soup e.g. Bisques.

Fruit coulis are sauces made with ripe or cooked fruits and served as an accompaniments to hot or cold desserts, including ice-cream.

Crème fraiche Fresh cream to which lactic acid bacteria culture has been added, which thickens the cream and gives it a slightly sharp but not sour flavour.

Cromesqui or **Kromesky**A hot hors-d oeuvre of Polish origin, which is made by binding a salpicon with a thick sauce and when cold it is cut into rectangles and dusted with flour. These are then wrapped in a thin savoury pancake or caul before being dipped in batter and deep fried. They may also be made with a sweet salpicon.

CroquemboucheA decorative cone shaped dessert constructed from balls of choux pastry filled with custard and glazed with caramel or spun sugar, usually placed on a base of nougat.

DarneA thick, transverse slice of a large round fish cut on the bone. e.g. salmon or tuna.

DaubeA method of braising meat/fish/vegetable/mushroom in red wine stock, the name is derived from Spanish „en daube (to braise).

DécoupoirA small S.S. or G.I. cutter that cuts decorative slices in the form of a star/trefoil/heart/diamond/spade or leaf from soft foods such as jelly/truffles, etc.

DeliceNeatly folded fillet of a large fish.

DégorgerA French term, referring to soaking of meat or fish, etc, in cold water to eliminate impurities. It also means sprinkling certain vegetables (e.g. bitter gourd) with salt to draw out excess water and bitter juices.

Dim sumA Cantonese speciality, consisting of a collection of steamed and fried snacks, e.g. spring rolls, dumplings, etc.

DodineA dish of boned, stuffed and braised poultry, similar to ballontine.

DolmaRefers to Greek/Turkish cuisine where a Vine leaf is stuffed with rice/

mince, in place of Vine leaf cabbage or fig leaf may be used.

Du barry Dishes containing cauliflower, as the foundation ingredient. These dishes were dedicated to Countess du Barry the favourite of King Louis the fifteen.

DuxellesA basic preparation consisting of chopped onions, mushrooms and shallots sautéed in butter.

Em BallerA French term, meaning to wrap up an article in Caul or muslin, that is to be poached or stewed in stock.

Entrecote (rib steak)A piece of prime quality Beef which should be cut from between two ribs.

EscalopeSame as Scallop, a thin slice of white meat.

FalafelSpicy, Middle Eastern food consisting of chickpeas, onions and spices rolled into small balls and fried in oil.

FeuilletéPuff or flaky pastry shaped into fingers or triangles filled or garnished with cheese, ham, seafood, etc. May be served hot or cold as an entrée.

Filet mignon Filet mignon(French for "cute fillet" or dainty fillet)is a steak cut of beef taken from the tenderloin.

Forestiére a' laA garnish consisting of wild mushroom, potato noisettes or rissoles and bacon.

FrangipaneAn almond flavoured pastry cream used in the preparations of various desserts, cakes, pastries, sweet and pancakes. It is made of milk, sugar, refined flour, eggs and butter mixed with ground almond.

FricadellesBalls of ground meat(beef or pork or both) which are deep or shallow fried. Of Belgium, German and north France cookery.

Frittata patataA Spanish egg and potato omelette.

FumetA liquid obtained by reducing a stock or cooking liquor that is added to a sauce or stock to enhance its flavour or give it extra body. The word is used for concentrated fish or mushroom stocks.

Ganache

Ganache is a glaze, icing or filling for pastries made from double cream and chocolate.

GodivauDelicate forcemeat of veal and fat, for making quenelles or to fill a vol-a-vent.

GougonSmall strips of fish breadcrumb coated and fried.

GravadlaxA classic Scandinavian dish consisting of thin slices of dried salmon pickled in sugar, salt, pepper, and herbs, especially dill, originates from an ancient method of preserving by burying it in sand for a few days the fish would ferment and become slightly sour. May be served thinly sliced with a slightly sweetened sauce of mustard and dill as an appetizer.

Green bacon Side of pork only cured.

GuacamoleIt is a dip originating in Mexico and consisting of avocado, tomato, onion, lemon juice and spices. It is eaten with totopos or maize chips.

Gum TragacanthA reddish or white mucilaginous gum extracted from the genus *Astragalus,*

Found in Asia and used in the manufacture of stabilizers, emulsifiers and thickeners of the food industry. It prevents the crystallisation of ice-creams and jams.

HaggisHaggis is a Scottish national dish, a type of a spicy offal sausage. Traditionally consisting of a sheep s stomach stuffed with a spicy mixture of the animal s heart, liver and lungs minced with onion, oatmeal, suet, spices and salt. The Haggis is poached in stock and served with mashed swede or rutabaga(Swedish turnip).

Ham Hock The hock is the lower portion of a hog s hind leg made up of meat, fat, bone, gristle and connective tissue.

Hongroise à la Dishes that contain paprika. Of Hungarian origin.

JardinièreA mixture of vegetables consisting of carrots, peas, turnips and French beans served as a garnish for roast and sautéed meats, etc.

KottbullarThese are Swedish meatballs, which are part of the smorgasbord table at a Swedish party..

LardingThe process of adding fats to cuts of meat or certain types of fish to provide moistness, whilst it is being cooked in an oven. It consists of threading thin strips of pork fat into a cut of meat with a larding needle.

Leberwurst

Literally liver sausage made with finely ground pork, onions pork liver and seasonings. It is soft and spreadable. A product of Germany.

LoretteLorette is a garnish consisting of chicken croquettes, asparagus tips and sliced truffles

Marron Chestnuts that have been poached in syrup and then glazed, marron glace as they are known were created during the reign of Louis XIV and sold in the syrup they are cooked.

MeringueA very light sweet mixture made from sugar and stiffly beaten egg whites that when baked becomes crisp and firm. Invented by a Swiss pastry chef „Galasparini who practised his art in a small town of Meiringen.

MortadellaA lightly smoked Italian sausage served cold and very thinly sliced as an hors d oeuvre, a speciality of Bologna. The recipe dates back to 1484.

MoussakaA dish common to Turkey, Greece and the Balkans made with slices of aubergine arranged in layers alternating with minced mutton, onion, tomatoes and cheese, and baked in an oven.

MousselineA mousseline is a dish based on meat, shellfish or foie gras(usually puréed) to which whipped cream has been added. It may be any of various mousse like preparations most of which have a large quantity of whipped cream. Mousseline is also denotes a sauce which is hollandaise sauce mixed with whipped cream, it is also known as Chantilly sauce. It is also used to describe the paste or forcemeat used to make fish or meat balls.

NageAn aromatic court bouillon in which crayfish or lobsters are cooked.

NesselrodeA name given to various cooked dishes and pastries all containing chestnut purée, dedicated to Count Nesselrode, the 19th century Russian diplomat who negotiated the treaty of Paris after the Crimean war.

NougatA sweetmeat made from sugar, honey and nuts.

Oven spring The rapid rise or increase in size in a loaf of bread during the first few minutes of baking.

Over run The increase in volume in an ice-cream mixture due to incorporation of air whilst it is being frozen.

PaellaA traditional Spanish preparation made from rice cooked with vegetables, chicken, shellfish, etc. Its name is derived from the container in which it is prepared. Originated in the district of Valencia, its three basic ingredients are rice, saffron and olive oil. Garnish may include vegetables like French beans, peas, red peppers and artichoke and meats like chicken, rabbit, duck, lobster, prawns, squids and chorizo.

Pan-bagnatA speciality of Nice, France consisting of a kind of sandwich sprinkled with olive oil and filled with onion, anchovy, celery, black ripe olives, etc.

PaniniAn Italian sandwich made with very white bread brushed with olive oil and filled with crudités, charcuterie, etc.

En PapilloteA small decorative paper frill used to garnish the bone end of a lamb, veal or chicken drumstick. It also means cut of meat or fish baked in a wrapping of grease proof paper or non stick baking parchment or foil.

PastillageA paste used in confectionary made from a mixture of icing sugar and gelatine dissolved in water or gum tragacanth and powdered starch. It is kneaded until firm enough to be shaped easily may be coloured and left to dry. Centre pieces may also be made using pastillage.

PaupietteA thin slice of meat or fish spread with a layer of force meat, and then rolled up into a neat sausage shape, it may be barded or tied with string or secured with toothpicks before being cooked.

PellicleThe drying operation after raw items are cured in brine is important for a thin glossy skin like sheen will develop on the item that has been dried properly and is known as Pellicle.

PestoA cold sauce, from Genoa in Italy Large quantities of basil are ground with garlic, pine nuts and parmesan cheese, olive oil is added gradually to make a bright green aromatic and full flavoured sauce with a thick pouring consistency

PiccataDescribes a small round veal escalope sautéed and served with a spicy lemon and butter sauce.

PlombièresAn ice-cream made with almond flavoured custard cream and kirsh.

Quenelles

Chicken forcemeat, pea shaped, which may be poached or fried and used as a garnish.

Rameki A small round straight sided soufflé dish 8-10 cm. In diameter in oven proof china or glass, it is used to cook and serve individual portions of a variety of hot entrées, small cheese or seafood or fish soufflés. It is equally useful for serving aspics as well as for cold creams and custard. The word is derived from German „rubm a little dish with cream.

Sabayon or ZabaglioneA light foamy dessert of Italian origin made of egg yolks, sugar and marsala wine beaten over hot water until pale and foamy

SalsaSauce made from tomatoes, onions, chilli peppers and spices, served with Spanish or Mexican food.

SpatzleA speciality common to Alsace in France and southern Germany, consisting of small dumpling or noodle made from flour, egg and cream, poached in water or broth then pan fried in butter, and is used to garnishmeat dishes and may also be served as an entree.

Stramer maxA type of sandwich in which a bread slice is fried on it is placed sautéed bacon and on the top of the bacon a fried egg is placed, it may be garnished with sprigs of parsley and quarters of tomatoes.

SundaeA dessert originated in the U. S. A. Consisting of ice cream and fruit coated with jam or syrup and topped with nuts, confectionary and cream. Originally it was reserved for the family on Sundays.

TammyMuslin or cheese cloth used as a strainer.

TempuraTypically Japanese shrimp and vegetable fritter using a light batter made with wheat flour, cold water and eggs. It is traditionally accompanied by a lightly sweetened sauce and a white radish puree sprinkled with ginger.

Tex Mex

A mixture of Texas and Mexican cuisine.

TofuTofu also known as soya bean curd is a soft, cheese like food made by coagulating fresh hot soya milk with a coagulant. It is of Chinese origin and was prepared as early as 2nd century B. C.

TournedosAlso known as filet mignon is a small round slice about an inch thick, taken from the heart of the fillet of beef and sautéed or grilled.

Viennoise, à la Veal escallops coated with egg and bread crumbs, sautéed and served with hard boiled eggs, capers and parsley and a slice of lemon.

WalweskaThe name given to fish poached in fumet garnished with a slice of lobster and thinly sliced truffle coated with mornay sauce, finished with lobster butter and glazed in the oven-dedicated to Count Walweska, natural son of Napoleon one.

WashingtonA garnish for poached or chicken braised with sweet corn and bound with a very thick cream.

In Russian cooking an assortment of small hot or cold savouries served before a meal as hors d oeuvre. Zakuski are larger in size than canapé.

ZamponeAn Italian speciality from Modena consisting of a boned and stuffed pig s trotter, it may be served hot or cold. It is stuffed with a force meat of pork, green bacon, truffles and seasonings and then cured, smoked, boiled and often served with lentils. A large trotter is called zampone and a small one zampino.

ZingaraGarnish containing paprika and tomato. Zingara means gipsy in Italian. It consists of demi glace and tomato sauce mixed with ham, pickled tounge, mushroom, truffle and paprika served with veal escallops or sautéed chicken.

ASPIC

Definition:-Aspic jelly or gelée is clarified stock that contains enough gelatine that it solidifies when cold. The gelatine may be naturally extracted from bones or added from a package.A good stock naturally contains a certain amount of gelatine but in most cases it must be supplemented with additional unflavoured, packaged gelatine.Aspic jelly may be nearly colourless or various shades of amber.It must be crystal clears. This is achieved by clarifying.White or light coloured aspic is used when the natural colours and decorations must show through.Amber or golden aspic enhances the brown colour of foods such as roasted meatsand poultry.

Aspic is used as a coating for foods and as binding agent. When it is used for coating foods, it has 3 main purposes.

The Protect food from the air, which would dry them out and discolour them.

To improve appearance and give shine.

To add flavour in this case the stock must be of a high quality

As a binding ingredient aspics is used in mousse, terrines and aspire moulds. It is also the binding agent in chaud froid sauces.

In addition, when congealed and chopped or cut into various shapes aspic jelly is used as a garnish for platters.

Procedures for converting stock to aspic jelly.

Test the stock for gelatine content if less, add powered gelatine.

Clarify as for consommé remove all traces of fat

The aspic jelly is now ready to use.

Chaud Froid

Meaning of Chaud froid

Making of Chaud froid & Precautions

Types of chaud froid

Uses of chaud froid

Chaud froid translated means "hot-cold" the name refers to the fact that this sauce is applied hot and served cold. The high gelatine content of the sauce makes it possible to apply it to an item while still warm and flowing. As the cooling sauce gels, it adheres to the product. It gives a smooth, pristine surface and seals the item from the air.

The reasons for using chaud froid sauce are:-Protection of an item from the air while sitting on a buffet The sauces act as a background on which to decorate. Besides the chaufriod is adornment in itself. The sauce can complement the flavour of the coated item

TYPESThe most common method of categorizing chaudfroid sauces is colour. There are a wide variety of additions made to chaudfroid sauces, depending on the intended end use. The result is a broad range of flavours and colours.

They may be classified as:-

Chaudfroid Blanche (White)

Chaudfroid brune (brown)

Chaudfroid a l aurore(Red)

Chaudfroid vert (green)

Chaudfroid Mayonnaise

PRERERATION OF CHAUDFROID

Basic white Chaudfroid yield: 2 cups.

Reduce $1^{1/2}$ cup veloute and ½ cup mushroom fumet in a thick bottomed sauté dish. Reduce over full heat stirring continuously, and then add 1¾ cup aspic and $2/3^{rd}$ cup cream.

Continue reducing until the white sauce coats the back of the wooden spoon. Ensurea good consistency by cooling a small quantity of sauce on ice, if is not sufficientlyfirm, add a few more spoonfuls of aspic to it and reduce again.

Strain through asieve or Muslim cloth and stir until it reaches the desired consistency by cooling iton a bed of ice

Yellow Chaudfroid

Same as above – a little turmeric powder is needed.

Red Chaudfroid- a l aurora- To above add 50 gms. of fine tomato puree.

Green Chaudfroid – Vert

To above add fine puree of spinach.

Brown Chaufroid- brune.

Same as above- only substitute Demi- glace for veloute

Chaudfroid mayonnaise

To the mayonnaise sauce a little gelatine may be needed to bring it to the right consistency.

Precautions whilst using chaudfroid

Food to be coated must be completely cooled or the coating may not adhere to it,

The item to be coated must be placed on a rack and must be coated with aspic to smoothen the surface. First coat sides of the item then the top. The first layer must be allowed to set in a refrigerator before the second coat is applied.

Do not coat too much – min. 2 mm.

If there are lumps remove coating and start all over again.

The coating must be firm before decorating.

All decorations must be dipped in aspic of before placing to avoid falling off.

Aspic must be clear and transparent to show the designs clearly.

Food surface must be fairly dry when coating with aspic or chaudfroid or it with run down.

Platters or mirrors must be used in proportion to the food to be displayed.

All food used must be edible.

If using silver platter it is better to coat the base with aspic.

The proportion of garnish must be in relation to the size of the item to be decorated.

Planning and sketching of the layout must be done much in advance.

Avoid handling foods with your hands to often.

Tempering the chaud froid

Chaudfroid sauce should be tempered before applying. Once the item has been properly prepped, the sauce may be tempered this is a matter of bringing the temperature of the sauce by either slightly heating or cooling, to a point which will allow the best, and easiest coating. The gel takes place at approximately 85°F

The closer you can maintain the sauce to this temperature without it getting too thick, the more evenly it will coat. It should take two to three coats of chaudfroid for a smooth, glistening finish.

Chaufroid that is too warm when applied results in problems:-

It tends to wash over the item leaving a very thin layer.

If extremely warm it will melt away the layers already present.

It increases the possibility of bubbles on the surface.

It takes more time than necessary to apply.

Chaufroid which is too cool (thick) when applied creates its own set of problems:-

The sauce will not coat the item smoothly.

It will form lumps.

The layer of sauce will be too thick and uneven.

A sauce which is tempered to the right temperature will do the following:-

The sauce will be easy to manipulate.

It will give a smooth even coating.

It will make the application of the coating easier and more efficient.

There are two ways to apply chaud froid sauce. It can be either ladled on the item or the item can be dipped into it.

The ladling method is suitable for both large and small items.

Place the item(s) on a wire rack over a clean sheet pan.

Whilst lining small items on the rack keep at least one inch space between them.

Ladle the tempered sauce over small items using even strokes in one direction only.

Try to cover each item entirely with each pass.

Avoid dripping on previously coated items.

Large items, which cannot be covered in a single pass, must be started with the lower areas first and finish with the higher areas.

The dipping method is ideal for smaller items e.g. timbales.

Whichever method of coating is used, the items should be refrigerated between each coat and before final trimming.

After applying chaudfroid the items must be TRIMMED for decoration

Carefully remove the items from the rack/screen.

To create a smooth even surface trim the bottom with a sharp paring knife dipped in hot water. They are now ready for the FINAL STEP.

After decorations they are chilled after which they are glazed with a single coat of well tempered aspic jelly.

The final gaze of aspic keeps the chaud froid looking fresh and sparking

FORCEMEATS

One of the basic components of Charcuterie and Garde Manger items is a preparation known as Forcemeats.

Definition: Forcemeat is a lean meat and fat emulsion that is established when theingredients are processed through together by grinding, sieving or pureeing. Depending on the grinding and emulsifying methods and the intended use, the forcemeat may have a smooth consistency or may be heavily textured or coarse. The result must not be just a mixture but an emulsion, so that it would hold together properly when sliced. Forcemeat should have a rich and pleasant taste and feel in the mouth.

Uses: Forcemeats has many uses, it may be used for making quenelles, sausages, pâtés,terrines, roulades, galantines and to prepare stuffing for other items.

STYLES: Each Forcemeat style will have a particular Texture. The four basic forcemeat styles are:-

Straight.

Country style or Champagne.

Gratin.

Mousseline.

Straight Forcemeats combine pork and pork fat with a dominant meat in equal parts, througha process of progressive grinding and emulsification. The meats are cut into cubes, seasoned and marinated, ground and then processed.

Champagne County style forcemeat is rather coarse in texture. It is traditionally made frompork and pork fat, often with a percentage of liver and other garnish ingredients.

Gratin Forcemeat made by sautéing some portion of the dominant meat which is cooledbefore it is ground.

Mousseline is very light Forcemeat, based on white meats and fish. The inclusion of creamand eggs give a Mousseline its characteristic light texture and consistency.

Components of forcemeat and their contribution

Meats:Meat is the major component of Forcemeat. Its contribution to the particular character of the force meat will depend on the dominant meat chosen. The type of meat used includes pork, lamb, beef, veal, poultry, game and fish. The dominant meat is often combined with pork because it has a high capacity for water retention which aids in the production of a moist forcemeat and readily allows for extension of volume in the final product. The functions of meat as the major component in forcemeats are extremely important to the production of a quality product. The body and structure of the product is dependent upon the meat for the matrix of protein into which the fat particles of the forcemeat are suspended. As the meat is broken down into progressively smaller particles more proteins are exposed, these proteins encapsulate the smaller particles of fat, trapping it in the forcemeat giving it a moist flavourful product with a pleasing mouth feel.

***Fats*:**Fats contribute flavour, binding power and texture to the forcemeat. Pork fat primarily fatback is considered the best type of fat for use in forcemeat. It has a neutral flavour and is relatively pure. It has an ideal melting point for forcemeat production. It is soft enough to melt in the mouth yet hard enough to stand up to cooking temperatures. Lamb fat is limited to forcemeat production to those which contain lamb. The strong flavour and hardness of this fat makes it less desirable in forcemeats. Beef fat is also very hard and also undesirable. Poultry fat is soft, has a strong flavour and a low melting point making it difficult to emulsify.

Panada:Panada as it is applied to forcemeats, indicates a paste prepared from flour, bread, rice or other starch products. It aids in binding the fat, it lightens the density of the product, and it contributes to the seasoning of the product. However it should be noted that improved modern technology and equipment makes it possible to create better emulsions without the addition of panada. According to Escoffier there are five types of panadas: 1. bread panada.2. Flour panada. 3. Frangipane panada. 4. Cooked rice panada. 5. Cooked potato panada.

N. B. List not Exhaustive.

Eggs:

The major contributions of eggs to the forcemeat are binding power and firmer texture. Eggs are not used in sausage making.

Seasonings:

Seasonings serve a far greater function in the forcemeat than simple enhancement of flavour. It facilitates the exposure of myosin, the protein largely responsible for binding forcemeat. It also enhances water retention and flavour.

Curing salt:

It is also sometimes called T.C.M. (Tinted Cure Mix) or Prague powder. It is composed of 94% salt (NaCl) and 6% Sodium Nitrate. Curing salt is tinted pink to distinguish it from ordinary salt. The two primary reasons it is used are to fix the colour in a processed meat and to inhibit the growth of Clostridium Botulinum. Curing salts converts to nitric oxide when it combines with processed meats. This nitric oxide combines with myoglobin, the red meat pigment; this combination preserves a pink color in the meat after it is cooked.

Spices:

Spices are primarily responsible for the distinctive flavour characteristics of various forcemeats. Some of the spices used are; white and black pepper, cloves, paprika, bay leaves, marjoram, thyme, basil, nutmeg, mace, ginger, garlic, etc. Other flavourings used are wine, brandy, shallots, etc.

Garnishes:

Garnishes may be added to forcemeat after it is completed. There is a wide range of possibilities for this purpose and may include mushroom, dried currants, dried fruits and nuts as well as traditional garnishes of pistachios, smoked tongue and truffles. Garnishes should be at least partially cooked and cooled before adding.

METHODOLOGY OF PREPERATION

The basis of successful forcemeat preparation starts with:-

Careful selection of ingredients which are to be used and assemble them before beginning.

Choose the right equipment and prepare them properly for production, the most important being the grinder and food processor.

The preparation of forcemeat consist of 3 main steps:

Fabrication and grinding.

Moulding, forming and stuffing.

Cooking.

Fabrication and grinding.

Basic fabrication will include four steps:

The meats should be trimmed of fats, gristle and silver skin.

The rind should be removed from the fatback.

The meat and fats should be cubed.

The cubed meats and fats should be well chilled.

NB. Partial freezing of fats could be done to maintain low grinding temperature, however freezing of meat should be avoided.

Seasoning and curing is the next step. Salt, curing salts (if used) and any other seasonings are distributed evenly. The mix is then allowed to marinate preferably overnight.

Grinding: grinding procedures followed, must be able to keep intact meat proteins until the cooking stage for the success of the emulsion. Maintaining the temperature of meat between 7°c to 13°c during the grinding process prevents the denaturing of the proteins and will increase the binding power. The marinated meat and fat mixture through a large ¼ inch die, on medium speed. If finer textured forcemeat is required then the mixture is ground a second time through a smaller die. This is referred to as progressive grinding. For pureed forcemeat the mixture would be transferred at this point to a well chilled food processor and processed to a smooth paste. At no time during grinding should the temperature rise above 15°c.

Moulding, forming and stuffing.

Prior to filling moulds, the forcemeat mixture should be tested. Poaching a small quantity quenelle in lightly salted water will allow the determination of correctness of flavour, seasoning and binding.Forcemeats should be placed into terrines and pate moulds in several layers to minimize the possibilities of air pockets.

When layering, garnishes may be added to the forcemeat, random garnishes should be evenly distributed and inlaid garnishes should be carefully positioned within the terrine, pate or

galantine.

Cooking

Various methods of cooking may be used depending on the reciepe in which the forcemeat isused.

POINTS TO BE KEPT IN THE MIND FOR HANDLING & STORAGE OF FORCEMEATS

The preparation of a wholesome product calls for strict sanitary practices. There is a constant danger of cross contamination of the various components of forcemeat.The meats and other components in the forcemeat must be held at safe temperatures both before and during processing.Once processed they must be quickly cooled and then held at safe temperatures.

Always fully dismantle and clean processing and grinding equipment between batches of different types of meat to avoid cross contamination.

Always chill everything involved in the production.

On completion of production always store forcemeats covered and under refrigeration.

Galantine & Ballonttine

Definition: A cold jellied loaf made of lean poultry veal, game, pork or fish mixed withforcemeat containing eggs, spices and various other ingredients in its own skin and tied. Galantines are cooked in a well flavoured stock and served cold as an entrée. The name comes from the old French galantine meaning felly.

The galantine is made up of:

The skin as an outer layer

Force meat

Garnish

Recipe of galantine de volaille

Singe a large 2 kg chicken, cut of feet and pinions.

Slit the bird along the back, carefully separate the skin without tearing it from the carcass, including legs.]

Scrape the skin clean and soak in cold water.

De bone the carcass separating the flesh from the bones

Dice the flesh-keep aside.

Now prepare forcemeat consisting of:-

1.	Finely minced or ground loin of pork	250gms.
2.	Finely ground shoulder of veal	250gms.
3.	Diced fat bacon	150gms.
4.	Diced ham	
5.	Pickled tongue diced	150 gms.
	for garnish take	
6.	The breast of the chicken cut into strips.	150gms.
7.	Blanched pistachio	25 gms.
	Marinated in brandy	
8.	Diced truffles	50 gms.

To make forcemeat.

Take the chicken meat minced meat, and grind to a fine forcemeat along with 2 eggs, 30 ml brandy salt, spices and a little gelatine.

Remove this force meat and with wet hands blend it together with the garnish consisting of diced ham, diced fat some pistachios, strips of Chicken breast and diced truffles.

Shape into a ball and then into a rectangular block.

Place this block of forcemeat over the central third of the chicken skin and gently fold the chicken skin.

Soak a coarse linen cloth in water and wring it out, then spread it flat on the table. Place it so that a flap 20 cms wide hangs over the edge of the table.

Place the galantine horizontally on the cloth about 10 cms from the edge of the table.

Wrap the galantine in the cloth as tightly as possible, sausage shape.

Tie both ends of the cloth securely.

Tie the galantine with string in three places to keep it in shape.

Bring to boil rich aspic stock add the galantine and poach for approx 1 ¾ hour.

Drain carefully, cool slightly, unwrap the cloth rinse it in luke warm water and wring thoroughly.

Again spread it on the table and reroll the galantine and tie security, set to cool under a slight weight, till cold.

When cold, remove cloth, coat with aspic and decorate.

Serve cold in slices with tarragon mayonnaise, along with a lively red wine such as Chinon.

BALLOTTINEA hot or cold dish based on meat, poultry, game birds, or fish. The flesh is boned, stuffed rolled and tied up with a string usually wrapped in muslin-similar to galantine then braised or poached.

HAM & BACON Ham is the most distinctive of all cured products, universally popular and may be eaten raw or braised or boiled or roasted.

The term used describes specifically the hind leg of a pig above the hock joint cut from the carcass and cured. GAMMON is also from the leg but is cured while still attached to the side of the carcass.Ham in its more general meaning of the hind leg is applied to cured meat made from other animal, including wild boar mutton, goat venison and even badger.

The process of curing all hams being with salting. This may be done with dry salt or brine, or a combination of the two. Wet cures penetrate the meat more quickly.The flavour of Ham depends on many factors breed and age of pigs, its diet, kind of wood burned for smoking the meat, and the length of the time it is aged.The interplay of these factors give Ham a diversity almost as rich as that of wine or cheese.A good ham should be plumb with an ample, though not too thick layer of fat under the rind.The method of curing hams was also done by the Chinese, where the province of Yunnan is known for fine quality hams.

There are two main types of cured Hams :-

Those eaten raw and

Those eaten cooked

HAMS eaten raw

When eaten raw they are usually served finely sliced. They are cured, matured and dried, they may be smoked. Although they are suitable for serving raw, they may be used in cooked dishes. These hams are normally dry cured. The most important aspect of the curing process is the MATURING PERIOD.

The maturing period consist of the drying process which may take several months to a year. Only "Certified" pork may be used so as to eliminate the possibility of TRICHINEA bacteria growing. This is done by freezing the pork according to a specific schedule.

VARELIES OF RAW HAMS

Jambon d "Ardennes- The best known Belgian ham smoked to dark brown.

Jambon de Byaonne – French smoked Ham with a smoky flavour and brown exterior made around Orthez and Peyrechorade east of the ancient port city of Bayonne. The red seal guarantees that the ham comes from good quality Carcasses that has been rubbed with a mixture of salt from Salies-de-Béarn, saltpetre, sugar, pepper and aromatic herbs and has been dried fro 130-180 days.

eg. Jamón ibérico, Spanish from the native Iberain pig, which is reared in the woodlands of south and Western. Spain, also known as PATA NEGRA (black trotters).

Jamón Serrano –Mountain Ham- produced from white pigs especially large, white, landrace, Belgian white species,

Jamón Serrano de Jabugo is considered the best.

Knochenschinken „ham on the bone - a hard heavily smoked, German ham.

Landrauch „country smoked a heavily smoked and dry German ham.

Prosciutto di Parma This ham is the most famous of raw hams because of its delicate taste. .These hams are dry cured and matured without smoking for at least eight months and sometimes two years. Connoisseurs are very fond of the ham from San Daniele and Langhirano near PARMA. also known as prosciutto crudo de Parma

Westfalishe schinken Westphalian ham- is protected by a trade mark- it is dry salted, then brined, scrubbed with cold water to reduce its saltiness and cold smokedover strongly resinous wood, like beech and juniper wood and juniper berries, then dried, it is dense textured and brown in colour.

Mainz Ham is brined, desalted, soaked in brandy or wine lees and cold smoked for a long period.

COOKED HAMS Hams to be served cooked are cured by traditional methods usually having a high salt content and have to be soaked several hours before cooking.

The best hams are salted by injecting the brine into the veins before the joint is boned. It is then put in brine for four days. The drained ham should be brought to the boil in fresh water. Jest as the water boils it should be drained away and fresh water added. When the water boils and the scum has been skimmed off, flavouring agents such as onions, vegetables, a bouquet garni, peppercorns, are added.

The ham is then simmered gently, alternatively it may be baked a combination of boiling for half the time and then baking gives excellent results.

As a guide cooking times are calculated at 40 minutes. per kg, plus an extra 40 minutes.

Cooking hams are also produced commercially by pressing into a mould before steaming e.g. block shaped PARIS Ham

ExamplesYork Ham. One of the best known cooked hams. Traditionally. it is dry salted,smoked over oak and matured for 3 to 4 months. It is cooked on the bone either in stock or steamed. It can be served hot or cold, accompanied by Madeira or port sauce and spinach.

VIRGINIA HAMS is a general term for a ham made from the meat of hogs fed onacorns, peanuts and peaches. Dry cured in barrels for several weeks, they are then coated with molasses, pepper and brown sugar. They are cured for a further two weeks and then hung to dry slowly for 10-12 months. Some varieties are also smoked over very aromatic woods such as hickory and matured for up to a year. This involved process gives the ham a distinct flavour and deep reddish brown colour.

SMITHFIELD HAM is a trade name for a variety of Virginia Ham, available onlyfrom Smithfield Virginia. They are dry cured for several months resulting in a dense, dark, red meat. They are not smoked.

Williamsburg ham is a milder version of Smithfield Ham.

Pennsylvania ham is brine cured. It is pickled in vinegar & sugar, then smoked overapple or hickory wood resulting in a fully cooked ham. Prosciutto (PARMA) COTTO, a cooked version of prosciutto Crudo, which takes less time to produce and less expensive.

CANNED HAMS are available for Holland, Denmark and Poland they may or not besmoked. No refrigeration is required if they are sterilized.

PRAGUE HAM is the most celebrated European Ham from Czechoslovakia. It issweet cured and smoked over beech. If raw it must be cooked before service it is also available cooked.

Nutritionally ham has a fat content of 2 to 5% and has 300 kcal/100 gms when cooked and 380 kcal/100 gms when raw.

GAMMONGammon is also from the hind leg of pork but is separated from the carcass after salting. It may be smoked or left un smoked.

BACONThe side of a pig cured with salt in a single piece. Bacon is peculiarly a product of the British Isles, or is produced abroad especially in Denmark. Bacon held a place of primary importance in the British diet in past centuries. Large scale bacon curing business was set up in the 1770 s by John Harris in Wiltshire, still a bacon centre. The standard commercial method of curing bacon is known as the Wiltshire cure. This was originally a dry cure.

The prepared sides of the pig, legs still on, were strewn with salt and stacked skin side down. After two weeks the salt was brushed aside and the sides matured for a week before packing.

In modern times the sides are both injected and immersed in brine in place of dry salt and smoked. A Wiltshire side is a large piece of meat and is divided up for various purposes. The shoulder yields the cheapest bacon, the most valued is back and streaky bacon from the loin and belly respectively. The leg yields Gammon and the other parts of the side may be used as "boiling bacon". The breeds of pig used for bacon are hybrids of Yorkshire large and Landrace. The French use the term lard to mean any kind of bacon. Streaky bacon is termed „Lard de poitrine (fumé is added if it is smoked). The German word for bacon is speck LACHSSCHINKEN speck for back bacon. The Italian use streaky bacon and call it

PANCETTA. The Spanish call streaky bacon TOCINO. American bacon is cured meat from the belly of hog, which has particularly soft fat which allows the bacon to become crisp on heating.The word derives from the old French BAKKO which means a piece of salted pork. Bacon remains a gourmet product in the English breakfast. They are sold as thin slices

„Rashers in Britain which are eaten fried, grilled or broiled, especially with eggs. Bacon is a useful flavouring in many dishes such as casseroles, stews, salads, charcuterie, Choucroute, etc.They are also used for barding, larding etc.Green Bacon are sides of Pork only cured. Bacon is high on calories.

CURINGThere are four methods of curing Hams.

Brine pumping

Spray pumping

Brining

Dry curing

Brine Pumping An apparatus similar to a large syringe is filled with the prepared brine. The meat is injected with brine at several points, insuring even distribution. The ham is then immersed in the same brine for three to four days to insure the exterior portions are fully cured.

Spray pumping:This is done by commercial processors with special pumps. It is also known as stich pumping. The pump has multiple needles and can deliver brine to every part of the Ham s interior in one step. Both types of pumping are considered the best method for curing ham and is combined with immersion to produce the best results.

Brining:By immersion only is done for small pieces of Ham. It is not a method which can be used for large joints of ham, because the interior may spoil before the cure has a chance to reach it.

Dry Curing: is done by rubbing the cure mixture thoroughly into the ham. Several hams are cured by stacking them in a barrel the dry cure mix is the same as brine minus liquid.

PâtéPâté on its own signifies a dish consisting of a pastry case filled with meat, fish, vegetable or fruit & is baked in the oven & served hot or cold. In England these are known as "pies".

The word is used in three ways in French

pâté

pâté en croûte

pate en terrine

The pastry used in most cases was made with lard.

If made with lard, the pastry must be made well in advance.

The pastry lid must be sealed at the edges so that the filling does not escape.

The centre at the top is pierced with a chimney for steam to escape.

The fillings or forcemeat is based on pork, veal, ham, chicken, fish, game and sometimes vegetables, and, or mixtures combining the above.The ingredients are generally minced or ground, but some of them may be cut into juliennes, dices, etc.

The ingredients may be marinated separately.

The filling is placed in the centre of the rolled out pastry and the edges are folded over and sealed, or alternately, as is done in England by using pie dishes and covering them with a pastry.

Baking starts in a hot oven which is then turned down to medium.

Hot pâté have a little sauce or gravy poured into through the chimney before serving.

In case of cold pate aspic flavoured with Madeira, port, etc. it is poured through the chimney filling up the space caused by baking .The aspic should be ready to set.

They are served cut into thick slices.

Pâté is synonymous with pate en croûte.

Pate en croûte (reciepe)

Place 500 gms of sifted flour on a work top and make a well in the centre.

In the well add two whole eggs and 100 ml of water & 175 gms. of lard.Mix together kneading lightly till a smooth paste is formed.Refrigerate 2 hours before use.

Def. Pate en terrine is a meat, poultry, game, fish, or vegetable forcemeat, put into a terrine dish lined with bacon, cooked in the oven and always served cold. After making the forcemeat into a smooth consistency mix in 80 gms lard and 80gms foie gras.

Pour this mixture into a small terrine, press down and leave to cool.

Melt lard on a very low heat, pour into the terrine, cover it and allow cooking in a bain-marie.

Cooking time is approximately 45 minutes to 1 hour per kg at 160 deg C.

Recipe for pate maison

Sr.no..	ING	QTY.
1.	Chicken liver	500 gms.
2.	Lean pork	125 gms.
3.	Fat bacon	125 gms.
4.	Chopped onions	50 gms.
5.	Parsley	10 gms.
6.	Garlic	7 gms.
7.	Butter	100 gms.
8.	Cream	65 gms.

METHOD

Clean chicken liver properly by removing all veins, connective tissue &. tubes. Wash & cut into dices.

Fry diced fat bacon in butter add diced lean pork & diced chicken liver.

Add onion, herbs, garlic & seasoning.

Sauté for few minutes.

Mince this mixture finely then rub it through a fine wire sieve , add cream

Pour this mixture in a terrine lined with larding baco

Cook in an oven in a bain marie till warm in the centre and fat on the surface is quiet clear.

Cool under pressure by keeping some weight on it.

Serve from the terrine or turn out and slice.

Foie gras (French for "fat liver") is afood productmade of theliverof aduckorgoosethathas been specially fattened. This fattening is typically achieved through gavage (force-feeding) corn, according to French law, though outside of France it is occasionally produced using natural feeding.

Foie gras is a popular and well-known delicacy in French cuisine. Its flavor is described as rich, buttery, and delicate, unlike that of an ordinary duck or goose liver. Foie gras is sold whole, or is prepared into mousse, parfait, or pâté, and may also be served as an accompaniment to another food item, such as steak. The technique of gavage dates as far back as 2500 BC, when the ancient Egyptians began keeping birds for food and deliberately fattened the birds through force-feeding. Today, France is by far the largest producer and consumer of foie-gras, though it is produced and consumed worldwide, particularly in other European nations, the United States, and the People's Republic of China. Each liver weighs approx. 700-900 gms. for geese and 300-400 gms. for duck. The colour ranges from ivory white to creamy to pink.

Forms of foie grasIn France, foie gras exists in different, legally-defined presentations, from the expensive to the cheap

1.*foie gras entier* (whole foie gras), made of one or two whole liver lobes; either cooked (*cuit*), semi-cooked (*mi-cuit*), or fresh (*frais*);

2.*foie gras*, made of pieces of livers reassembled together;

3.*bloc de foie gras*, a fully-cooked, molded block composed of 98% or more foie gras; if termed *avec morceaux* ("with pieces"), it must contain at least 50% foie gras pieces for goose, and 30% for duck

Foie gras are available in four forms.
*fresh raw foie gras sold during Christmas
*freshly cooked foie gras
*semi cooked pasteurized foie gras available in cans.
*preserved foie gras prepared in traditional ways, sterilized and preserved in its own fat.

TRUFFLE

Truffles are *hypogeous* (underground) versions of mushrooms. They don't form a prominent stem and their spore-bearing surfaces are enclosed. They rely on animals eating them (*mycophagy*) to distribute their spores, instead of air currents like mushrooms. Truffles resemble small potatoes, and often between the size of a marble and a golf ball.

There are hundreds of different kinds of truffles, and while none are known to be poisonous, only a few of them are considered to be delicacies by humans. Truffles (and mushrooms) are only the "fruit" of the fungus (like an apple to an apple tree); the main perennial fungal body exists as a web of filamentous hyphae in the soil. All of the truffle fungi form mycorrhizae with the roots of trees, and are essential to the trees' ability to acquire nutrients. The belowground fruiting habit of truffles is thought to be an adaptation to forest fires or dry or frosty periods, in which aboveground mushrooms are more vulnerable.

A subterranean fungus which lives in symbiosis with certain trees, mainly the oak but also the chestnut, hazel and beech. They belong to the family "tuberaceae", order tuberales, class ascomycetes, a large class of fungi known also as sac fungi because their spores are formed in a sac like structure called "ascus".

A highly esteemed food stuff, the truffle- from latin "tuber" meaning over growth is spherical, of variable size and irregular shape and black, dark brown or sometimes grey or even white in colour, it is found in chalky-soil about 12 inch below the ground.

The truffle has been known and appreciated since ancient times. The Egyptians ate truffles coated with goose fat en papillote.

The ancient Greeks and Romans attributed therapeutic and aphrodisiac powers tothem.

Legend says that during thunder storms when lightning strikes the ground gives rise to truffles. During the middle ages they fell into oblivion. However they returned to popularity during Renaissance.

Pigs or even dogs are used to seek out the truffles and it was common in the 17th century. They spring up spontaneously when the fungal spores or mycelia encounter the rootlets of oak and form a mycorrhiza which takes its nutrients from the trees. The truffle itself is the fruiting body of the fungus and does not appear to be connected by any filaments to the mycorrhiza.

There are approx. 70 types of truffles, 32 of which are found in Europe. The most highly esteemed is the black truffle of Perigord which matures after the first frost; it has black flesh streaked with whitish veins and gives off a strong aroma.

The black must be rounded and in a single piece and it is not at its best until ripe. It is also known as diamond of cookery and the famous chef Brilliant Savarin called them black pearl.

Truffle are now sold in cans, peeled or scrubbed, ripe and whole. They are graded

Surchoin- firm black flesh, uniform size.

Extra- Surchoin: with firm flesh more or less black, irregular in size.

Premier choix: with more or less firm flesh, sometimes light in colour, of irregular size.

Canned: Truffles are also canned in pieces, peelings and fragments.

J.K. Vandoyer observed that "there are two types of people who eat truffles, those think truffles are good because they are dear, and those, who know they are dear because they are good".

Truffles are eaten raw or cooked, cut into strips or slices, diced or shredded in the form of julliene or fumet or essence or simply for their fragrance. They are best eaten for themselves fresh and raw with butter or salads or cooked in embers or braised in white wine or in a puff pastry. They are not cooked before canning, simply scrubbed and salted.

Shelf life of truffles is about a week, white is more delicate than black. Truffles must be kept in an air tight container as they very readily give off their moisture and aroma, and can lose up to 10% of weight overnight.

Truffles have twice the calorie content of cultivated mushrooms and 3 times that of wild mushrooms. 100 gms gives approx. 90 K cal. Some of truffle species are:

Tuber Melanosporum.

Tuber Magnatum.

Tuber Aestivum.

Tuber Indicum.

APPETIZERS

An excellent definition has been given by Escoffier which states "To perk up the spirit of some and to give spirit to others who are without it" this is the supreme role of the Hors d oeuvre on a menu".

Hors d oeuvres are meant to pique the taste buds and perk up the appetite. Hors d oeuvres and appetizers are synonymous.

Hors d oeuvres is a French expression and its true meaning is a preparation served outside of the menu or at the beginning of the meal before the main course. It comes from the French term „hors (outside) and goes back to early times, when at Banquets the appetizer (hors d oeuvre) was served in a separate room (antechamber) where the guest assembled and waited for the arrival of the „Host and the Chief Guest.

Guidelines for foods served as Hors d'oeuvres

Should be small enough to eat in one or two bites some hors d oeuvre may be eaten with the fingers, while others may require a plate and a fork.

Should be kept light, delicate and unsubstantial.

Should be Attractive. Because hors d oeuvre customarily precedes the meal, they are considered a means of teasing the appetite. This is partially accomplished through visual appeal.

Designed to complement the meal that is to follow. It is important to avoid serving too many foods of a similar taste or texture e.g. Lobster canapés/ lobster bisque.

Guidelines for presentation of HORS D'OEUVRE to assist the Chef: -

Keep in mind the nature of the event, as well as, the menu that follows, when selecting hors d oeuvres.

Ice carvings and ice beds are often used to keep seafood and caviar very cold, as well as for their dramatic appeal.

Hors d oeuvre served on platters or passed on trays should be thought fully presented, so that the last hors d oeuvre on the plate is still attractively presented.

CLASSIFICATIONThe possible variations of hors d oeuvres are almost limitless. Being virtually unlimited, the selection of hors d oeuvres served by the Chef may be dictated by specific occasions or by the circumstances. Almost every culture has their version of what is referred to by Americans as Appetizers, and the French as hors d oeuvre.

Some Examples.

RUSSIAN "Zakuski" –are various preparations patronized by the Russians. Theseare laid out on a table to be enjoyed by the arriving guest for an hour or so before the main meal. These are blinis and breads of various kinds with savoury toppings, served in Russia with vodka.

ITALIAN –Antipasto–means before the pasta. A typical selection would includemarinated mushrooms, artichoke hearts, sliced salami and prosciutto ham, smoked sardines, anchovies stuffed olive, roasted red peppers- etc.

SPANISH – „Tapas means lid . It refers to variety of items-e.g.:- kidney beans invinegar sauce boiled sliced potatoes with garlic and mayonnaise, small meat balls, salt cod, black olives etc.

SWEDISH – "Smorgasbord" means bread and butter table- It includes shrimp,pickles, meatballs, herrings, smoked salmon, caviar aquavit etc.

INDONESIAN "Rijsttafel" meaning rice table, a Dutch meal of Indonesian origin- Itincludes the service of a central dish of fluffy rice, surrounded by a large number of side dishes including sate spicy pork and goat, dumplings, hard boiled eggs, steamed veg. etc.

JAPANESE "Sushi –considered as the national dish of Japan. These are tinyportions of sliced raw fish, placed on mounds of vinegary rice. Sushi and sashimi is the formal Japanese first course.

GREEK "Meze" –It includes such items as keftedakia (tiny meat balls, Kreatopita(triangular flaky pastry filled with ground meat) spanakopita (triangular pastries filled with spinach and feta cheese) and taramosalata (creamy pink cod roe paste).

DUTCH "Smørrebrød" –means buttered bread this is a Danish open faced sandwichusing pieces of meat, fish or vegetables, artfully arranged.

HORS d oeuvre may be classified in various ways because of its complexity: -

Hot & Cold Hors d oeuvre is the major division. There are further classifications within these major categories.

Classical and contemporary.

Vegetarian/Non vegetarian.

Hors d oeuvre singular and compound.

HOT HORS D'OEUVRE

They are generally served at cocktail parties or at dinner where it is more likely to be served after the soup, it is seldom served at lunch.

Warm and hot appetizers include small servings of pasta such as tortellini or ravioli, Puff pastry shells like vol-au-vent or made into turnovers and filled with savoury ragouts or foigras, broiled or grilled fish, seafood or poultry, Crepes, blini. Meatballs etc. vegetables such as steamed artichokes with a dipping sauce, asparagus, grilled vegetables may also be featured.

Examples of Hot Hors d oeuvre

Croquettes, Fritters, Kromeskies, Rissoles, Beignets, Bouches Quiches. Barbequed Spareribs, Sheik Kebab, Baked Clams, Baked Crab, Broiled breaded Scallops, Fish Cakes, Croustades Baked Beans, etc.

COLD HORS D'OEUVRE

The greatest variety and unbelievable diversity is associated with cold hors d oeuvre, for e.g. Hors d oeuvre a la francaise- In this hors d oeuvre is presented in small oblong dishes called „raviers . The dish is needed because the hors d oeuvre are usually served with a marinade, sauce, relish or other accompaniment and require a fork for service or for eating. Any foods can be used in this category but they must be bite size.

Zakushki or hors d oeuvre a la Russe or canapés a la Russe became very popular in the 1890 s. This cold hors d oeuvre are considered to be classical and made up of certain specified ingredients. Chefs in Russia were patronized by the Czars and reached the pinnacle of their profession. It consists of a base of blinis the famous Russian pancake made out of buck wheat flour. This was topped with a toping that would be meat, fish, vegetable or a combination of these. A characteristic of the topping is that it would most often be flavoured with a smoked meat or fish. The chef had a chance to demonstrate his imagination and skill. Intricate garnishes of exquisite designs would decorate the Zakuski.

This would then be finished off with a glaze of aspic. The Zakuski is a dinner hors d oeuvreand are larger in size than the canapé. They are presented to the guest individually without an accompaniment or sauce.

CRUDITÉS

Crudités essentially means food eaten raw "Common usage of the term is normally limited to raw Vegetables, particularly for hors d oeuvres. Vegetables often used for crudités are-red, yellow, and green bell peppers, carrots, celery stalks, summer squash, red radishes, Belgian endive, cucumbers, cherry tomatoes lettuce etc. these are cut into finger size pieces or decorative rounds and served with one or more varieties of dip or dressings.

CANAPÉS

The term CANAPE refers to a small open faced sandwich which may be topped withan endless variety of savoury food items.

The canapé is comprised of four parts: -

BASEThe base serves as the foundation of the canapé. It must be firm enough for the guest to hold with two fingers without its topping spilling into the guests lap. The base would normally be bread-toasted or plain, white or brown. However a variety of other base ingredients could also be used like puff pastry flaky pastry, short crust, pizza dough, choux pastry, etc.

SPREADThe spread applied to the base has a threefold purpose:-

Spread adds flavour & moisture to the canapé.

Spread acts as a glue to hold all of the components of the canapé together.

Spread provides a fat barrier to prevent the base from becoming limp and soggy from the juices of the main body.

There are primarily two types of spread: -

A basic spread of 50% butter and 50% cream cheese.

Any compound butter that is suitable for the main topping of the canapé being prepared.

Either type of spread should be softened sufficiently to allow easy spreading.

MAIN BODY or Topping: This part of the canapé may be almost any savoury food items such as sliced cold meats or seafood or vegetables. The main body is what gives the canapé its particular flavour and character. Items of food used for the main body must be cut so that each canapé has a consistent size and shape. e.g. a slice of cheese, hardboiled egg, ham, salami, mushrooms or chicken coated with a thick cream sauce, marinated mushrooms, and prawns could all be used as a topping. The list is limitless and can only be contained by the imagination.

GARNISH Garnish of a canapé increases the eye appeal. It should enhance not overshadow the main body garnish can be a small leaf or herb or a piece of food which is in keeping with the canapé as a whole.

GARNISH Definition:A single item or combination of items accompanying a dish. The garnish can be placed around meat chicken fish or game or served separately.

Whether simple or composite the garnish always blends with the flavour with the basic dish. It is derived from the French word, to adorn. The term refers to decorative edible items used to ornament or to enhance the eye appeal of another food item.

Simple garnishes consist of a single element, usually a vegetable, rice, or pasta.

Composite garnishes are made from several ingredients whose flavours blend with each other as with the main dish. They may consist of ordinary items such as pieces of bacon, small onions, fresh vegetables, mushrooms, etc., or more elaborate ingredients, such as, cockscomb, crayfish tails, truffles, filed croustades, quenelles, and croutons depending on the nature of the dish.

The garnish may also be a kind of ragout made up of a composite salpicon like calves sweetbreads, mushrooms etc blended with brown or white sauce, and arranged in small pastry shells.

In all cases the garnish should be placed around a dish so as to achieve an overall harmony of shapes and colours pleasing to the eye.

Modern Plate Garnish In classical cuisine food was brought to the dining area on large silver platters and then served. The practice is still widely used for banquets

Currently there is a shift towards smaller portion sizes with good nutritional balance, and the trend has shifted to plated service. Service on individual plates gives the chef ample scope to use more thought and imagination in presenting the meal. Plates should not be overcrowded. The plate is best when simple yet elegant to the eye. The plate should present a combination of foods working together. It should not be several components that happen to be on the plate. The portion size should match the plate size.

Many pates need no additional garnish if the accompanying vegetables and starches provide an attractive balance and colour combinations. Hence the accompaniment becomes the garnish.

A simple Garnish becomes necessary sometimes to provide colour or balance to a plate. A simple garnish must be edible, appropriate to the food, planned into the plate layout not just dumped into the plate.

SOME TIPS FOR PLATE ARRANGEMENT

Keep the food off the rim of the plate

Arrange the food in unity. The focus should be on the centre of the plate, not on the edges and the firm. Place the food in the most attractive manner-the better side of the meat on top. The bone of chop should face away from the guest. Sauces can improve plate presentation. Serve the sauce around or under the food. Serve just enough sauce so as not to drown the food.

Refrain from using the same pattern over and over again in different courses.

Garnish only when necessary. Simplicity is the key. It is more attractive to have a simple plate presentation rather than a complex one.

Examples of garnishes and accompaniments generally indicated by the term in today kitchen

Bouquetiere	:	Bouquet of vegetables
Jardiniere	:	Garden vegetables
Clamart	:	Peas
Crecy	:	Carrot
Doria	:	Cucmbers cooked in butter
Dubarry	:	Cauliflower
Florentine	:	Spinach
Forestiere	:	Mushrooms
Lyonnaise	:	Onions
Parmentier	:	Potatoes
Princess	:	Asparagus

CHAPTER 4

Food Presentation

As much importance should be given to food presentation as is given to food preparation. Poor presentation lowers the value of well prepared foods. The intent of food presentation is to enhance its visual appearance.

Presenting food properly requires a high level of skill, knowledge and imagination. The modern approach is to present the food in the plate-which is common in a la carte service. The key word in plate presentation is BALANCE. It is a balance of colour texture, size, shape and temperature. The food presented must be appropriate to the occasion. It must be matched to the likes and often the beliefs of the guest. Presentation must complement the food, not disguise or hide it. Failure to present the food properly will lead to the failure of the best of dishes.

Factors to be considered whilst presenting food.

Temperature: Food presentations first priority is the temp at which it is served, hot foodmust be cold. It is vital that hot food is served to the customer immediately. Cold food should be served on a children plate. It should then be thoroughly chilled before service.

Flavour: Everything served on the plate is intended to be eaten. When the guest begin toeat, they do not eat the meat first, then the potatoes and then the vegetables, they take pieces of each, at any given time the mouth of the guest contains the flavour of every food that is on the plate. If the combined flavours of the items are not pleasing then the meal is a failure. No matter how well the items on the plate are prepared, if the flavours are not complementary the effect is not pleasing. It is not enough to ensure good preparation; you must ensure a good balanced presentation of flavours. Escoffier said that a meal is like a symphony. It should begin softly, gradually building up to a good finale. He understood

that it is the meeting of the flavours in the mouth, which determines the pleasure of the meal. However, flavour is not always obvious to the eye. It is necessary to create eye appeal in presentation.

Colour: Although a plate of fried fish and French fries may taste good, it has minimaleye appeal. Everything is brown in colour and crisp in texture. It offers little variety or excitement for the eye. A simple addition of Cole slaw on a bright green lettuce leaf will transform the plate completely. It improves not only the flavour and the mouth feel of the dish, but provides colour and contrast to the eye. The colours used on the plate should be natural. Artificial and non-food colours should be avoided. Colours must be appropriate to the dish.

Shapes: Eye appeal can be gained not only through colour but through the shape of foodas well. As with colour variety is the key. A plate of meat balls, new potatoes and Brussels sprouts may taste good and have a pleasing colour. Yet it is so monotonous being round. Change the shape of the potatoes and use beans instead and now the effect is better.

COOKING WITH WINE

We all know the importance of wine on the menu. It serves as an accompaniment to various courses of a meal. Each type of food is best suited by a particular type of wine. It helps in providing contrast in taste flavour and in some cases helps digestion. Besides being served in the restaurant wine is also extensively used in the kitchen.

SUITABILITY: Before we go on to actual use of wine, let us examine which wines are bestsuited for cooking. If you survey the market one can find certain wines labelled as cooking wines. They are wines produced specially for cooking. They are not as superior as a table wine and are generally by products of table wine.

Cooking wines are not matured for very long and are generally cheaper than table wines. However cheaper table wines can also be used in the kitchen. Try to avoid strongly flavoured wines which may adversely affect the flavour of the food. Generally sweeter wines are preferred to dry wines. Champagne can also be used like other sparkling wines.

Wine is used in Soup making

The taste & flavour of the soup is considerably enhanced by the addition of a littlewine. A dessert spoon-full of wine is enough for 6 to 8 portions. White wines go very wellwith bisque and other fish based soup.

Use of wine in salad

Wine may be added as a substitute for vinegar or lime juice to create tangy salad dressings.

Wines are used for basting

Meat and poultry can effectively be basted with wine to a very good effect. Used veryeffectively for deglazing roasting pans for gravy. Champagne can be used to baste turkey and ham.

Wines are used in sauces and stews.

Red wine may be added to almost all brown sauces, white wine for veloute sauce and its derivatives or to fish based sauces. Wine is also used to prepare reduction for béarnaise and hollandaise and its derivatives. Wine can also be used to flavour stews.

Wine as a marinade Old and tough meat can be marinated in wine by which tough fibre are made tender, wine also enhances the flavour in old meats.

Poaching in wine A good way to enhance the flavour for fish and meats during poaching is by adding a glass of wine to the poaching liquor. Flat fish can be poached entirely in white wine while whole salmon can be poached in court bouillon to which a glass of wine is added. Wine can also be used to poach fruits pears, apricot etc.

Wines used in Desserts

Sweet wine and fortified wines such as port and also brandy are used extensively in desserts.

MOUSSE & MOUSSELINE

Definition: *Mousse is a French term meaning „foam is applied to dishes with a foamytexture, usually cold and often sweet but also savoury and soft.

*It is light smooth and soft preparation either sweet or savoury, in which the ingredients are whisked or blended and folded together and are more often, then not, lightened with beaten egg whites.

TYPES:

Svoury mousses are served as an hors d oeuvre or entrée, it may beserved hot and may bebased on fish, shellfish poultry, foie-gras, ham etc.

Sweet mousse is usually based on fruit or flavouring such as chocolate or coffee. They areoften set in individual moulds and are served cold. They may be stabilised using gelatine or Gum tragacanth may be substituted for gelatine

For the gardemanger chef, mousse is a fully cooked basic ingredient which is pureed, bound with gelatine or fat and lightened with an aerator of whipped cream or egg whites. The term is also used to describe preparations which are either hot or cold, for which the basic structures remains the same.

PREPERATION

Hot Mousse or cold mousse has three basic components:

Base: The base can be Poultry, ham, Meat, fish, shellfish, foigras truffle, vegetables,etc. the base provides flavour, colour, body and character to the finished product.

Binder: This provides the structure to the finished product. This is done by theinclusion of aspic jelly or gelatine which will set as the finished product is chilled, or cold flavourful fat such as butter, will also contribute to the same.

Aeration: The lightening of the mousse which is accomplished with whippedcream and/or whipped egg whites. Whipped egg white adds lightness without increasing the calories much.

The usual proportion of the basic components would be 1 kg of base: 30 gms of gelatine + 1 cup of water : 750 gms of prepared aeration.

RECIEPE of fish Mousse (HOT)

Pound 500 gms, fish fillets in a mortar sprinkle with fine salt and freshly ground pepper, then blend in 2-3 egg whites. Rub this forcemeat through a sieve and refrigerate fill almost setting. At this stage add thick fresh cream. Adjust seasonings, pour mousse into lightly oiled mould, cover and secure, then poach gently in a bain-marie in the oven at 190° (375° f). Wait for ten minutes before turning out, serve warm, coated with fish sauce.

MAKING OF COLD MOUSSE

Preparing a cold mousse is a tricky affair and requires the service of a skilled chef.

However, if these below mentioned seven steps are followed it will minimize the risk.

Moulds – should be prepared first to ensure that the mousse can be moulded before it sets.Individual moulds, such as ramekins or small timbales should be lubricated or lined in a manner consistent with the character of the mousse. Lining means coating the moulds with a thin layer of aspic jelly. Decorations are laid on the layer of aspic jelly and the mousse mixture is poured into moulds. When the mousse is unmolded, it is a finished product both coated and decorated. Alternately it could be moulded, allowed to set, then turned out and coated or garnished, as needed.

Base: - Preparation of the base is the next step. Fully cooking the base product ismandatory; however, overcooking will result in a dry texture and poor mouth feel. The base product should then be pureed. The consistency of the pureed mixture can be adjusted with one of the following items: Veloute, mayonnaise, béchamel, cream or some similar product. The resulting puree should have a smooth, velvety texture. If cream is used it must be added near the end of the puree process to avoid breaking the cream. The puree should be slightly over seasoned to allow for the aeration which will be added. For the highest quality preparations the pureed mixture should be put through a fine sieve. Modern equipment replaces hand sieving.

Binder: The amount of gelatine to be added with be proportional to the amount ofbase to be set. The liquid to be added is limited only by what is suitable to the character of the mouse and the setting power of the gelatine. Rehydrate the dry gelatine by sprinkling it evenly into the cool liquid. Allow sufficient time for the gelatine granules to absorb the liquid (bloom) then place the bloomed gelatine over a bain marie until melted.

Wisk: The binder into the base, both the base and the binder should be at room temp forthis step.

AERATION: Will require the whipping of either cream or egg whites or bothwhipped separately to soft peaks.

Fold: the aeration into the base/ binder mixture. If the base mixture is to thick orcold, the aeration will be deflated.

Mould: the mouse before it starts to set.

Velvety smooth texture

Light and airy consistency which is not heavy or rubbery no airpockets.

A delicate but distinctive flavour

If a mouse mixture is moulded into multi portion terrines or timbales, resulting item is referred to as a Mouse. If the mousse, mixture is made richer by addition of cream and is moulded into single portion timbales or moulds or shaped into quenelles, the resulting item is termed a Mousseline

NON EDIBLE DISPLAYS & CENTERPIECES In French they are known as "Piece Montée".

Originally a large ornamental item of patisserie used to decorate the table at a banquet or a party. It usually reflects the theme of the occasion. In France, it is still popular for a wedding or baptism and displays the artistic skills of the confectionary trade. It was very popular in the Middle Ages, today a simple type of piece montée is the croquembouche, made of profiteroles filled with cream which has been sweetened and suitably flavoured, glazed and decorated with fancy sugar work.

Although food holds the spotlight in all buffet presentation, the objective of buffet planning must be to achieve visual beauty both in the artistic presentation of each item of edible food and in the arrangement of the many dishes on the buffet table. Nothing heightens the beauty of the buffet more than an outstanding centre piece (piece montée) which may be made of ice, tallow or other such materials. The term non-edible is used generally, to indicate that the centre piece is not meant for consumption along with the rest of the food on the buffet.

The guest should be able to identify the theme of the buffet at a glance, just by observing the non-edible decorations that provide eye-catching background for the presentation. A non-edible decorative display piece should be a work of art, always in good taste, whether the figure is made of ice sugar, tallow or any other material. The may be classified into:-

ARTISTIC DISPLAYS	FOOD DISPLAYS
1. Ice carvings	1.Bread Displays
2. Fallow Displays	2.Cheese & wine displays
3. Butter/Margarine sculptures	3.Seafood Displays
4. Salt dough sculptures (Saltilage)	4.Pastry Display
5. Sugar craft (pastillage)	5.Spice Display
6. Chocolate Mouldings	6.Fruit & Veg.arrangements
7.Fruit and veg. carvings	7.Suckling pig Roast turkey Hams
	8 Chaud Froid
	9 Aspicm cut outs

ICE CARVING

The Ice sculpture is the highlight of any buffet, and its focal point. Ice can be carved into any shapes, size or figure that fits the theme or occasion. For e.g. Christmas-Santa Clause, Anniversary- a heart.

The essentials of Ice-carvings

Use 100-300 pound block of ice 40 inches high by 20 inches wide by 10 inches thick.

A pair of ice tongs for moving ends and handling the ice.

An ice shaver with 3 to 4 prongs used to carve out the details and do the small cuttings on the block of ice.

An ice pick is used to split block of ice.

A hand saw is used to remove large cuts of ice or to make rough outlines

Chisels ranging in size from ½ to 2 inches.

A good pair of gloves which have metal finger tips to prevent accidents.

A variety of templates

An electric chain saw-(optional)

Salt is used for mending broken pieces of ice.

Points to be kept in mind

The optimum temperature for ice carving is 28°F or less. An ice block will melt at the rate of half to an inch per hour at room temperature.

Such ice carvings must have a base that is at least 6 inches high, for stability.

If a piece of ice breaks off dip each broken edge into salt and press back together for a few minutes till it holds.

The table used for the carving must be sturdy to support the weight of the ice.

The carved ice block should be placed in specially constructed pans wider that the base of the wooden block, on which, the ice carving will rest securely on top of the wooden block.

Coloured rotating lights could produce dramatic effects.

The ice sculpture could be placed on a rotating turn table.

The pan under the ice sculpture on display should be decorated with a linen cloth, flowers, ferns or other decorative material.

TALLOW WORK: Patterns and sculptures made with animal fat creating an eye- catching tallow piece is always time consuming, and should be planned well in advance. Such displays can be used over and over again but they should be covered with translucent wrap when not in use as dust tends to stick to them.

To be successful in the execution of a tallow display, the person making the display should have a model or a photograph of the piece to be made. In general a formula made up in the following proportions work well in tallow displays: 1/3 beeswax, 1/3 paraffin wax, 1/3 beef fat the quantity of fat may be increased to make it more pliable.

A solid secure wooden base must be used.

BUTTER AND MARGARINE CARVINGS:-Very often in place of tallow, butter or margarine could be used, margarine is more preferred as it is easier to handle, and it could either be moulded or sculpted.

CHOCOLATE MOULDINGS Tempered chocolate can be used to make figures which can be attractively arranged to be used as centre pieces during festive times like Christmas and Easter, or may be used to adorn the dessert buffet.

SALTILAGE:-These are salt dough used for sculptures. Combine 1 cup of water and 1 cup of cornstarch. Mix well over medium heat, stirring constantly, to a very thick paste. Knead 2 cups of salt into the hot mixture. It could be coloured e.g. soya sauce for brown colour. When the sculpture is finished it must be painted with cornstarch mixture. Saltilage dries quickly and tends to crack easily.

Fruit & vegetable carvings Very attractive centre pieces can be made by carvings various shapes out of fruits andvegetables. Large pumpkins, melon and such vegetable vegetables can be used as containers or carved into objects such as boat, ships, birds etc. various flowers can be made, the variety in colour of fruits and vegetables adds to a lot of eye appeal and the presentation of the centre pieces. Care should be taken not to use non food items such as pins, staples, toothpicks, drawing pins to hold the arrangement in place. Water may be sprayed to make to look fresh.

SUGAR CRAFT "PASTILLAGE"

This could include (1) Pulled Sugar (2) Poured sugar (3) Blown sugar(4) Spun sugar

Cooked sugar can be used in various forms to provide stunning works of art that could adorn a dessert buffet.

SandwichesIn simple terms, sandwiches may be described as two pieces of bread with some filling between them. However, in modern times where time is limited, sandwiches have become extremely popular and can range from delicate tea sandwich to traditional Scandinavian smørrebrod. They may be served cold or hot, plain or grilled or even toasted.

As the story goes sandwich was invented by an English Earl whose name was John Montague, the fourth Earl of Sandwich and is named after him. He was a compulsive gambler and found no time to have an elaborate meal and would ask for a piece of meat to be put between two slices of bread and served to him.Sandwiches may be served as snacks, for breakfast, tea parties, barbeques, entree, cocktail parties, buffets, etc. In addition, may be had as a whole meal by them.

Parts of a sandwich:-

Bread.
Spread
Filling
Garnish
Accompaniment.

BreadBread may be sliced; they may be plain, grilled, fried or toasted. They may be cut into different shapes; however, this must be done after filling.

Types of bread used:-

Loaf bread
Brioche
French bread
Brown bread
Burger buns
Danish rye bread, etc.

In case of sweet sandwiches:-

Genoese
Fruit bread
Meringue
Croissants, and
Puff/short crust pastry.

Spreads

Spreads are substances applied on bread:-
To moisten the surface of bread.
To add to taste and flavour.
For binding
To add to nutrition

To prevent sogginess

To suffice, when there is no filling.

Types of Spread Most spreads are savoury butters, mixed with salt, pepper, Worcestershire sauce, tobacco sauce, etc. These butters should not be frozen but at room temperature and slightly creamed for easy spreading. Some of these butters are:

Lemon butter

Onion butter

Olive butter

Paprika butter

Mayonnaise

English mustard

Chutney butter

Lobster butter, etc.

FILLINGSFillings are foodstuff, which is kept either on top or in between the slices of bread. It should be crisp, colourful, fresh, dry, juicy, clean and hygienic. There are types and types of fillings the variety are endless and amazing, but they could be grouped as meat, fish, poultry, egg, chesses, raw & cooked vegetables, cereals, fruits, etc.

TYPES OF FILLINGs

Some examples for cold sandwiches

Chopped hard-boiled eggs mixed with crumbled blue chesse with a little milk.

Cold meat loaf slices mixed with sour cream & horseradish.

Tuna salad with ripe avocado slices.

Cream chesse with chopped ripe olives.

Pan-fried shredded steak topped with crisp onion slices.

Shredded grilled fish topped with seafood cocktail sauce and lettuce.

Stir-fried shredded chicken topped with green onions, bean sprouts and a dash of soya sauce.

GARNISHESGarnishes are important for an attractive appearance and are necessary for proper eye appeal. Some garnishes used effectively, are parsley-sprigs, pimentos, tomatoes, olives, angelica cut in various shapes, etc. Fruits such as lemon, pears, pineapples, etc. add to the appearance. Garnishes may also be placed on the plate along with the sandwich, which also serves as an accompaniment for e.g. slices of tomatoes, lettuce leaves, pickled onions, gherkins, capers, etc.

ACCOMPANIMENTSThe accompaniments for sandwiches may be hot or cold. The common accompaniments are Wafers, French fried potatoes, salads like Cole slaw, red cabbage salad, Russian salad, Woldorf salad etc. Propriety sauces like Tabasco sauce, Tomato ketchup, H.P. sauce etc. may be served along with sandwiches.

CLASSIFICATION OF SANDWICHES

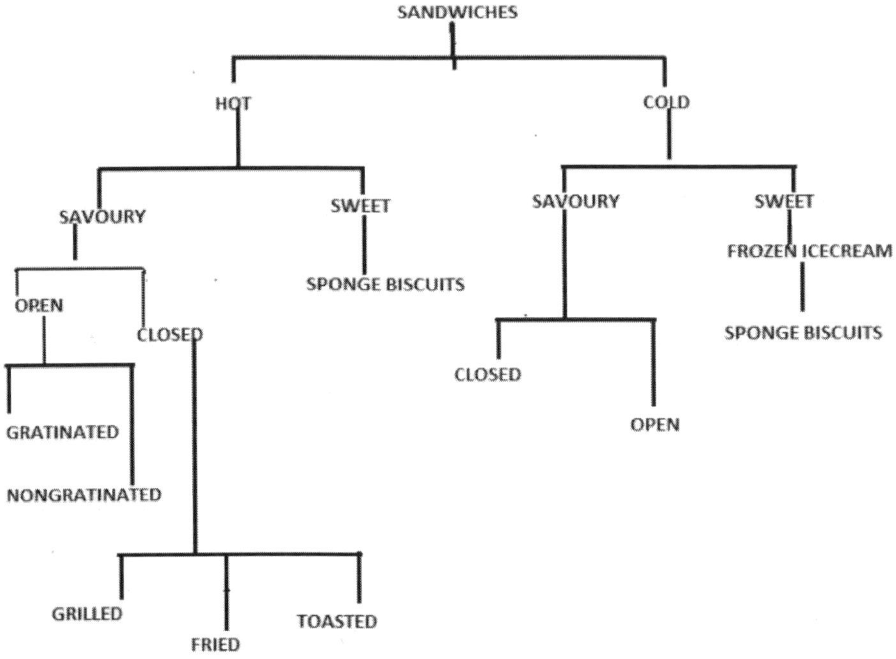

Points to be noted in sandwich preperation

Use stale one-day-old bread, which has a firm and a close fine texture for sandwiches

For rolled and pinwheel sandwiches use fresh bread.

For toasting use left over bread.

Use enriched and variety of breads for a wider choice •Keep loaves sliced for speedy service.

- Use adjacent slices of bread so that they are of even sizes and can be easily cut and wrapped.
- Since modern breads have high water content, they are packed whilst still warm and therefore mould could infect the bread. Before using we should discard bread having blue/green patches.
- Avoid removing the crusts. This save time and give more apparent value, prevents bread from staling and breaking during service and handling.
- Cream the butter for easy spreading.
- Use only fresh ingredients
- Take care in matching the ingredients eg. Pineapple slices with white meat.
- Ingredients with high moisture content should -be added just before service.
- Follow the rules of storage
- Since sandwich preparation involves skill & speed, planning is very important.
- Make sandwiches "to order" if possible.

- Store all breads in original wrappers, except for the loaves in current use store the wrapped breads' on a clean shelf well away from the floor.
- Handle bread and fillings as little as possible during all processes, avoiding the use of hands if tools or equipment can do the job efficiently.
- Make prepared fillings only in such quantities as will be used during one serving period. Hold them at 40^0 F or lower. Avoid leftovers. Never hold over any perishable foods or fillings that have been at room temperatures for four hours or more. Never expose fillings at room temperatures for long periods, as food poisoning bacteria grow rapidly in many sandwich fillings and even in bread moistened by mayonnaise or salad dressings, etc. •Serve unwrapped sandwiches immediately.
- Immediately following preparation, wrap all sandwiches not to be served at once, in semi/permeable, moisture/vapour 'proof; paper, refrigerate immediately. Never use a dampened cloth or towel to keep bread or sandwiches moist because this procedure provides an ideal media for rapid growth of harmful bacteria.
- Sandwiches may be stored for 12-24 hours at temperatures under 40°F, if they have been prepared carefully and quickly under rigid sanitary conditions. The best hold temperature is 40°F.
- Avoid stacking sandwiches in large units or placing them in cardboard boxes as these methods may affect the quality.

The danger incubation zone for most food poisoning bacteria is from 40°F. to 60°F. Maximum time limit for holding sandwich fillings at incubation temperature is four hours. Do not risk food poisoning by extending this. Display sandwiches only in such quantities as can be used during one serving period.

TYPES OF SANDWICHES

OPEN SANDWICH

These are made with one slice of bread and the filling is visible in this type of sandwiches.

CLOSED SANDWICHES

These are made with two slices of bread with fillings in between. There are many variations for e.g.

SWEET SANDWICH

Prepared with thin slices of stale Brioche and filled with chopped fruits or jam or thick sweet custard.

SANDWICH CAKE

These look like iced layer cakes and for these round bread loaves are used. They are sliced in two or three round slices and different savoury spreads/fillings are used and they are iced on top with soft icing containing butter, cheese, etc. it is cut into wedges.

PINWHEEL

The top crust is taken out of the sandwich loaf, it is then sliced length wise and butter and soft filling spread evenly. It is then rolled firmly. This sandwich is cut into roundels.

CLUB SANDWICH

This sandwich is served hot and consists of two buttered slices of toast. One slice is the base on which sliced cooked chicken, egg, lettuce, tomatoes, grilled bacon or ham may beplaced. The other slice is placed on top, pressed firmly, trimmed and decorated and served between folds of a paper napkin.

DOUBLE DECKER

In this sandwich, three slices are used, the middle slice is buttered on both sides and filling is placed in both the layers. It is pressed firmly, trimmed and held together with a cocktail stick with stuffed olive or cherry.

YIELD

Definition: The amount of a product that remains after the processing, performed as required, with-in an establishment is called the "yield" of that product.

In order to determine the yield of a given product the product must be weighed at the onset of the yield test. The formula for calculating yield is as follows:

Remaining weight x 100 = Yield %.

Original weight

A total yield test would require a product to be tested from the original state of purchase until it leaves the kitchen as a finished product to be served to the guest. This is done to determine the true food cost of the the final edible amount of the product as compared to the purchased original weight.

The types of Tests that are necessary in Meat and Fish products are:

TRIM TEST

A trim test determines the amount of the excess fat or unusable meat thathas been left on by the supplier. Fully trimmed Joint x 100 = Trimming yield % Untrimmed Joint

Boning yield: A product may be partially or fully boned.

Boneless weight x 100 = Boning yield

With bone weight

Yield by carcass weight

Usable meat x 100= Carcass yield%

Whole carcass weight

Cooking Yields: All meats will shrink to some extent during cooking, due to loss of moisture andmelting of fat. The amount of shrinkage depends largely on the amount of cooking time, as well as on the temperature at which the product was cooked. The method of cooking may also affect the shrinkage. Moist heat cooking may result in less moisture being lost, low temperature 120°C to 150°C is generally recommended as it results in less shrinkage from both moisture and fat.

Weight after cooking x 100= cooking yield %

Weight prior to cooking

Serving Yields: The Actual no. of portions that can be served form a joint, multiplied by the portion size determines the net serving weight. Yield is necessary to accurately arrive at or calculate the selling price of a product for e.g. a chef would bring a carcass of mutton and then butcher it into various joints and cuts. In order to do this he would need to buy the carcass, you would need a place as well as chefs to butcher it into various cuts, and then store it in a freezer until it is needed. All this cost money.

This method would be inefficient unless the entire carcass was utilized. In the modern context, with improved technology and services the chef may need only, to purchase those items directly from the market instead of buying the carcass, or he can outsource the work, thereby reducing the cost.

ARABIC

Arabic food refers to the food of the Arabian Peninsula, the largest country being Saudi Arabia, located in the southern region of the Middle East, which covers2149700 sq. Km., which is three quarters of the Arabian peninsula. It is bordered by the Persian Gulf and U.A.E. to the east, Oman and Yemen to the south, the Red Sea to the west and Jordan, Iraq and Kuwait to the north.

Sunni Muslims make up ninety percent of Saudi Arabia's 25 million inhabitants, the majority is of tribal ancestry. The indigenous Bedouin tribe's food culture and the cultural influence of Islam forms the main characteristic of Arabian food.

The Bedouin tribe were nomadic herdsmen who lived in the deserts of Arabia and North Africa. The Bedouin existence depended on their herds and flocks. The camel was the supreme possession providing transport, milk for food and beverage, meat, hair, hides and dung for fuel. The camel allowed men to conquer the desert as they are capable of sustained travel in the desert. It was because of the camel these Arabs became the middle men in the caravan spice trade. These trade links brought spices and seasonings from Africa, India, Far East and Iraq and supplied them to the European countries.

The Bedouin food culture was based on the simple scarce food available in the region and their famed hospitality culture of honouring the guest. The main dish is centred on meat, chicken, fish or prawns, cooked in a sauce or roasted, baked or grilled, as in kebabs, with rice accompaniments. Simply dressed salads including peppery cess and cucumbers are common. Flat bread, curds and pickles accompany meats.

Islam, which had taken roots in the 6th century A.D., has dominated the Muslim culture by initiating strict culinary taboos which forbids ingesting alcohol, pork and blood. Lamb is the most popular meat and Khouzi the national dish is a whole spit roasted lamb stuffed with chicken, eggs and spiced rice.

In Muslim culture mixing of sexes is discouraged, men and women dine separately; males eat before women and children.

Dates are commonly used in sweet and savoury dishes.

Coffee is the main drink and has strong association with the renowned hospitality of the people. It is prepared from finely ground, well roasted beans and may be flavoured with cardamons.

Originally, the Arabsof the Arabian Peninsularelied heavily on a diet of dates,wheat,barley,riceand meat, with little variety and heavy emphasis on yoghurtproducts, such as labneh(yoghurt without butterfat).

There is a strong emphasis on the following items in Arabian cuisine:

- Meat:lamband chickenare the most used, with beefand camelused to a lesser degree. Other poultryis used in some regions, and in coastal areas, porkis completely prohibited— for MuslimArabs, being both a cultural tabooand prohibited under Islamic law; many Christian Arabsalso avoid pork as they have never acquired a taste for it, although this is often not the case in Lebanon, where cold cuts of ham are frequently consumed in Christian neighbourhoods.[1]

- Dairy products: dairy products are widely used, especially yoghurtand white cheese. Butterand creamare also used extensively.
- Herbsand spices:mintand thyme(often in a mix called za'atar) are widely and almost universally used; spices are used much less than the Indian cuisine, but the amount and types generally varies from region to region. Some of the included herbs and spices are sesame,saffron,turmeric,garlic,cumin,cinnamon, and sumac. Spice mixtures include baharat.
- Beverages: hot beverages are used more than cold, coffeebeing on the top of the list, mostly in the Gulf countries. However, teais also served in many Arab countries. In Egypt and Jordan, for instance, tea is a more important hot beverage than coffee.
- Grains:riceis the staple and is used for most dishes; wheatis the main source for bread.Bulgurand semolinaare also used extensively.
- Legumes:lentilsare widely used as well as fava beansand chickpeas(garbanzo beans).
- Vegetablesand fruits: Arabic cuisine also favors vegetables such as cucumbers,eggplant(aubergine), zucchini(courgette), okraand onions, and fruits(primarily citrus) which are often used as seasonings for entrees. Olivesas well as dates,figsand pomegranateare also widely used.
- Nuts:almonds,pine nuts,pistachios, and walnutsare often included.
- Greens: parsleyand mintare popular as seasonings in many dishes, while spinachand mulukhiyah(leaves of plants of the Corchorusgenus) are used in cooked dishes.
- Dressings and sauces: The most popular dressings include various combinations of olive oil,lemon juice,parsley, and/or garlic, and tahini(sesame paste). Labaneh, thinned yoghurt, is often seasoned with mint and onion or garlic, and served as a sauce with various dishes.

Notably, many of the same spices used in Arabian cuisine are also those emphasized in Indian cuisine. This is a result of heavy trading and historical ties between the two regions.

CultureEssential to any cooking in the Arabian Peninsula is the concept of hospitality and generosity. Meals are generally large family affairs, with much sharing and a great deal of warmth over the dinner table. Formal dinners and celebrations generally involve large quantities of lamb, and every occasion entails large quantities of Arabic coffee. In an average Gulf Arab state household, a visitor might expect a dinner consisting of a very large platter, shared commonly, with a vast amount of rice, incorporating lamb or chicken, or both, as separate dishes, with various stewed vegetables, heavily spiced, sometimes with a tomato based sauce. Most likely there would be several other less hearty items on the side. Tea would certainly accompany the meal, as it is almost constantly consumed. Coffee would be included as well.

Structure of meals There are two basic structures for meals in the Arab world, one regular and one specific for the month of Ramadan.

Breakfast Cafés often offer croissantsfor breakfast. Breakfast is often a quick meal consisting of bread and dairy products with tea and sometimes with jam. The most used is labnehand cream,. Labneh is served with olives, dried mintand drizzled with olive oil. Pastries such as manaqeesh, sfiha,fatayerand kahi are sometimes eaten for breakfast. Flat breadwith olive oiland za'taris also popular. Most Arab families also consume hummusand falafelwith pita bread.

Lunch Lunch is considered the main meal of the day and is traditionally eaten after the noon prayer. It is the meal for which the family comes together and, when entertaining, it is the meal of choice to invite guests to. Rarely do meals have different courses; however, saladsand maza (an appetizer) are served as side dishes to the main meal. The latter usually consists of a portion of meat,poultryor fish, a portion of rice, lentil, bread or bageland a portion of cooked vegetables in addition to the fresh ones with the maza and salad. The vegetables and meat are usually cooked together in a sauce Drinks are not necessarily served with the food; however, there is a very wide variety of drinks such as shineena(or laban), Karakaden, Naque'e Al Zabib, Irq soos, Tamr Hindi as well as fruit juices. During the 20th century, carbonated beverages and fruit based drinks, sold by supermarkets, have also become very popular.

Dinner Dinner is traditionally the lightest meal, although in modern times and due to changing lifestyles, dinner has become more important.

Ramadan meals In addition to the two meals mentioned hereafter, during Ramadansweets are consumed much more than usual; sweets and fresh fruits are served between these two meals. Although most sweets are made all year round such as knafeh, baklawa and basbousa, some are made especially for Ramadan, such as Qatayef.

Futuur Futuur (also called iftar, Afur in Somali) or fast-breaking, is the meal taken at duskwhen the fast is over. The meal consists of three courses: first, an odd number of dates based on Islamictradition. This is followed by a soup, the most popular being lentil soup, but a wide variety of soups such as chicken, oats, *freeka*(a soup made from a form of whole wheat and chicken broth), potato, maash and others are also offered. The third course is the main dish, usually eaten after an interval when Maghreb prayer is conducted. The main dish is mostly similar to lunch, except that cold drinks are also served.

Sahur Sahar is the meal eaten just before the dawnwhen fastingmust begin. It is eaten to help the person make it through the day with enough energy.

BREAD The invention of leavened bread is attributed to the Egyptians. The Greeks baked on grids in an oven like stricture. Romans cooked their bread is household ovens made of brick and earth. It was in the Middle Ages that the bakery trade began to develop, bread became very varied and many different kinds of bread were produced.

Definition: Bread is food made from flour and water dough with yeast, which is fermented, kneaded and baked in the oven. The action of yeast gives bread its characteristic texture and flavour.

Bread is the only food, which, like wine, is present on the table from start to finish of any meal; bread constitutes the traditional accompaniment to all dishes. It is also the basic ingredient in sandwiches, canapés, toasts, croutons & breadcrumbs. In addition to this it is used widely in the preparations of the other dishes like, soups, gazpacho & garlic soup, panadas, stuffing's & forcemeats, timbales, charlottes &

pudding and even in sauces. Good bread must have a crisp crust, an attractive golden colour and as soft crumb. Growing state to quickly is a sign of bad quality. Most bread should be served fresh but not hot. A daily intake of 300 gms provides 125gms carbohydrates 25gms proteins, 2 gms fat calcium, phosphorus, magnesium potassium and it gives 750 calories.

The baking/making of bread comprises of 3 main operations kneading fermentation and baking.

The following ingredients are necessary for bread making

1.Maida

2.Yeast

3.Sugar

4.Fat and

5.Salt

1. Refined flour or Maida Only strong and not weak flour is used for making bread. Strong flour has reference to the character of flour. Wheat flour contains both soluble and insoluble proteins. Proteins along with other components join when water is added. When this occurs, two of the insoluble proteins namely glutenin and gliadin join in the presence of water forming a tough, somewhat rubbery material called gluten. Glutenin gives solidity to the product whilst gliadin is the binding imparting the soft, sticky character to gluten. The gluten of strong flour is tough, resists extension is capable of withstanding prolonged periods of fermentation without breaking down producing good loafs. Flour containing such gluten is capable of absorbing a high percentage of water. Diastatic enzymes present in the wheat flour affect the gassing power of the flour. If flour is deficient in diastase the final proving of the bread will be unsatisfactory. On the other hand, if too much diastatic action occurs the bread will still be unsatisfactory having a strictly crumb.

SALT Why salt is used in Bread making? Bread made without salt is insipid and flavourless; therefore, salt makes bread palatable and appetizing. The quantity of salt needed is also the right quantity to exercise adequate control over the speed of yeast action (1 Kg of flour is to 30 gm of salt) If too much salt is added the bread will be too salty for pleasant eating whilst there will also be slowing down of yeast action. Dough with too little salt in them suffers because of the lack of control over yeast activity and fermentation, allowing the production of excessive acidity. Sat has a physical effect on the gluten of flour. In reasonable quantities, it strengthens gluten and increases its resistance to the general softening effects of fermentation. Too much salt will completely rob it of its power of holding gas.

If salt is not added at all, then the yeast in the dough will be able to consume excessive quantities of sugar during its uncontrolled speedy action during fermentation that there may be insufficient sugar left at baking time to give perfect crust colour. Loaves made from dough containing too little salt will lack volume because the gluten has not been strengthened sufficiently. The weak gluten strands will break down giving crumbly bread with large holes in texture.

Dough made with rather too much salt will have toughened gluten, which will have been insufficiently ripened, producing bread of subnormal volume and with unsightly holes in the texture.

Yeast Yeast is living micro organism, the one used for bread making is known as baker's yeast or scientifically as ¯Saccharomycees Cerevisiae . Like all living things yeast can only work well between certain temperatures. The ideal and optimum temp, for the working of yeast is between 78^0 and 82^0 F. It works steadily at 76^{0}F but rather too slowly. Above 84°F the speed of fermentation is very great but fermentation of dough may be undesirable. Above 140^{0}F the proteins in yeast get coagulated, the cells cease to function and then die. Yeast grows better in a slightly acid medium.

Yeast may be stored in a refrigerator at 36to 40^0 F. If no refrigerator is available, remove from packet and press it into a clean, dry earthenware vessel. Stand the jar in cold water and cover with a piece of clean muslin the ends of which dip into water. For fermentation to occur normally dough must be made at a suitable temperature. In very cold weather very hot water may be needed. But under no conditions should the water temperature be above 110^{0}F. If salt comes into direct contact with yeast in sufficient concentrations the yeast will be destroyed. This is because salt will deprive the yeast cells of its water. The salt should be dissolved in water separate from the yeast solution. When salt is approx 3% of the solution its effect on yeast is not deadly but merely restrictive. After making dough at the right temperature it is essential to see that the dough retains that temperature during fermentation. If it becomes chilled yeast action will slow down. The dough should be protected from draught of air especially cold air. They should preferably be fermented in bowls, which are bad conductors of heat. **Fats** Fats used in small quantities, act as a gluten lubricant, the strands of which then slide over one another and so appear to extend more easily, and the dough ripens more readily. The crumb is made moister, is wither and more even in texture. Crust are thinner and more biscuit like owing to the shortening properties of fats, and the general build of the loaf is better. If fats are used in heavy quantities it causes bread to be clammy and alter its eating qualities. The undesirable characteristics that would be apparent when using large quantities of fat can be counteracted by the use of milk powder. Milk powder imparts bloom to the crust, makes the crumb a delicate creamy yellow colour but makes the bread crumbly. Where both fat and milk are used the crumb is creamy, soft, and even in texture crusts are thin and short eating and the loaf volume very satisfactory.

SUGAR There must be sufficient sugar in the dough at the final proving stage from which the yeast can generate gas. Sucrose or glucose may be added to dough if greater gassing powers are required. Therefore sugar is needed for final proving to give sufficient volume to the loaf and for caramelization on the crust of the bread during baking. The quantity of sugar used in dough should be small. Sugar has a dispersing action on the gluten of flour and large quantities can completely destroy its tenacity and extensibility.

Bread Making There are many satisfactory methods of making bread given below are details of each of the methods that may be employed for making bread

I Straight Dough Method When the whole of the flour, yeast, salt, water yeast food and enriching materials are taken and, at one operation, amalgamated by hand or machine into dough, the method is called the straight dough method of bread making. It is the least complicate of all dough making processes. The greater the quantity of yeast the shorter the length of time the dough will require in which to reach maturity and vice-versa. Excellent bread can be made by suing extra yeast in a cool dough and adding a little extra salt. However to obtain good results it is not advisable to speed up fermentation by use of high temperature and a small quantity of salt.

II Delayed Salt Method A simple but very effective variation of the straight dough process is the delayed salt method. In this the whole of the ingredients except the salt are mixed together to make the dough which is then allowed to ferment for approx 30 min the salt is then sieved over the surface of the dough and thoroughly mixed. By this process stronger flour are ripened more quickly and extra flavour is produced in the bread. This is achieved because no salt is present for most of the fermentation period hence yeast works more rapidly as do acid forming bacteria present in the dough.

III FERMENT AND DOUGH Ferment is a thin liqueur prepared at a suitable temp containing all the essential food that is required by yeast. It is generally prepared with only a portion of the water that must eventually be used to make the finished dough. All he yeast, yeast food and some of the flour are mixed in to the selected quantity of water and a period to time allowed to elapse during which the yeast can set to work and reach an active, vigorous condition before it is called upon to undertake the more serious and difficult work of fermenting the whole of the flour. Ferment offers yeast a period to recuperate, so that when the remaining ingredients are added to make the dough it can get on with the heavier work efficiently. The ferment is usually allowed to work until it has risen up the vessel in which it is contained to the fullest limits of the extensibility of the gluten. When this point is reached and passed the gluten strands break and the mixture subsides. The ferment is then ready for dough making.

IVSponge & Dough A quarter of the amount of the total flour needed for the final dough is removed and mixed with sufficient water to make very a soft dough. Into this mixture a small quantity yeast and salt are mixed and allowed to ferment slowly over a long period. The time can be regulated by the amount of yeast used and the temperature at which the sponge is set. When the sponge has cradled the production of an increased army of yeast cells, the remaining ingredients are added and the dough is made.

V Flying sponge

Instead of making a sponge to lie for many hours a similar mixture can be prepared with larger quantities of yeast that are normal for straight dough process, and allowed to lie for an hour. They are referred to as flying sponges because it takes less time to prepare the dough.

VI No time dough method In this method dough is not fermented in the usual manner. It is allowed to ferment for a short period so the twin function of fermentation i.e. production of gas and conditioning of gluten are achieved to some extent by increasing the amount of yeast and by vigorously beating the dough using mechanical dough mixers so that the dough becomes a little slack and warm. The dough is then shaped and directly deposited in bread moulds for final proving before they are baked. It is possible to get a good product using this method but the product has poor keeping quality and lacks aroma due to short fermentation time, the gluten and starch are not conditioned to hold moisture and there is no flavour because flavour producing bi-products of fermentation are absent because of increased quantity of yeast present.

The bread may have a strong yeast flavour.

Staling of Bakery Products and Mold Infectnion There are three ways in which bakery products stale. They are, Starch Retrogradation (firming of the crumb), getting infected by molds and rope; See Below. In simple terms, staling of crumb (firming of crumb) is the process the starch molecules go through when they shrink upon cooling. Starch molecule consists of a very long chain of Carbon, Hydrogen and Oxygen that are stretched out when warm and feel soft. Upon cooling, the chain shrinks and thus become firm which is called staling. You have probably experienced that when a stale product is warmed, it becomes soft. The starch chain has stretched again. Upon cooling, it shrinks again and become firm.

Anti-Staling Ingredients:

1. Emulsifiers. For the past several years bakers used emulsifiers called bread softeners to produce bread that will remain soft for a longer period of time. It is added to the dough during mixing. Some of the more common ones are monoglycrides, calcium stearoyl lactylate, and sodium stearoyl lactylate. The softening action takes place after the bread is baked. Also, Potato bread will resist staling because potatoes act as anti-staling ingredients to some degree. Some anti-staling ingredients also perform as dough conditioners or dough strengtheners.
2. Enzymes. Enzyme manufacturers are hard at work on generic engineering and protein engineering producing enzymes to extend the shelf life of bread many fold. In a paper presented at the 1999 American Society of Baking's Annual Convention, it was stated that some of these enzymes are available now. However, since every baker wants to have one better, enzyme manufacturers will continue to work on developing better ones. It was also stated that there is a lag time of between 2 and 3 years between the time a specific enzyme is identified and actually having it available for the baker to use.

   Advantages of Using Enzymes instead of Chemicals. Since enzymes are produced from natural ingredients, they will find greater acceptance by the housewife than when chemicals are used.
3. Mold and Mold Inhibitors. Sanitation plays a very important role in preventing mold in bread. Mold spores do not survive baking temperatures. The interior of the loaf, when it comes out of the oven is about 210 to 212 degrees F. which will destroy any mold spores which may be present in the dough. Therefore, bread

and other bakery products can only be contaminated after they leave the oven.

Some of the more dangerous areas for mold contmination are storage rooms, and slicing machine blades which come in direct contact with the interior of the loaf where there is an abundant supply of food and moisture. Mold spores also thrive in dark places. You can extend the length of time that it takes bakery products to mold by several days by using Mold Inhibitors such as Calcium Propionate for yeast raised doughs and sodium propionate in chemically leavened products. Propionates are present in many foods, but in very small amounts. Swiss Cheese, however is an exception. For this reason, Swiss Cheese rarely molds, unless it is improperly developed. Propionates may be obtained by the oxidization of propyl alcohol, forming propionic acid. The propionic acid is in turn combined with other chemicals to form the well known Sodium and Calcium propionates sold under different Trades Names. Mold Inhibitors react as an alkaline in doughs, and since yeast doesn't like an alkaline condition, Mineral Yeast Foods containing monocalcium phosphate are added to the dough. Monocalcium Phosphate reacts as an acid in doughs therefore counter-acting the alkaline which is formed by the propionates. Also, vinegar can be used at the rate of about 1 pint per 100 pounds of flour. Inhibitors are called inhibitors, because not enough is used to kill the mold. They only retard the growth of molds. Bread will mold eventually if kept in a warm moist invironment. The amounts of Calcium Propionates to use in bread varies with the climate, season of the year, or type of product. Dark Breads require more than White Breads. For average climates, 2.5 to 3.5 ounces are used per 100 pounds of flour in White Breads and 4.0 to 5.0 ounces are used in Dark Breads.

Types and Color of Molds. There are many different types of molds and they have different colors. Mold spores are practically everywhere, because they are very tiny and are carried in the air. They are so tiny that they can only be seen under a microscope. Mold Spores are like seeds that you plant in the garden. When they come in contact with the proper food, moisture and warmth, the spores produce mold plants which you can see with the naked eye.

Rope. Rope is a bread disease caused by the bacteria, Bacillus mesentericus. This disease breaks down the cells of the bread and leaves a sticky, pasty mass. When the crumb is pressed together, and pulled apart, it will stretch into long, sticky, web-like strands. The product will have the odor of over-ripe cantalope. The rope bacteria are too small to see with the naked eye, but they can be seen with a microscope. The bacteria can be present in the ingredients, especially flour and yeast. Unlike mold, rope spores are not destroyed by baking temperatures. Calcium propionate, sodium diacetate or one pint of vinegar per 100 pounds of flour can be used in bread doughs to increase the shelf life of the product. If the bakery is contaminated, thorough cleaning with special chemicals will be necessary and/or the bakery may have to be steam cleaned.

External Bread Faults

CUISINE OF SPAIN AND PORTUGAL

Situated in southwest Europe is the Iberian Peninsula which juts out from France and the Pyrenees mountain range into the waters of the Mediterranean Sea and the Atlantic Ocean. It lies between 10°W to 4°E longitude and 36°N to 43°N latitude and includes two countries Spain and Portugal with Spain covering more than three quarters of its landmass. The proximity of the two countries with their large coastline regions

Symptom	Causes
Crust too dark	- Oven temperature too high - Excessive milk or sugar. - Excessive baking time. - Over proofing.
Crust too light	- Oven temperature too low. - Insufficient milk or sugar. - Insufficient baking time. - Insufficient proofing. - Insufficient mixing.
Crust broken	- Insufficient proofing. - Insufficient liquid.
Crust too hard	- Oven temperature too high - Insufficient proofing. - Insufficient sugar or shortening. - Excessive steam. - Insufficient liquid. - Baking time too long.
Crust too soft	- Oven temperature too low - Excessive sugar/egg yolks/shortening. - Excessive oil/margarine as a wash. - Insufficient steam during baking. - Baking time too short or wrong bread machine setting.

Internal Bread Faults

Symptom	Causes
Coarse and irregular grain	- Improper mixing procedures. - Stiff batter. - Careless or poor depositing in the pans. - Oven too cool, (baked too slowly).
Dense grain	- Excessive liquid in the batter. - Improper mixing procedure.
Off-color breads	- Improper mixing procedure. - Oven too cool, (baked too slowly). - Unclean equipment.

If raisins, nuts or dried fruit sunk to the bottom	- Pieces of fruit were too large and too heavy. - Sugary syrup on the outside of the fruit was not washed off- causing the pieces of fruit to slide through the mixture as it heated. - Washed and dried fruit was not dusted with flour before being added to the mixture. - Bread mixture was over beaten or was too wet so it could not hold the fruit in place. - Oven temperature was too low, causing the mixture to melt before it set to hold the fruit in place.

General Bread Faults

Symptom	**Causes**
Batter over-flowed the pans	1. Wrong adjustments to recipes (too much 2. liquid, flour etc.) 3. Wrong size pan used. Mixture should fill 2/3 of pan.
Poor flavor	1. Improper mixing procedure. 2. Improper cleaning and greasing of the pans. 3. Faulty baking conditions. 4. Improper cleaning of the equipment.
Breads too tough	· Excessive mixing. · Batter too stiff (insufficient water). · Batter too thin (excessive water).
ˌacks body/structure	· Excessive mixing · Insufficient liquid.
)ries out too soon	· Excessive baking time. · Insufficient liquid. · Improper mixing procedures. Cooled in a drafty location.

and overlapping historical influences, bind their culinary traditions.

HISTORICAL AND CULTURAL INFLUENCES

Since ancient times waves of invasions of the Iberian Peninsula have radically influenced its food. In the north the Celtic people introduced pigs and pork which is still popular today. The Romans brought irrigation and olive trees which changed the economic conditions for the better. Arabs (Moors) who ruled the region for 800 years left an indelible mark on the food habits of the inhabitants. They brought in saffron, rice, citrus fruits, almonds, eggplant, eastern spices and this has had a dominant influence on the cuisine. Being very powerful seafarers both Spain and Portugal travelled all over the world in search of spices bringing back home spices like cloves, cinnamon, nutmeg, and black pepper. With the discovery of the New World i.e. Americas, foods such as chillies, corn, beans, tomatoes, vanilla, chocolate, squash, guava, pecans, pine nuts, turkey and potatoes were incorporated into their cuisine. Their cuisines amalgamated with the colonies they ruled.

SPAIN

The Spanish landscape is dominated by a high plateau surrounded and dissected by mountains, creating regional cuisines. Spain borders the Bay of Biscay, France, Andorra and Pyrenees to the north, the Mediterranean Sea and the Straits of Gibraltar to the east and south the Atlantic Ocean to the south and Portugal and Atlantic Ocean to the west. Agriculture is a significant part of the economy. Spanish population is almost 43 million and almost all are Roman Catholic, making Christian holidays occasions for culinary celebrations.

Although distinct dishes are found within culinary regions nationally the Frittata patata An egg omelette with potatoes is a clear favourite, Paella the rice, meat and seafood dish is another favourite so is Cocidas a brothy soup and gazpacho a cold cucumber soup and almond based sweets. The Spanish are good eaters and sometimes may eat both an early and mid-morning breakfast as well as full lunch and dinners and in between snacking on Tapas. Lunch is considered a heavier meal than dinner. A full meal may begin with Tapas followed by an entree, then the main course and lastly sweet or dessert.

PORTUGAL

Portugal has a passion for seafood because of its long coastline. For culinary purposes Portugal may be divided into north and south separated by the Tagus River. Portugal is situated on the innermost edge of the European Continent. The population is 11million mostly Roman Catholic and Christian Culinary traditions have shaped their eating habits. Portugal terrain is generally mountainous north of Tagus River and rolling plains south of it and it has a sizeable rural population. Its main agriculture products are wheat, corn, rice, potatoes, grapes and olive oil. Dairy products are scarce especially in the north. Portuguese tend to use more varied and intense seasonings.

North is famous for its Caldo Verde a soup of potato, onions, shredded cabbage and Linguiça sausage, may be thickened by cornbread. Portugal is famous for sardines and cod which are canned and salted. Specialities of Portugal are chestnut soup and almond & egg confections.

South is more hotter and fertile climate. Wheat is the staple crop and food, especially bread. Bread is also used to thicken soups or stews. Algrarve is the southern most region, from it comes Piri-Piri a hot chilli sauce which is now famous in all former Portuguese colonies. The warm climate is good for cultivating figs, apricot, lemons, carob, almonds, sugarcane, citrus and rice. Portugal like Spain has a lot of Moor's influence especially in the use of almonds and egg yolks in sweets.

The Portuguese eat a light breakfast followed by a mid-morning snack then lunch followed by a leisurely dinner. The main meal will start with soup followed by a meat or fish dish accompanied with vegetables, especially green salads. Desserts are simple like rice pudding or cheese or fruit followed by coffee.

FRENCH CUISINE

In France, cuisine is not simply a source of pleasure but a multifaceted discipline. With a focus on tradition, technique and mastery of style, French cuisine is arguably the most aesthetic cuisine in the world. The development of French cuisine may be attributed to the fact that France has historically had a gastronomique capital ¯PARIS . Culinary resources are concentrated there—the best ingredients and the most sensitive palates were all to be found at one place.

France is situated between 43°N and 51°N latitudes and between 5°W and 9°E longitude. The hexagon shaped mainland of France is located in western Europe and is bordered by the English Channel on the north west, Belgium and Luxembourg on the north east, Germany, Switzerland and Italy to the east, the Mediterranean sea to the south east, Spain and Andorra on the south west and the Bay of Biscay and the Atlantic ocean to the west. The Pyrenees mountain range divides France from Spain.

France has an area of 547000 km^2, the terrain to the north and west is flat with rolling hills, while the south and east are quite rugged and mountainous. The climate is mild winters and summers in the west, cool winters and hot summers inland, tough winters in the mountains and mild winters and hot summers along the Mediterranean in the south. About 57% of the land in France is dedicated to agriculture and the population of France is approximately 61 million.

HISTORICAL AND CULTURAL BACKGROUND

Throughout its history France has been invaded by explorers from many foreign countries. In certain areas of the country Celtic, British, Basque, Spanish, Italians, Greek and Arab influences are evident. The Celtic Gaul introduced farming to this area and also developed Charcuterie for which France is famous even today. The Romans who took over introduced cheese making and the Moors introduced goat rearing and spices. Arab influence is evident in the use of almonds and rice. With the marriage of Catherine de Medici to Henry II the foundations for modern French cuisine were established. Marie Antonio Carême (1784-1833)the great Chef who organised and detailed dishes according to courses laid the foundation for Grande Cuisine. It was further refined by Chef Georges-Aguste Escoffier whose approach was based on simplicity and called it Cuisine Classique. The next major shift in French cuisine was initiated by Chef Fernand Point (1897-1955) who further simplified the menu and laid the ground work for Nouvelle Cuisine.

France may be divided into four culinary regions—the North West, North East,

South West and South East. There are in all 22 provinces, each province has its own culinary specialities, impacted by history, terrain and climate.

THE NORTH WEST REGION

The North West region includes the provinces of Brittany, Basse-Normandy, haute Normandy, Pays de la Loire and the Loire Valley. This area has a long coastline and maritime climate- cool summers, warm winters and heavy rain. Proximity to the ocean results in a cuisine heavily influenced by sea food. Clams, lobsters, Dungeness crabs, oysters, skate, mackerel and Dover sole are all relished. Wild game including boar, rabbit, duck and pheasant, along with domestic goat and lamb are all popular. Normandy is renowned for cow's milk cheese ¯Camembert and superior butter which is utilized heavily in local cuisine. Fruits and vegetable of this region include pears, plums, apples, potatoes, artichokes, endive and pumpkins. Wheat is the preferred grain and walnuts the favourite nut.

THE NORTH EAST REGION

The North East region of France includes Nord Pays de Calais, Picardy, Champagne,

Alsace, Lorraine and Franche-Comte. This region's cuisine is influenced by its neighbouring nations – Germany, Switzerland and Belgium. Thus foods traditionally associated with Germanic cuisine such as sauerkraut and sausages are popular as are waffles and beets, items of Flemish origin. Pork, wild game, foi gras, freshwater fish, escargots(snails) and frogs are commonly utilised. The products of this region are wheat, barley, endive, beets, potatoes, cabbage, wild mushrooms, truffles, plums, apples, cherries, grapes, asparagus and cheese. Wheat is used to make spaetzle and egg noodles.

SOUTHEAST REGION

The southeast region of France consists of Burgundy, Auvergne, Limousine, Rhône alps, Côte d' Azur and Corsica and is the home to the city of Lyon the culinary capital of France. Beef, pork, lamb, duck and rabbit are all common as are cheeses derived from cow's, sheep's and goat's milk. Artichokes, eggplants, tomatoes, garlic, olives, herbs, apricots, cherries, plums and figs flourish in the cool Mediterranean climate. Common fish include anchovies, sardines, red mullets and monkfish. Specialities of this region include Dijion mustard, Le Puv lentils, bouillabaisse, ratatouille and tapenade.

SOUTHWEST REGION

The provinces of Midi-Pyrenees, Languedoc-Roussillon, Aquitaine and Poitou-Charentes make up the southwest region of France. This area borders Spain and is heavily influenced by Spanish cuisine and the Arab moors conquerors from Africa. Seafood is popular including monkfish, eel, tuna, oysters, cod and mussels. Poultry, walnuts, chestnuts, porcini and chanterelles mushrooms are harvested. The Moors introduced exotic spices such as pepper, cumin, anise, ginger, cinnamon and caraway. Specialities are fish soup with peppers and onion and jambon de Bayonne. The staples are wheat, barley and corn and like the Spanish use almond paste for thickening sauces.

Frozen Desserts

Definition:- They are cold desserts made by freezing a flavoured mixture or a concoction made from favoured full milk and cream.

History: - The Chinese knew the art of making iced drinks and dessert long before the Christian era. This art may have travelled Westward through the Greeks. Both the Greeks and Romans were known to serve fruit salads and purees mixed with honey and snow. Macro Polo the great traveller may have made it popular when he returned back from China.

Catherina de Medic introduces cold desserts in the form of ice creams to the French aristocracy when she married the future king HENRY-II. However the credit for introducing the ice cream to the public goes to Francesco Procopio which then became the rage.

Around 1775 ices became more delicate in flavour, richer and with more body so that it could be moulded easily. By the end of the 18th Century ice cream became a fashion.

TYPES & CLASIFICATION

Cold dessert is made by freezing a favoured mixture and they are of two types.

A. They may be made by freezing the mixture without any agitation – STILL FROZEN

B. They may be made by mechanically churning during the freezing process which result in a smooth creamy texture FREEZE CHURENED ICES.

A STILL FROZEN

- Mousses
- Soufflés
- Parfait
- Biscuit Glace or ice cream Cake
- Bombe glace

B. FREEZE CHURNED

- Ice creams
- Fruit Ices
- Sorbet
- Granita
- Marquises ? Punch.

Mousse A French term meaning foam is applied to dishes with a foamy texture. They are usually cold, and often sweet but also savoury and sometimes even hot. Some confections are naturally foamy; others may need beaten egg white and/or whipped cream, and possibly gelatine to achieve the desired texture. Soufflé is used as a synonym with Mousse however mousse is used for a wide range of dishes such as those incorporating savoury items such as mousse de jambon or mousse de asparagus.

Soufflé:-A French word which literally means ¯puffed up and is used as a culinary term in both English and French. It is a light, frothy dish just stiff enough to hold its shape, and which may be savoury or sweet, hot or cold. Cold soufflé is difficult to distinguish from a mousse and is made in the same way. The hot soufflé is started with a Roux blended with egg yolks and savoury or sweet flavouring ingredients to which are added stiffly beaten egg whites by folding it in. It is then baked in a high sided dish to contain its puffing.

Parfait An iced dessert very similar to Bombe, made from fresh cream, which gives it smoothness and prevents it from melting easily and can be cut into slices. It is made by beating 8 eggs yolks over a bain-marie and then gradually adding boiling syrup (110°C) till it becomes light and fluffy, whisk away from fire till cool, and add the chosen flavour, (Syrup is made with 60 ml water +200gms. caster sugar) whip in 115 gm double cream and freeze for 6 hours. In N. America this term has come to mean a combination of fruit and ice creams served in a tall glass which exposes the layers.

Ice cream Cake/ Biscuits glace An iced dessert made of alternate layers of different flavoured ice creams & a bombe mixture- frozen brick shape. After removing from the mould the ice cream is cut into even sizes/ slices and then arranged in small paper cases and kept frozen till serving. The same name is also used to describe a round/oblong cake having a sponge cake or meringue base with ice-cream or sorbet or parfait or bombe mixture on the top, decorated with whipped cream and crystallised fruits in syrup.

Bombe A frozen dessert made from a bombe mixture, enriched with various ingredients and frozen in a mould. This dessert was named after the spherical moulds with rounded tops which were used to make it. Traditionally bombe moulds are filled with two different mixtures. The bottom and sides of moulds are lined with ice cream or fruit ice. They are then filled with a bombe mixture made with 32 egg. yolks per litre of sugar syrup at specific gravity 1.285. The syrup is made with 700 ml of water and 700gms of sugar. Wisk egg yolks and syrup over a Bain Marie till cool. Finally add an equal volume of whipped cream and the chosen flavouring

FREZE CHURENED

Ice cream It was only in 1620 A. D. that it was discovered that by mixing Saltpetre (Potassium nitrate) Sodium Nitrate and common salt it was possible to liquefy ice and in so doing reduce the temperature below freezing point. This endothermic effect of the mixture of ice and Salt which was packed around a container of ice water allowing the water to freeze, and so was born the potential for making frozen dessert.

During the 18th Century it was recognised that a superior ice cream could be created if the mixture was churned till it semi froze and then froze.

The word's first ice cream plant opened in America in 1851 founded by Jacob Fusseell.Kulfi an Indian Ice cream was cited in a 16th Century document.

Definition Ice creams are cold desserts made by freezing a flavoured mixture. Freezing is carried out commercially in an ice cream maker or churn freezer so that electrically driven blades stir the mixture throughout the operation to incorporate air and make it smooth. They may then be moulded and frozen. **Method of Preparation** Beat 7 egg yolks with 150 gm sugar till thick and creamy. Heat cream to boiling point add to above gradually and cook over double boiler till it coats the back of a wooden spoon, cool immediately and then freeze in ice cream maker. **Fruit Ices and water Ices** The most important factor in making these desserts is the density of sugar syrup+ flavoruing+ Lemon juice which must be appropriate for it to freeze to a slushy density-

1.425 to 1.2407 sp gravity. In case of fruit ices the puree of the fruit used should be equal to sugar syrup of the above mentioned sp. gr.

Sorbet or Shorbet ***Definition***: - A type of water ice that is more granular than ice cream as it does not contain any fat or egg yolks. The basic mixture for all sorbet is a combination of sugar syrup and fruit or fruit juices and other flavouring. It is the lower fat content and higher acidity content (0.35%) that distinguishes sorbet from ice cream. Historically sorbets were the first iced desert. The Chinese are the first to be credited for making sorbets. The word sorbet is derived from Arabic- Turkish ¯chorbet to Latin ¯Sorbetto . There are several variations of the sorbet representing differences in smoothness, flavour, density and degree of hardness due to comparative degree of sugar concentrations.

MarquiseAny of various delicate deserts eg chocolate marquise is a dessert half way between a mouse and a parfait. It is based on butter, eggs. sugar and flavouring and served with custard creams or Chantilly cream.

Punch A Cold Punch is an iced drink, which can be made with tea, sugar, spices, fruits or fruits or fruit juices, rum or brandy. The word originally described a British colonial drink derived from the Hindi word Panch‘ which means five, for five ingredients i.e. tea, lemon, sugar, cinnamon and rum which were used, a forerunner of the cocktail.

GRANITA It is a type of an Italian sorbet, popularized by Tortoni in Paris in the 19th Century. It is a half frozen preparation with a granular texture (hence its name) made of lightly sweetened syrup and a flavouring strawberry or pineapple or coffer or Kirsch. Granita does not contain any Italian meringue.

ADDITIVES

Only permitted additives must be used and this may differ from Country to country depending upon their local laws. However, the standard adopted by the European Union, is followed quite universally.

Special alphabetic codes are used which describes a particular group of items e.g. E for colour.

Some of the additives used for frozen desserts are:-

Colouring agents E signifying nature identical exact synthetic copies of natural substances a) Natural caramel. b) Cochineal c) Chlorophyll e) Yellow lacto flavones; f) Xanthophylls

- **Anti oxidants** – Which prevents fats and Oils from going rancid

a) Tocopherols b) Sulphurous anhydride c) lactic acid

Antioxidants and general stabilizers;-

a) B.H.A Butylatedhydroxyanisole b) Citric Acid c) Lecithns

- **Emulsifiers** – e.g. a) Gum Arabic, b) Pectin, c) Polyglycerol esters of polycondensed fatty acids
- **Improvers** such as coal Tar dyes.

CHINESE CUISINE

Introduction

As one travels around the world today, one cannot help being impressed by the extent to which Chinese food and cooking has been established in-almost every corner of the earth. The popularisation of Chinese cuisine lies in the unique traditions and techniques of Chinese cooking, and in the inherent appeal of Chinese food and flavours to the palate, and also Chinese food can be extremely economical as well as being highly nutritious, because, most ingredients are cut into small pieces, then quickly cooked so as to retain their natural goodness. Chinese culinary' art has gone through thousands of years of refinement and develop pment, but the Chinese unique way of cooking and preparing food, remains basically unchanged. Archaeological finds of the Bronze Age (around 1850 BC) indicate that the Chinese had utensils such as bronze Cleavers for cutting up foods into small pieces and cooking them in animal fat, using a bronze pot not dissimilar to the modern wok. There is data to prove that as long ago as the ZHOU dynasty (12 C BC) the Chinese used Soya sauce, vinegar, rice wine, fruit jam and spices as seasoning for their cooking and that elaborate and complicated cooking methods were already being employed. By the time of China's greatest sage CONFUCIUS (551 - 479 BC) who was an acknowledged gourmet recorded that the importance of heat application and blending of different flavours were emphasized in Chinese cooking; and the uses of high, moderate or low heat, the blending of sour, piquant, salty, bitter or sweet flavours were all given their correct application in order to achieve a harmonious whole. This theory of harmony is one of the main characteristics of Chinese cuisine to this day.

Today, Chinese cuisine is generally considered along, with the French as one of the two greatest cuisines. It is simple, highly adaptable to the taste of the other countries and best of all it can be prepared by anyone, possessed of a little patience. Tai See Foo - or Master Chef is a much-disciplined man, no where is the Tai See Foo in such importance as in China, where, in relation to the Chinese philosophy of life, his profession over the centuries has been looked upon with the greatest respect in the community. The Chinese value food highly and rarely wastes any, many recipes require the use of leftovers and cooking ahead is standard practice. The basic flavours are six – Sweet, Sour, Bitter, Spicy (sharp) Pungent and Salty. Their distribution, proportion and use must be controlled for proper blending. Meat has always been a major item in Chinese diet; however the meat ration per person was small. Efficient utilisation, proper colour arrangements and palatability often required highly imaginative combinations. Often the meat could only be flavouring for a dish rather than the main ingredient.

China's economy has seldom been able to afford such animals as the cow and the lamb, inadequate pastureland for cattle has made raising these animals difficult. Pork is therefore China's most common meat. In the north, mutton is commonly used, particularly by the Chinese Muslims. Many Chinese Buddhist for religious reasons, will eat only vegetable, the cooking of which was developed to a high degree. The scientific study of vegetable became a part of Taoism and its devotees devised a highly nutritional vegetarian diet, an art so refined that their vegetarian dishes resemble meat in taste as well as in texture.

The elements that contribute to the wide sensual appeal of Chinese food, which make it so acceptable to all people world over are:

1) Chinese meals are communal meals and communal dishes served on the table are of necessity, bigger and fuller than the average dishes, they are therefore

bound to create a greater visual impact and are more sumptuous in appearance. The exoticism of size and variety is further enhanced by the Chinese use of heat as an integral part of flavour - the use of heat to induce, ignite, and set ablaze all the latent desires in our appetites. Hence in a well-served Chinese meal, the time-lapse between the food leaving the hot pan and its arrival on the table is measured not in minutes but in seconds.

2) Chinese dinner is a multi-dish or multi-course meal.
3) The frequent and deliberate exploitation of changing textures both the harmony and contrast of textures are exploited.
4) The bulk intake of rice produces the ultimate physical satisfaction in eating along with several soups.
4) The use of soya beans and their by-products - soya sauce, soya paste, soya-cheese, soya bean curd, etc. are able to seduce our palate and taste buds.

The basic purpose of cooking is primarily to render food edible, and secondly to render it more enjoyable to eat. To achieve these purposes two methods are generally employed, heating and flavouring.

HEATING: Take the heating of food, which is basically capable of only a limited number of variations such as heating by air, baking, roasting, heating by fire or radiation, grilling, barbequing, heating through the medium of water or by oil or heating by conduction. By combining the different methods, by varying the pace of heating (Fire - Power), by varying the speed or lengthiness (time) of treatment by varying the stability of mobility (stir frying) of food while being heated the Chinese have developed some forty different accepted heating methods, each with its well defined and established terms of reference and conception.

FLAVORING In the case of flavouring the Chinese have developed and advanced even farther than in heating (cooking). This is due to the normal Chinese practice of cross cooking different types of food which results of large scale cross blending of flavours. Although not all Chinese dishes are mixed dishes - some consists of only one ingredient cooked in the simplest way. The seasoning materials and sauces are often applied at the last stage of cooking. The flavouring of Chinese cooking is achieved through a multi layer process i.e. Through the use of -supplementary ingredients for cross cooking to provide variety and difference in texture and material, the use of flavouring ingredients, seasonings and sauces to further enhance the taste and flavour and finally through the serving of table condiments to provide the individual diners with the opportunity to do their own personal "touch-ups" before consumption. In order to reduce confusion, it is normal practice in Chinese kitchens to divide the job of cooking into two clear stages: Preparation and actual cooking. The task of preparation and the task of cooking are usually carried out by two different persons. The preparations and portioning of the principal and supplementary ingredients are usually carried out by the assistant cook, while the chef attends to the firing (control of the heating) and all the work over the stove including flavouring and the application of all the sauces and seasonings.

THE MAIN CHARACTERISTIC OF CHINESE CUISINE

Actually, Chinese cooking is often simple, even for beginners provided you follow a few firm rules. The first thing to remember is that preparation and cooking are separate procedures; all preliminaries must be completed before actual cooking begins. Chinese foods must often be cooked quickly and at very high temperatures. Chinese use oil in their cooking - usually vegetable oil. With this oil one can get the high temperatures needed to seal in the flavour and original colour of the foods and also to preserve the all important crispness and vitamins of vegetables. They do not use butter and many other dairy products either vegetables rather than meat predominate. Soups play various parts in the symphony of a well composed meal - not only is there one as a light appetizer but clear soups are often used between courses as palate cleansers. Richer soups like velvet corn, may however be served as a separate course.

There exists a certain 'uniqueness' that distinguishes Chinese cooking from other food cultures. There is the Chinese division when preparing and serving food between TAN' (grain & other starch food) and 'CAT (meat and vegetable dishes) Grains in various forms of rice or wheat flours (bread, pancakes, noodles or dumplings), make up the FAN half of the meal. Vegetables and meat (including poultry, meat and fish) cut up and mixed in various combinations into individual dishes constitute the CAI half. A balanced meal must have an appropriate amount of both FAN & CAI. It is combining' various ingredients and the lending of different flavours for the preparation of CAI that lies the fine art and skill of Chinese cuisine.

The other distinctive feature of Chinese cuisine is the harmonious blending of colours, aromas, flavours, shapes and textures in one single CAI dish. The principle of blending complimentary or contrasting colours and flavours is a fundamental one - the different ingredients must not be mixed indiscriminately. The matching of flavours should follow a set pattern and is controlled and not casual. The cutting of ingredients is another important element of Chinese cooking in order to achieve the proper effect. Slices are matched with slices, shreds with shreds, cubes with cubes, chunks with chunks and so on. This is not only for the sake of appearance but also because ingredients of the same size and shape require about the same amount of time in cooking. This complexity of interrelated elements of colours, flavours and shapes in- Chinese cooking is reinforced by yet another feature: TEXTURE. A dish may have just one or several textures, such as tenderness, crispiness, crunchiness, smoothness and softness. The textures to be avoided are: sogginess, stringiness and hardness. The selection of different textures in one single dish is an integral part of blending of flavours and colours. The desired texture or textures in any dish can only be achieved by the right cooking methods. In all different methods of cooking the correct degree of heat and duration of cooking time are of vital importance.

REGIONAL COOKING STYLES.

China is a vast country and as such is exposed to extremes of both geography and climate. This naturally results in the growth of different agricultural products, so it is of little wonder that cuisines vary from province to province .Looking at the map of China, it is not difficult to understand why there should be such .a rich variety of different styles, throughout the land. Even though there is no official classification of various regional cuisines in China, but it is generally agreed SICHUAN in the west .SHANDONG in the north ,CANTON in the south and JIANGSU in the east represents the four major regional cooking styles of China. In addition, four more provinces ZHEJIANG, FUKIEN, ANHUI in the east and HUNAN in the west are usually included in the role of honour while one talks of the "Big Eight" distinguished schools of cuisine in China.

Northern School

Archaeological evidence shows that in about 5000 BC, the inhabitants of North China had begun to farm, settle down and make painted pottery, eating and cooking vessels. Some of the most conspicuous traces of early Chinese culture have been found at sites that lie along the valley of the Yellow River, which is why this area is sometimes described as the "Cradle of Chinese Civilization . Two ancient capitals of LUOYANG and KEIFENG are both situated just south of the Yellow River in Hunan province ("HU" is the Chinese word for "river" and 'NAN" means "south"). The noblemen and the imperial families live in such luxury that their chefs invented and perfected many of the Chinese classic dishes. These recipes were passed down through the centuries, and were moved to the capital, Peking and beyond.

China's North has two very long and distinct seasons (winter and summer) with short transitional periods in between. Winters are dry and cold, with temperatures often below freezing. Summers provide intense heat and rain. Its diverse terrain (hills, valleys and rivers) give variety to the region's agriculture.

Due to the extremely dichotomous climate, the land's produce is hearty: mainstays of wheat and corn, especially important to the Northern China economy, dominate the northerner's dietary needs. Crops are then manufactured into wheat-flour for use in common cuisine: noodles, stuffed buns, dumplings and steamed bread are just a few of the wheat products consumed in the provinces of this region. Although little rice is grown in this region, other hardy plants such as barley, millet, soybeans, cabbage, squash and apples predominately appear in northern Chinese agriculture and cooking

In the northern school the staple food is not rice but wheat flour, from which are made many noodle, dishes, steamed bread and dumplings. Northern food tends to be lighter than that of other provinces. From Peking (meaning northern capital) and its neighbouring districts come notable dishes prepared with wine stock. Northern cooking includes pungent sweet and sour dishes and more subtle, delicately seasoned foods. The use of garlic and spring onions is also characteristic.

Much of the north is bordered by Mongolia where people eat a lot of mutton. Food from Inner Mongolia and Shantung forms the backbone of northern cuisine.

Now Peking cuisine is quite a different matter, it is not a separate regional school, but rather the combination of all China's regional style of cooking. Being the capital of China for many centuries Peking (or Beijing as it is now called) occupies a unique position in the development of Chinese culinary art. Peking cuisine has been defined by the eminent Chinese gourmet Kenneth Lo as "The crystallization of many inventions and performance of the generations of imperial chefs of different dynasties winch have ruled in Peking for nearly a millennium, and the local dishes of the people of Shandon and Hubet which have been in the habit of preparing together with all the culinary contributions which over the years have established their reputation in the old capital Peking cooking is in short, the top table of Chinese culinary art. Peking cooking exhibits the greatest ingenuity and inventiveness.

Notable flavours and dishes—

Beijing is known for jiaozi, the traditional Chinese dumpling, and Peking duck. Jiaozi dumplings are often filled with pork and vegetables, but variations may include sweet fruits (dates) or chestnuts. Peking duck is a traditional delicacy perfected during the Qing Dynasty and served to important and wealthy individuals throughout history. The duck and its skin (a delicacy) are served with Hoisin (Peking) sauce in flat-bread wrappers..

Northern cuisine includes the Henan (north of the river) region. Strikingly unique from other northern flavours is the Shaolin vegetarian cuisine. Chinese Buddhist belief has for centuries prohibited the eating of animal flesh, and the monks here have spent an age perfecting the cooking of all types of vegetarian food. This cuisine is very nutritious and healthy.

The western school

The Szechuan style of cuisine arose from a culturally distinct area in the central western of part of China, a province known as Sichuan. This area of China came into its own culturally towards the end of the Shang Dynasty, during the 15th century. However, it was also the climate of the area that helped to shape the culinary traditions that were to arise from Sichuan province and make their way into the realm of international cuisine.

The province from which the cuisine that the world knows as Szechuan evolved is often hot and humid, and this contributed to this necessity of preparing foods in ways that differ significantly from other regions of China. Szechuan cuisine is primarily known for its hot and spicy dishes, though naturally there is more to Szechuan food than spice and sauces rich and strong in flavour.

Much of the spicing of regional Chinese cooking is based upon bringing together five fundamental taste sensations – sweet, sour, pungent, salty and bitter. The balance of these particular elements in any one dish or regional cuisine can vary, according to need and desire, especially as influenced by climate, culture and food availability.

In Szechuan cuisine, there are a variety of ingredients and spices used to create these basic taste sensations. These include a variety of chilli peppers, peppercorns over various types,

Sichuan peppers, which are in reality a type of fruit, not pepper, and produce a numbing effect in addition to their warm flavour. Sichuan peppers, also called flower pepper and mountain pepper, are a traditional part of the Chinese five spice powder, or at least of those that are modelled upon the most authentic versions of the spice combinations common to regional Chinese cooking.

Other ingredients used commonly in Szechuan cuisine to create the five fundamental taste sensations include different types of sugars, such as beet root sugar and cane sugar, as well as local fruits for sweetness. The sour comes from pickled vegetables and different varieties of vinegar. A special bitter melon is added to many dishes to offer the touch of bitterness that complements other flavours. Other spices and flavours include dried orange peel, garlic, ginger, sesame oil and bean paste. Salt is important to Szechuan cuisine, and the area produces uniquely flavoured salts that help to distinguish authentic Szechuan cuisine from the other regional cuisines from China.

Szechuan cuisine is marked by its rich traditional flavours, which stem from a culture of hundreds of years and are in part shaped by the natural forces of climate. Authentic Szechuan cuisine offers a unique dining experience made up of adventurous and creative taste sensations.

Specialities

Hunan (south of the river) cuisine: Renowned for its soups, is one of the oldest and richest also noted for its spicy, pungent and flavourful dishes. Hunanes are especially fond of using chillies, sweet peppers and shallots in cooking. Sichuan (Szechuan) cuisine: hot, spicy chillies, ma po doufu, hot pot Famous for its heat and distinct flavours, Sichuan cooking mastered the light cooking techniques of stir-frying, sautéing, and dry-braising. One of the region's most famous recipes is ma po doufu, a spicy bean-curd and vegetable dish cooked with some of the most powerful chillies in the world. In traditional Chinese medicine and nutrition, hot chilli peppers are considered helpful in reducing the ‾internal dampness . The humid climate also compels a creativity and variety in food preservation, including techniques such as picking, salting, drying and smoking. lnland cooking also makes much use of the fungus called Cloud ear or, Tree ear.

Tea smoked duck, Chicken chilly, Liver Paste Soup, Hot & Sour Soup, Beans A La Szechwan, Dong An Chicken, Fried crab, Soy Braised duck, sliced Hoi sin Pork, Bean curd, Spiced Turnip etc., are some of the famous dishes of this region.

The Eastern School

The Yangtze, China's longest river which traverses the width of China from west to east flows through China's leading agricultural regions-Sichuan and Hunan (on the upper) Hubei and Jiangxi (on the middle) Jiangsu and Zianzgi (on the lower),which contains some of the most fertile land in China. :

Both wheat and rice are grown here, as well as other crops which include — barley, corn, sweet potatoes, peanuts, and soya beans. Fisheries abound in the multitude of lakes and other tributaries and deep sea fishing has long been established in the coastal province of Jiangsu and Zhejiang The areas that cover the middle and lower regions of the Yangtze are traditionally referred to as "Land of Fish and Rice', and is collectively known as Jiangnan ("JIANG" means "great river' referring to the, Yangtze and 'NAN" referring to the south), and it boasts a number of distinctive cooking styles.

The Yangtze River delta has its own cooking style known as HYAIYANG with the culinary centre in Shanghai that is China's largest city which lies on the Yangtze estuary. South East China has always been regarded as the most culturally developed and economically prosperous region. Both Nanjing in Jiangsu and Hangzhou in Zhejiang have been China's capital of several dynasties; other culinary centres are to be located in YANGZHOU (Yangchow), SUZHOU and ZHENJIANG. Yangchow fried rice, chow mien (open fried noodles), wantons, spring rolls, dumplings and many other Cantonese dim sum dishes have all originated from here.

South of Zhejiang is the province FUJI AN (FUKIEN) which is sometimes grouped in the Eastern School, but its cooking style is more influenced by its southern neighbour Canton, so very often Fukien cuisine is included with Cantonese in the Southern school.

Taken as a whole, Eastern cuisine is rich, decorative and rather on the sweet side; unlike Peking food, garlic is used sparingly, if at all. The area as a whole is renowned for certain products and dishes: the specially cured Chinhua ham, with its pinkish red flesh and succulently savoury-sweet taste, the rich dark Chinkiang vinegar and the amber-coloured Shdaohsing rice wine. Classic dishes include Crisp stir-fried shrimp, Eel cooked in oil, Yangchow fried rice, Lion's head and fish from the West Lake with a sweet and sour sauce.

One special cooking technique of the region has been adopted nationally. This is hungshao the red-braising method of cooking, whereby the ingredients (mainly meat, poultry and fish) are cooked slowly in an aromatic mixture of thick dark soy sauce and rice wine. When, at the end of cooking,' the sauce is reduced and spooned over the main ingredient, the resulting taste is both rich and fragrant.

Shanghai cuisine is the least known outside China. Its oiliness and sweetness are perhaps less appealing to the Western palate, and because it is decorative, it tends to be labour-intensive. Moreover, it depends largely on fresh local produce; the famous Shanghai crabs, studded with yellow roe in the autumn, have no counterpart elsewhere and for the delicate taste of the famous West Lake fish one has to go to Hangchow.

The staple food of this region is rice. The cooks on the coast use more soya sauce and sugar and specialise in salty and gravy-laden dishes. Fish and shell fish from the many rivers and the neighbouring sea are popular ingredients. These are gently spiced concoctions of meat, chicken, duck and sea food with, of course lots of vegetables. Fukien produces the best soy sauce and therefore its cuisine has a good deal of stewing in this sauce or "red cooking" as it is called because of the colour the sauce imparts. The soups are clear and light. The Fukienese excels in their soft spring rolls and sea food. Fukien is also famous for its pork and chicken dishes made with sweet-tasting and fermented rice paste.

Speciality and Popular dishes

Yangchow fried rice, Chow mien, Spring rolls, Dim sums, White cut pork, lion's head (pork meat balls with cabbage - the alarming name of this dish refers to the pork meat balls which are supposed to resemble the shape of a lion's head and the cabbage which is supposed to look like its mane), Squirrel fish.

The Southern School

The Pearl River delta, with Canton as a provincial capital of GUANGDONG (KWANGTUNG), is undoubtedly the home of the most famous of all Chinese cooking styles. Unfortunately the reputation of Cantonese cuisine has been badly damaged by a so called 'chop suey' food outside China. Authentic Cantonese food has no rival and has a greater variety of food than any other school because Canton was the first Chinese port open for trade, therefore foreign influence are particularly stronger in its cooking There are many pig and poultry farms and fish ponds. High, quality tea is a special product of Fukien, while all along the coast fish and sea food - crabs, cray fish, shrimps, prawns, scallops, clams - are plentiful. This wealth of ingredients has helped to make

Cantonese cooking the most versatile and varied of Chinese cuisines. Cantonese food is not highly seasoned, instead a harmonious blending of different flavours is sought in order to bring out the best of the ingredients. Cantonese cooks are at their most skilful when they stir-fry dishes. Red-braised dishes are an eastern contribution to the Chinese gastronomy but southern stir-fry dishes reign supreme nationwide. Their 'wok fragrance' a term used to describe the aroma so desirable in stir-fry dishes is matchless.

Southern cooking is subtle and the least greasy of all the regional styles. The cooks excel in stir-frying. At its best, the cuisine tends to be more costly than the others because the cooks use highly concentrated chicken bouillon as the basis of their soups and general cooking: They like to use nuts and mushrooms in their dishes. They prepare many varieties of sea food and lots of roasted and grilled pork and poultry. Steamed dishes are also featured.

Fisheries play a major role in the economy, Guangdong contributes about one fourth of China's fish catch (over 20% of the fish caught here are fresh water fish). Rice is a dominant food grain; the other crops are tea, tobacco, peanut, sugarcane and sub tropical fruits such as bananas, pineapples, oranges, tangerines and lychees.

HAINAN Island is the only truly tropical area of China and produces coconuts, coffee, natural rubber and figs..; The Southern School consists of three distinct styles of cooking: CANTON, CHAOCHOW. (Sv.atow), and DONGJIANG (also known as HAKKA), which means 'family of guest', which refers to the immigrants from North China who settled in the South during the Song Dynasty after the invasion of Mongols in the 13th Century. So it was the Hakka's who introduced noodles, wantons and dumplings etc, into the Contonese diet.

There was a mass immigration overseas after the 17th century both by the Cantonese and the Hakka. When Swanton was opened to foreign trade in 1858, it became a major port for Chinese immigration to South East Asia, America and Europe. That is why; the first Chinese restaurant to open abroad introduced only Cantonese cooking to the outside world. Schools of cooking there are two other schools, though not regional in character, nevertheless should be included here among China's various styles of Schools of Cooking, namely the Moslem and Vegetarian School.

Specialized and popular dishes

Dim-sum, Shao-mi, Cantonese roast duck, Sweet & Sour Pork. Pork Goose, Ducks webs in oyster sauce, Stuffed green peppers, Shark's fin soup, Turtle soup etc. are very famous.

The Moslem School

The Chinese Moslem known as "HUI though Chinese speaking are distinguished from the Chinese by their affiliation with the Sunni branch of Islam. One theory is that they are descendants of the Moslems who settled in China in the 13 century and adopted the Chinese language and culture.

There are nearly 5 million Hui widely distributed throughout almost every province in China, but their traditional areas of settlement is in the North-West with heavy concentration in Hunan, Shanki, Hubei and Shangdong. They form the Chinese Moslem school, together with two other national minorities: the UYGOR group in XINJIANG (4 million, virtually all Moslems), and about 1.5 million MONGOLS who are traditionally nomadic, and therefore, like the Moslem, do not eat pork. Their daily diet consists of beef, mutton, milk and butter, items an average Chinese has no taste for.

The Vegetarian School

Chinese vegetarians are not allowed anything remotely associated with animal including egg and milk. They obtain their proteins mainly from soya beans and its byproducts such as bean curd (tofu), nuts and fungi.

Chinese vegetarian has a long history; its origin can be traced to as far back as around 500 BC, when the TAOIST SCHOOL of THOUGHT developed the hygienic and nutritional science of fruit and vegetables. Some centuries later when Buddhism which abhors the killing of any living creature and the eating of flesh in any form was introduced into China from India, this philosophy was readily grafted into TAOIST school of Cooking and a new form of vegetarianism was born.

Apart from the extensive use of fresh and dehydrated vegetables the vegetarian chefs have developed a new art by creating food that has become known as imitation meats. This imitation pork, chicken, fish and prawns and so on bare an amazing resemblance to their fleshy counterpart in form and texture, though not quite in flavour.

EQUIPMENT

UTENSILS

The Chinese batterie de cuisine consists of very few basic implements unlike the western kitchen. To start with .only four of the most rudimentary implements are essential to cook Chinese food, i.e. Cleaver, chopping block, wok and stirrer. The Chinese cooking utensils are ancient designs, they are made-of basic and inexpensive materials and they have been in continuous use for several thousand years. As for the rest of the cooking utensils such as sieves, spatula, strainer, casserole, steamers you will find the western version to be less effective. The other tools which are used in the Chinese kitchen are cooking chopsticks, bamboo steamers, strainers, Mongolian fire pot ladles, fish slices, wok-brush, wok scoop, bamboo mat, etc."

CLEAVER

The Chinese cleaver is an all purpose cook's knife that is used for slicing, shredding, peeling, pounding, crushing, chopping and even for transporting cut food from the chopping board or to a plate directly to the wok. At the first site, a Chinese cleaver may appear to be hefty, gleaming ominously sharp but in reality it is quite light, steady and not at all dangerous to use provided you handle it correctly and with care. Cleavers are available in a variety of materials and weight. They all have a blade of about 8-9 inches long and 3-4 inches wide. The heaviest weighing almost a kg called CHOPPER is really meant for the professionals and is excellent for chopping bones such as drumsticks, pork spare ribs etc. The smaller and much lighter SLICER with a thinner and sharper blade is convenient for slicing, meat and vegetables. But most Chinese cooks prefer a medium weight, dual purpose cleaver known as the CIVIL and MILITARY Knife (wen-wu-dao in Chinese).The lighter front have of the blade is used for slicing, shredding, and scoring etc. and the heavier rear half of the blade is used for chopping and so on. The back of the blade is used as a pounder and tenderizer and the flat side is used for crushing and transporting. The end of the handle acts as a pestle for grinding spices.etc,. The blades of a cleaver should be made of tempered carbon steel with a wooden handle. Stainless steel cleavers with metal handles may look good but require more frequent sharpening, also the handle gets slippery .therefore they are less satisfactory for both safety and steadiness. Always keep the cleaver blade sharp and clean. To prevent it from rusting and getting it stained wipe it dry with cloth or kitchen paper after use. Sharpen it frequently on a fine grained whet stone. Try to get a whetstone that has two different' grades of surface. Use a rough grain only if the blade has become blunt and the finer grained surface for a sharp finish to the edge. Lubricate the stone with vegetable oil or water and then put a damp cloth beneath it for stability. A cleaver of medium weight made of carbon or stainless steel is ideal for general use.

CHOPPING BLOCK

The traditional Chinese chopping block is a cross section of a tree trunk. Made of hard wood they range from about 12.inches in diameter and 2 inches thick, to giant ones up to 20 inches by 6-8 inches .The ideal size should be about 16 inches in diameter and at least 3-4 inches thick to be of any real use. To prevent it from splitting, season a new block with a liberal dose of vegetable oil on both sides. Let the wood absorb as much oil as it will take and sponge the block with salt and water and dry it thoroughly .Never soak the block in water nor wash it with any detergent - after each use., just scrape it clean with the blade of a cleaver then wipe the surface with a sponge or cloth wrung out in plain hot water. Always stand the block on its side when not in use. Never cut raw ingredients and cooked food on the same surface .Use different block or board for the two types of food for hygienic reasons .Use one side for chopping only then the other side should remain smooth enough for pastry making.

WOK

The Chinese cooking utensil known as "WOK" is the POT or PAN the correct translation should be GOU. The wok was designed with a rounded bottom to fit snugly over a traditional Chinese brazier or oven which burned wood .charcoal or coal. It conducts and retains heat evenly and because of its shape the food always returns to the centre of the wok where the heat is most intense that is why it is ideally suited for quick stir frying .Of course the wok is far more versatile than just a frying pan, it is also ideal for deep frying , its conical shape requires far less oil than a fiat bottomed deep fryer, and has more depth which means more heat and more frying surface, which means that more food can be cooked more quickly at one go .Furthermore since the wok has a large capacity on the upper end as the oil level rises when the raw ingredients are added to it, there is a little chance for the oil to overflow and catch fire as often is the case with the conventional deep fryer. Now days a metal collar or ring purchased with the wok adapts it neatly to any gas or electric range.

Besides being a frying pan (deep or shallow) , a wok is also used for braising, steaming, boiling, and even smoking in other words the whole spectrum of Chinese cooking methods can be executed in one single use utensil. Basically there are only two different types of wok- the DOUBLE HANDED WOK with two handles on two opposite sides and the frying pan type SINGLE HANDED WOK .Both types are usually made of light weight iron or carbonized steel, and the diameter ranges from about 12-18 inches. The single handed wok may appear to be unsteady and slightly tipped to one side, but in fact it is quite safe and much easier to handle particularly for quick stir frying since it offers you plenty of leverage of tilting and tossing .the disadvantages of using a double handed wok is that you need strong wrist and oven gloves to lift it, as the metal handles get very hot even if they are reinforced with heat resistant plastic or wood. A dome shaped lid would be another useful item for certain braising and steaming dishes . Wok lids are usually made of light metal such as aluminium with a wooden or plastic knob on top as a handle. The dome shaped allows the cooking of a whole chicken or duck in a wok and the natural curve will guide the condensation inside the lid sliding down along the edge rather than dropping down directly onto the food that is being cooked.

STIRRER.

' Some wok sets often consist of a pair of stirrers in the shape of a ladle and a spatula, made of iron and stainless steel; both have a long handle with wooden tip. Of the two, the ladle or scooper is more versatile. It is an indispensable utensil in the professional kitchen, since it is used for adding ingredients and seasonings to the wok besides being a stirrer and scooper during cooking as well as transferring food from the wok to the serving dish or bowl. It is also a measure for the cook, as the standard ladle will hold 6 fi oz (180 ml or 2/3 cup) liquid, slightly smaller than the rice bowl. The spatula or shovel has a rounded end to match the contours of the wok therefore it can be very useful for scraping and lifting fried food the bottom of the wok such as when cooking a whole fish etc. Sometimes it is used in conjunction with the ladle for stir frying, rather like when you are mixing or tossing a salad with a pair of spoon and fork.

INITIAL PREPARATION.

Cutting Techniques. The cutting of various ingredients into different sizes, thickness and shapes is an important element in Chinese cuisine .As mentioned earlier, the Chinese always cut their food into small neat pieces before cooking, partly because of fuel conservation, small pieces of food can be cooked quickly before the sticks of fire wood burn out and partly because, small pieces of food are easier to be served and eaten with chopsticks, since knives and carvers have never been used on Chinese tables. The fact that small pieces of food only require a short time for cooking ,thus retain much of the natural flavours and nutritious value is an added bonus in Chinese cooking ,which must be regarded as an incidental discovery..

When it comes to the actual cooking, the two most important factors are the degree of heat and the duration of cooking. These two factors are so closely related to each other that it is very difficult to give a precise cooking time in most recipes, since much depends on the size and condition of the ingredients, and above all, on the type of the stove and cooking utensils used.

All in all, there are well over 50 different distinct methods of cooking in Chinese cooking. They fall roughly into the following four categories:-

1. WATER COOKING: : Boiling, Poaching, and Simmering

2 OIL COOKING : Deep frying, shallow frying, stir frying, braising.

3. FIRE COOKING : Roasting, Baking and Barbecuing
4. STEAM COOKING: Steaming.

COOKING METHODS

The Chinese divide the temperature of heat into "Military"(high or fierce and • medium) and 'civil' (low or gentle and weak) And proper control of temperature and cooking time is the key to success.

High or fierce heat is usually used for quick cooking for and tender foods. Different kinds of frying, .steaming, instant boiling etc and call for a high heat.

Medium or moderate heat can be used for quick -braising, steaming, and boiling.

Low or gentle heat is used for slow cooking allowing the flavours to penetrate through all the ingredients such as roasting and simmering.

Weak heat is used for long cooking turning hard ingredients soft. It is used for simmering, braising and stewing.

Here are some 25 commonly used methods in Chinese cooking .One dish may require one ,two or three methods each will produce a different effect.

1. CHAO Stir frying. By far the most common method of Chinese cooking .Practically all vegetables will be cooked this way. Here a wok is most useful Heat the wok first then add the oil until it smokes add the ingredients, stir and toss .constantly no more than 2-3 minutes. In other way stir fry the ingredients in a little hot oil over a very high heat. This method is widely used and has many variations.

a. Pure stir frying: the raw ingredients are not marinated nor coated with a batter, they are just stir fried in hot oil and seasonings are added towards the end of cooking .Most vegetables are cooked in this way.

b. Braising stir frying: The main and supplementary ingredients are cooked in this separately .at first and then brought together with the addition of seasoning and stock or a thickening agent (usually of corn flour mixed with water) and braised very quickly over high heat.

c. Twice cooked stir frying: One ingredient has been previously cooked and is here cut into smaller pieces and stir fried with other ingredients and seasonings.

2. **ZHA** Deep fry in hot oil over a high heat. Food is fried in a large quantity of oil over a high or medium heat. There are different variations of deep frying

a. Neat deep frying: the raw ingredients are not coated with batter or flour.

b. Dry deep frying: Raw ingredients are coated with dry flour or breadcrumbs.

c. Soft deep frying: Raw ingredients are coated with batter, first and then deep fried for crispness.

3. **JIAN.** Shallow frying over a moderate heat. Similar to tire western way except that in some cases stock or water is added at the last minute forming a gravy .A flat bottomed pan is used . a little oil and medium or low heat .Seasonings are added when food is half done. The pan should be turned from time to time during cooking so that the heat is evenly distributed.

4. **BAO.** Rapid frying literally means to explode. It takes an even shorter time Than stir frying using very high heat .Rapid stir frying is another form of stir

frying , the ingredient or ingredients have been deep fried or rapid boiled first, they are then quickly stir fried over very high heat for a short period of time. Variations in this method include rapid stir frying in oil rapid stir frying in bean sauce and rapid stir frying with spring onions,

5. **SHAO.** Braising literally meaning to burn or in this case to cook. The ingredients are first fried in a little oil over a moderate heat, then simmered in stock until very little liquid or juice is Ieft. Redcooking In this widely used method of cooking the meat is cut into small chunks then deep fried or par boiled or steamed until half done .Seasonings (Soya sauce, wine vinegar sugar etc) stock or water are added to it ,the whole thing is brought to a boil and simmered until done.
6. **MEN.** Stewing, it is very similar to braising except that it usually takes longer over a low heat. Slow braising- the food must be fried first (light brown) then all the ingredients (seasonings etc.) are put in a tightly covered pot and simmered over a very low heat slowly like a casserole.
7. **DUN.** Simmering In this method of cooking no oil is used at all and the food is cooked over low heat .Slow cooking, there are two kinds of slow cooking in water. Slow cooking in water is a form of stewing , slow cooking, out of water involves a double boiling technique .When the pot that contains the food is immersed in a large pot of boiling water. .
8. **ZHU.** Boiling over moderate heat. Boil the ingredients directly in water over low heat.
9. **CHUAN.** Rapid or fierce boiling over high heat for a very short period of time. This simple cooking is often used for making soups Bring the water or stock boil over-high heat add the ingredients and seasonings, serve as soon as the soup re-boils. No thickening agents added and the vegetables will be crisp and fresh.
10. **ZHENG.** Steaming needs no explanation .Traditionally the Chinese use bamboo steamers which sits in the wok .Another widely used in China not only for cooking .but also for treating raw ingredients before cooking by other methods , or to keep food warm after they have been cooked.
11. **.LU.** Stewing in stock made of Soya sauce five spice powder and sugar over low heat .Soya stewing- a Soya-gravy is made first the ingredients are stewed in this gravy over a low heat.
12. **HUI.** Another form of braising - literally means "Assembly Normally a number of ingredients, some cooked, some semi cooked are blended together for the final stage of cooking in a gravy using a high to moderate heat. A method of cooking a dish that consists of several different ingredients. Stir fry the ingredients first add stock or water and seasonings, boil over high heat for a short while, then thicken the gravy before serving .Alternately prepare the gravy first then add the partly cooked ingredients (deep fried or steamed), cook over low heat .thicken the gravy and serve..
13. **KAO.** Roasting which hardly needs explanation, except that in China most kitchens are not equipped with ovens , therefore most of the roasting is done as barbecuing in a restaurant. The ingredients are first marinated or treated then either cooked in an oven or over an open fire like barbecuing

14. **BAN.** Mixing raw food or salad or-cold dishes which are mixed together with a dressing. Mixing salads. This method does not actually involve cooking, but simply calls for cutting the raw or cooked ingredients and dressing it with seasonings.
15. **SHAUN.** Instant boiling or rinsing thinly sliced ingredients are dipped into boiling water for a second or two, and then served with a sauce. This cooking method keeps the ingredients fresh and tender.
16. **AO-Stewing or braising.** Flavour a little hot oil with spring onions and ginger root then stir fries the ingredients for a short time. Now add the stock or water and seasonings, simmer over a low heat .The food should be soft and tender.
17. **QIANDHot salads.** Here the raw ingredients are parboiled or blanched first, then dressed with seasonings. The difference between cold salad and hot salad dressings is as follows:- Cold salad dressing- Soya sauce, vinegar, and sesame seed oil. Hot salad dressing: Ginger shreds, Sichuan pepper corn, salt, sugar and sesame seed oil.
18. **YAN Pickling-** Pickle the food with salt and sugar or with salt and wine .Dishes prepared this way has a subtle fragrance and is crisp.
19. **TA Pan frying-** The ingredients are coated with batter fried in a small amount of oil on both sides over a low heat until done. The ingredients may be deep fried first, and then finished off by pan frying .Seasonings and sauce is added towards the end of cooking.
20. **TIE-PAN. Sticking frying.** This is basically a form of shallow frying, but only one side is fried, the food is not turned over, so that one side is golden brown and the other side is soft and tender.
21. **LIU sauté** This is a special technique which involves two stages of cooking .First deep fry , quick or rapid boil steam or boil the ingredients until done, then mix with seasonings to make a sauce.
   a. Dark brown sauté Pour the sauce over the cooked foods and serve.
   b. Slippery sauté Stir fry the raw ingredients and pour the sauce over half way through cooking, stirring constantly until done.
   d. Soft sauté Steam or boil the ingredients and then, while they are still hot add a thin and delicate sauce.
22. **PENG.Quick braising.** This is one of the important cooking techniques and is always used with deep frying .The ingredients are cut into small pieces and deep fried first, then taken out of the oil and a sauce is added .While the sauce is hot stir fry over high heat and remove the wok from heat and continue stirring for few more times before serving.

23 **.JIANG:A soya braising.** The difference between soya stewing and soya braising is that the ingredients are marinated first in the sauce in which it is cooked, with the additional stock and water. The sauce is reduced or thickened and is served with dish.

24 **.PA. Braising in sauce.** In this method, a little oil is first flavoured with spring onions and or ginger root; the ingredients are then placed in the wok or pot and simmered until done.

25. **SHUN Smoking.** Cooking with heat and smoke from burning materials such as saw dust, tea leaves, cypress branches, bamboo leaves or granulated sugar.

The Chinese menu

Chinese menu bears no resemblance to western menus which are course wise. The Chinese cooking tradition makes for a greater harmony of living, an aspect of Chinese cuisine which has often been over looked. There is a great feeling of togetherness in the way the Chinese eat. They gather around a table and partake all the dishes which are placed on the table in a communal style. Nobody is served just an individual portion in the western way. The chop-sticks are used not only as eating implements but also to help others to a choice piece especially from a particular dish this is usually an expression of respect and affection.

Due to the multi course nature of the Chinese meal, eating and dinning have always been very much a family or communal event and Chinese food is best eaten this way, for only then can you enjoy a variety of dishes. An informal Chinese dinner served at home is essentially a buffet style affair, with more hot dishes then cold served on the table at the same time, to be shared by everyone.

A Chinese meal is served absolutely ready to eat there is neither last minute carving on the table, nor dishing out separate item such as meat, vegetables, gravy or sauce and no long prelude when you wait for everybody to be served before you start. At a Chinese meal, as soon as the first dish or course of dishes is placed on the table the host will raise his glass and say

¯**Gan bei** or cheers or bon appettit.

A SAMPLE MENU Prawns in garlic sauce Wonton soup Stir fried pork with leeches Beans Sichuan Apple toffee

CHOCOLATES Historical background Cocoa was well known to the classic Mayan civilization which flourished and died in the Yucatan and Guatemala in the 1st Millennium. Alongside deceased Maya dignitaries were buried implements like jars and bowls which were used for making chocolate. They called it Ka-ka-w. Linguistics believes that the Maya's probably learnt to use the product from the earlier Olmec civilization which flourished between 1500BC to 400BC.

The beans became a commodity for trade, an object of warfare and also a currency. The Mayans spread the chocolate far and wide to the west of Yucatan where the Aztec established their power. In due course Cocoa became a major source of wealth of the Aztec. To the Aztec chocolate was the drink for the warriors and the elite. Chocolate lent itself to flavour mixtures like maize flour and herbs. It was offered to the Gods and was used to anoint new born children on the forehead, face, fingers and toes. It was, only, under the invader Cortez, when the Europeans, first learnt the full value of cocoa. Its new name ¯chocolate appears to be a Spanish inspired blend of Maya and Spanish. The word was soon applied to all products of cacao. As a commodity of trade cocoa beans began to reach Spain in 1558. As an expensive exotic spice Chocolate was gradually introduced to the rest of Europe. By the 17th century the Italians experimented with new flavourings for chocolate including musk, jasmine, citron and lemon peel. In1659 A. D. David Chaliou was granted a monopoly for selling chocolate throughout France. Chocolate was first sold in London in 1657

By the end of the 18th century there had been a perceptible increase in the amount of chocolate being consumed in stabs, in ices and sorbets, as an ingredient in desserts and main dishes and in pastas and soups.

It was in 1828 that a Dutchman ¯Van Houten patened the screw press which removed 2/3rd of cacao butter. The residue so obtained was known as Cocoa. This dispersed easily in water and was considered to be more digestible.

Mr. Van Houten, also developed an Alkalizing process by treating cocoa during processing with potassium carbonate which led to a milder flavour and darker colour.

By adding the excess cacao butter to ground beans created a smooth paste which could be moulded and remain solid when cool yet melted easily in the mouth.By 1842 Cadbury Bros. was selling block chocolates. By 1847 Fry were marketing chocolate déleciux à Manger. Major contributions were made by Swiss for e.g. In 1880 Randolph Lindt increased the amount of cocoa butter in his formula and developed CONCHING. In 1876 Daniel Peter produced the first milk chocolate.

SOURCES The Cocoa tree provides with its seed the raw material for making chocolate. The scientist Linnacus' assigned the species to a botanical genus, which he named Theobroma' – food of the gods. Botanically the leathery fruits are giant berries or pods.

In this genus 22 species are now recognized, all native to central and South America, of these two are cultivated. Of greater importance is ¯Theobroma Cacao from which nearly all the world's chocolate is produced. Cacao is the term for the tree and for its seeds corrupted to cocoa in English.

It is now cultivated all over the world within an area of 20degrees on both sides of the equator. This tree requires shade when young and is susceptible to fungi and pests. There are many varieties however the Forestero variety accounts for 80% of the world production.

Cacao flowers are pollinated by a species of Midge and grow directly on the trunk of the tree. Only a few flowers develop into fruit or pods and average yield annually being 30 per tree. Full grown fruits are about 8 inches (20cm) long and 4 inches (10 cm) across in an oblong shape. The green pods when ripe are saffron, yellow or red in colour and contain on an average 30 to 40 seeds, occurring in rows and embedded in a white or pinkish pulp.

West Africa is now the largest producer of Cocao and produces over 60% of the world's production.

MANUFACTURE & PROCESSING OF CHOCOLATE Ripe pods are collected, split and the contents scraped out. The seeds and the surrounding pulp are exposed to the sun allowing the pulp to ferment. This fermentation process is completed in 5 to 7 days. Fermentation is essential for the development of good flavour, for use in the making of chocolate. Fermentation develops ¯flavour precursors breaking down sugar to glucose and fructose and turning some protein into free amino acids and smaller peptides. After fermentation the beans are dried and exported to manufactures. They lose 50% of their weight on drying and the yield of a single tree is approx. 500 gms to 1 kg.

At the manufacturers a complex process of roasting and grinding turns the seeds into chocolate mass i.e. cocoa and cocoa butter. These two are mixed in varying proportion to form chocolate. Chocolate that contains a very high percentage of cocoa butter and is known as

CHOCOLATE COUVERTURE.

Before preparing chocolate for dipping, moulding, coating, sauces, etc. they must be stabilised or tempered.

TEMPERING Before preparing chocolate for use they must be stabilised or tempered. This process applies only to genuine chocolate containing very high cocoa butter or chocolate couverture. Cocoa butter consists of different fats, some melt at low temperatures others at higher temperatures those with lower melting points are the first to solidify on being cooled giving chocolate an undesirable grainy texture. It is the high melting point fats that give high quality chocolate its shine and snap. The objective of tempering is to distribute these fats evenly by creating very fine crystals evenly throughout so that it becomes smooth, sets evenly and quickly.

Tempering consists of 3 stages

1. Melting: Chocolate couverture must be melted over a Bain Marie to 49°- 50° C (120122°F)at this temp all fats would have melted, it should be stirred constantly to evenly distribute the fats.
2. Tempering: When the chocolate has melted it is removed from the Bain Marie on to a marble top and stirred constantly to about 29°C (84°F). The object of this process is to seed the mixture with cocoa butter crystals of a uniform and stable type which will keep well during storage. At this point nuts, fruits, etc. may be added.
3. RE-WARMING: After tempering and cooling, if the mass is to thick for using it must be re warmed over Bain Marie till it reaches a temp of 29°C(84°F). This step must be done carefully for if the temperature rises to 44°C or 111° F the chocolate is no longer tempered, it SEIZES i.e. it goes hard and grainy.

Chocolate which has not been tempered will take excessively long time to set and its texture will not be good. Also some of the cocoa butter with float and then set making a whitish coating called the BLOOM'.

CHOCOLATE MAKING Manual: Chocolates can be made by hand dipping, the centres being lowered on a special dipping fork into molten chocolate, covered and then deposited on paper to set. It is a skill which takes years to master and is a method used mainly by craft confectioners, who wish to produce high quality individual chocolate selections.

AUTOMATED: There are two automated methods:-

a) Enrobing: It is a method in which the centres are transported under a curtain of molten chocolate and then allowed to set.

b) Shell moulding: Molten chocolate is deposited into moulds to form a shell which is then filled. A lid of chocolate seals the filling in before it is de moulded.

Hand Moulding: This is done using moulds made of plastic, metal or rubber which must be kept clean and dry as well as smooth. Molten chocolate is then deposited by hand into moulds to form a shell which is then filled and covered by a layer of molten chocolate and allowed to set. Chocolate shrinks when set thereby pulling it away from the moulds so it can be easily de moulded.

TYPES OF CHOCOLATE:

TEMPERED Chocolate is used for dipping, making moulds, pastries, cake icings, cookies and meringues.

LIQUEUR CHOCOLATES can be made by shell moulding or by depositing the syrup into impressions made in trays of starch & left undisturbed for some time, the syrup ¯crusts forming sugar crystals and can be lifted out and enrobed.

TRUFFLES: Are based on a ganache flavoured with sprits, essences and nuts.

WHITE CHOCOLATE is made by using only cocoa butter

Block Chocolates

Cocoa powder Cocoa powder is made by dehydrating cocoa mass.

Drinking Chocolate: is made by dehydrating prepared Chocolate into powdered form.

Chocolates contain Phenylethlamine a naturally occurring substance in the brain which stimulates euphoric feelings. It also contains THEOBROMINE a stimulant which acts on the muscles and Caffeine, but in much smaller quantities.

YIELD is 600 calories per 100 gms.

CUISINE OF GREAT BRITAIN Great Britain lies to the northwest of Continental Europeand east of Ireland. It is separated from the continent by the North Seaand by the English Channel, which narrows to 34 kilometres (21 mi) at the Straits of Dover. It is situated between longitude 50°N to 61°N and latitude 8°W to 2°E and occupies an area, of 209,331 km^{2} (80,823 sq mi), approximately. The

North Channel, Irish Sea, St. George's Channel and Celtic Sea separate the island from the islands of Ireland to its west. Geographically, the island is marked by low, rolling countryside in the east and south, while hills and mountains predominate in the western and northern regions. Great Britain comprises of England, Wales and Scotland on the island of Great Britain, while the United Kingdom includes Great Britain as well as Northern Ireland.

ENGLAND England is a country which historically has been invaded by successive waves of different people right from Celts, Picts, Romans, Vikings, Saxsons, Normans, etc., right from ancient times, and all of them have left a mark on the English kitchen. In recent times immigrants from West Indies, Asians, especially from Indo-Pak has turned contemporary cooking across Britain to reflect its multi cultural society with its vast array of ingredients and culinary skills imported from around the World.

The English have a reputation of generous meat consumption, some of the traditional meat dishes are: mixed grill, Lancashire hot pot, Roast beef with Yorkshire pudding, beef steak with oyster sauce beef and kidney pie and Sheppard's pie. Ham and sausages are an important part of the diet, famous Hams are York Ham and Black Braden ham.

The large consumption of meat encouraged the development of interesting accompaniments like Cumberland sauce, red currant jelly, pickled walnuts, numerous chutneys and pickles. Poultry dishes include stuffed chicken, stuffed duck and stuffed turkey. Stuffed Turkey is the speciality for Christmas along with cranberry sauce, bacon and chipolata sausage.

Amongst vegetables potatoes are a complete favourite and feature in a vast array of dishes. Peas, fava beans, asparagus, parsley, watercress, cabbage and parsnips are other commonly used vegetables.

British also consume large amounts of fish e.g. Dover Sole fried in butter; mackerels served with gooseberries and baked crabs dressed in their shells.

Regional specialities

*Hindle Wakes from Lancashire is chicken stuffed with prunes and herb flavoured herbs, cooked with vinegar and glazed with a lemon cream sauce.

*Toad in the hole is a dish of sausages baked in batter.

*Angles on horseback are bacon wrapped oysters grilled and served on croutons.

*Black puddings are blood puddings from Lancashire.

The English are known for having a heavy Breakfast and would include selection of juices, eggs to order, grilled mushrooms, bacon and sausages, selection of breads, jams and preserves and of course Tea.

Afternoon tea is a characteristic meal of the English and may include scones with strawberry jam, sandwiches, teacakes, muffins, buns, crumpets and ginger and brandy snaps.

Cakes include the famous Victoria sponge cake and the traditional Sinnel cake and marzipans. Puddings are very popular and include desserts like Cabinet pudding, Prince Albert pudding and bread and butter pudding.

Cheeses are a favourite after meals and are accompanied with cream crackers, some famous chesses are Stilton blue veined cheese, Cheddar cheese. Beer is the all time favourite beverage.

SCOTLAND

Scotland lies to the north of England and although being surrounded by sea on all three sides it still has the resources of the mountains, the mild lush farmlands as well as the sea. Scotland's fine cooking has more in common with France than its neighbour England.

Breakfast and High Tea are elevated to full hearty meals, breakfast is served with bannock- a griddle baked flat bread made from barley and oats or baps a traditional soft breakfast roll, or Dundee cake a rich buttery Scottish fruit cake containing sultanas, ground almonds and candied peel, Dundee marmalade, porridge, lightly poached kippers and eggs. High tea would feature hot or cold savoury dish followed by a sweet pudding or fruit pies or cakes or scones. The favourite dish is Scotch eggs made of ground sausage meat wrapped around a hardboiled egg which is coated with breadcrumbs and deep fried until golden.

Fresh fish is readily available anywhere in Scotland, traditionally herrings, herring's roe cakes, trout are enjoyed fried in oatmeal. Shellfish dish includes Limpet stovies which is shellfish stewed with sliced potatoes. Pratan Bree is crab soup made with cream and rice.

Meat dishes include Scotch broth made from cured lamb, hotchpotch is a stew made from neck of lamb and vegetables, haggis is an offal sausage, cock-a-leekie is the famous chicken and leek dish cooked in beef stock with prunes and herbs.

The Scots love strong flavoured vegetables like rutabaga and turnips. The famous dessert of Scotland is cloutie dumplings which is a spiced boiled pudding with dried fruits. Cheddar is the most famous cheese from Scotland. Whiskey is the national passion of Scotland.

WALES

Wales is situated to the west of England and its cuisine is based on the agricultural lifestyle prevalent in rural households. The day starts with a hearty breakfast followed by a substantial main mid-day meal and a relaxed supper.

Wales has the seaweed named LAVER which is hand gathered and sold ready cooked in markets to be made into cakes or Laver bread which are fried and served with bacon for breakfast. Mutton is the favourite meat and is traditionally cured and served with prune sauce and black currants. Leeks, potatoes, carrots, Swede and cabbage are the commonly served vegetables.

Specialities of Wales is the Welsh rarebit a savoury snack of melted cheese grilled on toast, Glamorgan sausage which is made from cheese, breadcrumbs, leeks, and mustard and is served grilled or fried. The famous cake of Wales is the Bara brith which is a yeast fruit loaf.

IRELAND

IRELAND is an island situated to the west of England and unlike the rest of western Europe remained free of Roman influence and remained true to the ancient Celtic culture. The food and cooking of Ireland is based on the simple use of good ingredients in heavy peasant style dishes.

The staples of Irish diet were cereals like oats, barley, wheat and rye, and dairy products. Potatoes when introduced readily substituted cereals, especially amongst the poor so much so that in the mid 19th century failure of the potato crop caused the great potato famine. Other popular vegetables are cabbage and leeks. Ireland produces a lot of dairy products including excellent cheeses.

Ireland has an extensive coastline and is known for excellent seafood like cockles, mussels, scallops, Galaway oysters, Dublin Bay prawns, mackerel, Irish salmon and trout. Carragheen whose scientific name is Chondrus crispus also known as Irish moss is a species of red algae which is used for its setting properties. Sloke the Irish name for laver and is the same seaweed used by the Welsh is also cooked in Ireland.

Traditional meat dishes include Irish stew made from lamb, onions and potatoes, Limerick ham is a traditional smoked ham which may be boiled and baked. Dublin coddle is a hearty stew of sausages and bacon. Soda bread is the local favourite made using buttermilk and soda bi-carbonate, they are slashed with a deep cross on the top, this soft bread rises high and tastes wonderful when warm.

A Sample menu
Scotch broth
Roast beef
Yorkshire puddinglazed carrots and turnips
Roast potatoes
Apple crumble

Icings

Icings or frostings are sweet coatings for cakes and other baked goods.

Icings have three main functions:-

1. They improve the keeping qualities of the cake by forming protective coatings around it.

2. they contribute flavour and richness
3. They improve appearance.

There are seven basic kinds of icings:-

1. Fondant
2. Butter cream
3. Foam Type icing
4. Fudge type icing
5. Flat type icing
6. Royal or decorators icings
7. Glazes

Fondant

Fondant is sugar syrup that is crystallized to a smooth creamy white mass. When applied it sets up into a shiny, non-sticky coating.

Fondant is prepared by dissolving 500gms of granulated or cube sugar in 150 ml of water and 15 ml of glucose and then allowed to boil gradually till it reaches the soft ball stage 112°-116 °C (234-240°F) which may be tested by dropping a little syrup in iced water where it will from a ball under water but lose its shape immediately when it is exposed to air. The syrup must be cooled immediately and the air bubbles then subside.

The syrup is, then, poured out into a cold surface and worked first with a spatula until it turns from a clear liquid to a white crumbly solid. It is then kneaded by hand until smooth and finished by being left to ripen in a cool place for at least 12 hours.

The object is to produce minute crystals in a super staturated solution of sugar giving a creamy texture to the finished product.

Uses:

- v For first coating on fruit cakes before applying Royal icing.
- v For dipping fresh fruits to make confections for immediate consumption.
- v For casting into moulds.
- v Pastel coloured icing for cakes

Butter Cream Icings

Butter cream icings are light smooth mixtures of fat and icing sugar. They may also contain eggs to increase their smoothness or lightness. This icing is very popular and is used for covering many kinds of cake.

They are easily flavoured and coloured to suit a variety of purposes.

There are four types of basic kinds of butter cream:

1. Butter icing is made with butter and icing sugar which are creamed together to the desired consistency and lightness.
2. a) Simple butter cream are made by creaming together fat and sugar to the desired consistency, a small quantity of egg white may be whipped in to obtain the desired lightness.

   b) Decorators butter cream is a simple butter cream used for making flowers and other cake decorations. It is creamed only a little, because if too much air is incorporated, it could not be able to hold delicate shapes.

3. Meringue type butter creams are prepared by first beating egg whites and adding a boiling syrup or just sugar. Soft butter is then mixed into the meringue. This is a very light smooth icing.
4. French butter creams are similar to above but the mixture is made with whole eggs, and boiling syrup. This is a very rich, light icing. N.B. Unsalted butter is the preferred fat for butter creams because of its flavour and melt in the mouth quality.

Recipe for: Butter icing

i) Beat 125 gms. of butter add 125 gms. of icing sugar with 30 gm of milk and flavouring. Beat until creamy and smooth.

ii) Butter cream or crème au beurre.

Place 2 egg whites and 125gm of icing sugar in a mixing bowl and whisk until mixture holds shape. Cool slightly. Cream 125 gm butter until soft then beat in the meringue mixture a little at a time. Flavour or colour as desired.

Foam type icing

They are also known as boiled icings. They are simple meringues made with boiling syrup and may also contain gelatine as a stabilizer. Foam type icings should be applied thickly to cakes and left in peaks and swirls. These icings are not stable and should be used they day they are prepared.

Flat type icings

These icings are also known as water icings and are mixtures of confectioners' sugar, water, sometimes corn syrup and flavouring. They are used for coffee cakes, Danish party and sweet rolls.

They are a simple mixture consisting of five pounds of powdered sugar 300ml water, 200 ml corn syrup and flavouring as desired. Egg white may also be added to lighten the frosting.

Fudge Type icing.

Fudge type icings are rich cooked icings. Fudge icings are heavy and thick and they may be flavoured by a variety of ingredients. They are used on cup cakes, layer cakes, loaf cakes, sheet cakes, etc.

To store fudge icings they must be properly covered with cling flim and then kept in an airtight container in the refrigerator.

To use stored fudge icing, warm in a double boiler until it is soft enough to spread. They are stable frostings which hold their shape well on cakes and cup cakes.

CHOCOLATE FUDGE FROSTING

Sugar	–	450 gms
Glucose or corn syrup	-	150 gms
Water	-	120 ml
Butter	-	150 gms
Sugar pwd	-	375 gms
Cocoa pwd	-	175 gms
Vanilla essence	-	to taste

Method

1. Combine granulated sugar, glucose and water and boil till 116°C.
2. Sift powdered sugar and cocoa together, cream sugar/cocoa with butter till light and fluffy and gradually add syrup and essence and blend well.
3. Use immediately while still warm and spreadable.

Royal Icing

This icing is the traditional covering for Christmas and wedding cakes, and is made from icing sugar beaten with egg whites and lemon juice; a teaspoon of glycerine may be added. In the hands of a skilled confectioner this can be used to produce perfectly flat smooth surfaces or piped into intricate borders, patterns or trellis work, which are very fragile but very hard when set. It is always applied over a layer of marzipan or fondant.

The recipe for royal icing needed for 6 inch round or 5 inch square cakes is as follows.

1.	Egg whites	2. No.
2.	Icing Sugar	500 gms
3.	Lemon juice	1 Teaspoon
4.	Glycerine	1 Teaspoon
5.	Cream of tartar	2.5 gms

Method

- v Beat the egg whites with a fork until frothy
- v Gradually beat in 1/2 the icing sugar, using a wooden spoon (+ Lemon juice and cream of tartar)
- v Beat in the remaining icing sugar with the glycerine
- v Beat thoroughly until smooth and white, and having a consistency that stands in soft peaks.
- v Add colouring if required.
- v Cover the bowl with a damp cloth and leave it to stand for several hours to allow bubbles to escape. Before using stir well with wooden spoon but do not over beat.

The icings mentioned below are similar to Royal icing.

Sugar paste or Moulded Icing

Beat one egg white and 15 ml glucose gradually adding 500gm icing sugar to form a still paste. Turn unto a surface sprinkled with corn flour and knead until smooth. Wrap in cling film and keep and keep in a plastic bag to prevent it from drying, will keep refrigerated for 6 weeks.

This quantity is sufficient to cover 8 inch round cake.

SATIN ICING

Boil together 50 gms of butter + lemon juice +dissolved 250 gm of icing sugar and cook for 2 min. Remove from heat and beat in another 250 gm of icing sugar till stiff. Gradually mix in another 175 gm of icing sugar and knead until smooth preserve as above.

GLAZES or GLACE

Glazes are thin glossy transparent coatings that give shine to baked products and help prevent drying. The simplest mixture for this purpose is a syrup made from 250 gms of icing sugar in 30 ml of water or milk. They are brushed over small cakes or poured to give a smooth finish.

Syrup glazes may contain gelatin or corn starch. Fruit glazes, the most popular being apricot are made by cooking them till they melt and then forcing them through a strainer. Ganache may also be considered as an icing

GANACHE

A flavoured cream made with chocolate and fresh cream, sometimes with butter added. It may be used as a sauce, or to glaze a cake or it may be whipped and used a filling and/or icing. Ganache can also be made of stiffer consistency, chilled and rolled into truffles or as topping for petit fours. It was created in Paris round about 1850

Method:

Bring 100 ml of double cream to the boil. Remove from heat and add 225 gms of plain unsweetened chocolate broken into even squares. Stir until the chocolate has melted and is thoroughly combined with cream. Leave until cool but not set then whip until pale, thick and light or before whipping it may be poured over cakes as chocolate icing.

Toppings are anything that is used to cover a cake or a pastry and it may be fruits, jam, nuts etc. and Icings are that part of toppings which are sweet coatings that may be applied to cakes and pastries.

RULES For selection of icing

- v The flavour texture and colour of icing must be compatible with the cake.
- v In general use heavy frosting with heavy cakes and light frosting with light cakes. e.g. Angel food cakes with simple flat icings. High ratio cakes with butter cream or fudge type icings. Genoese sponge with French or meringue type icing.
- v Use the best quality flavourings and use them sparingly.
- v The flavour of the frosting should not be stronger than the cake.
- v Use colour sparingly, light pastel shades are more appetizing than loud colours.

Mexican Cuisine

The land of Mexico stretches from the arid border land with the USA to the North to the tropical Jungles of the Yucatan bordering Guatemala to the South from the humid coastline on the Gulf of Mexico on the East to the drier Pacific coast.

Mexico has been home to number of great civilization that are thought to date back potentially as far back as 40000 years. These civilizations advanced greatly over the centuries. However these native cultures of this area of the Americas did not have a written language and thus many of the specifies of their History are not known.

The arid north was sparsely inhabited by nomadic tribes who were hunter gathers who lived of the land. The original inhabitants of Mexico includes the Olmecs, Tolters, Lapotecs, Jotonais, Mayans and Aztecs.

The great Aztecs civilization contribution was the cultivation of maize which together with red beans and rice constitutes the staple food throughout the whole of Latin America. Tortillas (Pancakes made of cornmeal are eaten in a number of ways and is the signature dish/preparations of Mexico).

These cultures thrived on a mostly vegetarian diet because the availability of significant animal food was limited.

The arrival of Spanish in Mexico in the early sixteen century began a new chapter for the people and cuisine of this culture. After the Spanish arrived the native people incorporated many Spanish elements into their diets including pork, chicken olives, rice, cinnamon, radish, grapes, sugar cane, stone fruits, wheat, chickpeas melon and onions. This developed into a distinctive Mexican cuisine which combined the traditions of the natives with that of the Spanish. From the culinary point of view Mexico may be divided into the arid north, the rich central and the thickly forested south.

NOTHERN MEXICO

Northern Mexico comprises of nine areas which are known as the frontier. The Apache, Ute, Chichimec are native to this area. The life styles of the regions inhabitants had a large impact on the development of cuisine. Vaqueros (Cowboys) cooked on the open range over fire pits, Fajitas & Enchiladas are good examples, fresh salsas and guacamole accompanied the food, utilizing garlic, cilantro, tomatillos, lime and chilies native to the region.

Immigrants from Southern Mexico introduced corn based dishes to the regions diet. In coastal areas fish is a large part of the diet. The flavour profile of the region includes smoky, rich yet lean, spicy dishes with garlic, corn and wheat.

CENTRAL MEXICO

The capital of Mexico is situated in central Mexico. Most of central Mexico is a plateau surrounded by highland on all four sides. The rainy season last from May, to September. The remaining months are somewhat dry. When the Spanish arrived it was the Aztec civilization that was ruling Mexico. This is the land of chillies, both fresh and dried. Herbs such as epazote, hoja santa, avocado leaves, cilantro and Mexican oreganos are widely used. Cheese such as queso fresco is used as seasonings and toppings.

Name of some cheeses: Chihuahua, cotija, queso fresco and sardo.

Southern Mexico

Southern Mexico comprises of seven regions of which Tabasco is one (famous for Tabasco sauce). This region includes active volcanoes, pacific lowlands and highlands featuring dense jungles and a tropical climate. The diverse geography and isolated locations bed to the development of very different culture and hence cuisine. For e.g. Oaxaca which is quite remote retains its natural heritage. It is noted for its coffee and mescal.

Whereas Veracruz situated on the Gulf of Mexico was a port of choice for explorers and invaders. Veracruz was strongly influenced by Spanish, African and Caribbean culinary traditions. The cuisine has been able to blend the indigenous flavours and ingredients with those of the Mediterranean combining the use of olive oil, garlic, onions, capers and green olives with new world ingredients like jalapenos and tomatoes.

General Notes

The major Mexican meal is taken between 2 to 4 in the afternoon. In its full form it consists of 5 courses: a soup followed by a pasta of rice or noodles, a meat or fish dish accompanied by tortillas, beans and a fruit or dessert with coffee. Mexicans normally have an early light breakfast and later a mid morning breakfast consisting of eggs. Bacon, tomatoes and chilli sauces and of course tortillas. The evening meal except for special occasions is a simple matter of a pastry, fruit and perhaps some leftovers.

SPECIALITIES of MEXICO

TORTILLAS:

Maize remains the foundation of Mexican cuisine eaten in all areas and by all classes. The process for making tortillas starts the night before by boiling dried maize with water and lime, and leaving it to soak overnight. In the morning they drain it and rub the skins off the grains, after which the grains are ground into coarse wet flour, known as Masa or nixtamal. It will then be shaped by hand into flat cakes some 18cm in diameter and 2mm thick. These tortillas are cooked in seconds on a griddle known as ¯COMAL and are carefully wrapped in a hand embroidered napkin to keep them hot.

This technique of boiling in wood ash or lime and then soaking is known as ¯

Nixtamalization which was discovered by the local natives of southern Mexico and its southern neighbour Guatemala as early as 1500-1200 B. C..

This procedure makes it possible to remove the skin off the grain and allows the grain to be ground to a flour that produces a flexible bread, and renders the protein in the grain more accessible.

Tortillas may be served plain fried or baked, either flat or folded and topped or filled with various stuffing's.

Tortillas piled with savoury assortments are called ¯tostadas Enchiladas are folded stuffed tortillas, usually topped with a sauce and baked. ¯Tacos are plain tortillas, stuffed rolled and may be fried. Chilaquiles thin strips of fried tortilla covered with a highly spiced sauce and cooked in the oven.

Mole takes its name from molli, a nahuatt word meaning concoction.

Moles Pobiano De Gajolote- A very famous Mexican dish supposed to have been invented in the 16th Century by the convent of Puebla. They cooked Turkey in a sauce typical of Aztec cooking. The sauce (mole) is traditionally prepared by pounding various sweet and hot chillies such as ancho, mutato and pastitlla, onions, tomatoes, pieces of tortillas garlic, crushed almonds, aniseed, sea same seeds cinnamon, cloves and coriander seeds. The mixture is pounded with a little turkey stock till it is a smooth paste. It is then simmered with more turkey stock to which lard and plain dark chocolate are added. The cooked turkey is cut into pieces, liberally coated with the sauce, and served sprinkled with sesame seeds, sweet corn or small tortillas. It is served as main course.

GUACAMOLE: A dip or sauce originating in Mexico and consisting of avocado, tomato, onion, lemon juice and spices.

GERMAN CUISINE

Germany is situated North/Central Europe. To the north is the North Sea and to the North-East is the Baltic Sea, West of Germany lies Netherlands, Belgium and France. To the south lies Switzerland and Austria and to the East lies the Czech Republic and Poland.

Germany may be divided into three Culinary Regions, with the German speaking Prussians in the North and east. Saxony in the centre and Wurttemberg and Bavaria, in the south. Culinary specialities from each of these regions are influenced by climate, terrain as well as social status and Germany's history of localised governance.

NORTHEN REGION

In the cold damp North Germany where Dutch, Scandinavian and Polish influences mingle—thick soups, smoked meat and fish are popular, supplemented with dishes prepared from local crops, featuring beets, potatoes, cabbage, barley, hops and rye. Sausages and other charcuterie products are also a staple of the northern diet- e.g.Braunshweiger from the town of Braunshweig is a famous liver sausage. Sweet and soured creamed sauces and soups are very common. Meals are accompanied by beer or schnapps (strong liquor similar to gin).

CENTRAL REGION

This region is an area of rolling hills with wide expanses of forest and numerous spas. This region is basically an agricultural society famous for Pumpernickel and rye breads which are produced from local grains. Dumplings are the staple food of this area a number of varieties are made from potatoes, bread flour or oats. Frankfurter sausages are from this region and are now famous all over the world. Pfefferpotthast, a beef stew strongly flavoured with pepper are popular. Westphalia is famous for its ham and pork dishes. The thriving vineyards of this area produce excellent wine. Stolen is the traditional Christmas made from locally grown fruits and berries.

SOUTHERN REGION

This area includes the states of Bavaria, Swabia, Baden and Alsac-Lorraine. The cuisine of southern Germany features many of the same staples as its other counter parts but the dishes are much lighter. Vegetables including white asparagus, radishes and cabbages are consumed in large quantities here and vegetable salads are very popular throughout southern Germany. The cuisine of Bavaria which is located in south east Germany is influenced by Austria and the cuisine of Alsac-Lorraine situated in south west Germany is influenced by France. Fine wines are produced here. Spätzle a cross between a dumpling and noodle is a popular side dish. Very popular desserts are prepared with such fruits as plums, cherries, apple and berries that are grown in this region. This region is best known for its Schwartzälder Krichtorte also known as the Black Forest cake in English is a cherry cake flavoured with the cherry liquor ¯Krishwasser .

Other famous German Dishes are:

Lebkuchen

Lebkuchen is a traditional Germanbaked Christmastreat, somewhat resembling gingerbread.

Lebkuchen were invented by medievalmonks in Franconia,Germanyin the 13th century. *Lebkuchen* bakers were recorded as early as 1296 in Ulm, and 1395 in Nürnberg(Nuremberg). The latter being the most famous exporter today, of the product that is known as Nürnberger Lebkuchen (Nürnberg Lebkuchen).

Sauterbraten

This is a famous beef dish which involves marinating the meat in wine, vinegar and buttermilk and braising it. It is served with a sweetened sauce

Gansebraten

"Roast goose". Usually stuffed with apples and prunes.

Sauerkraut

SauerkrautGerman pronunciation: *zoyerkroyt* ,French *Choucroute*, directly translated: "sour cabbage", is finely shredded cabbagethat has been fermentedby various bacteria. It has a long shelf-life and a distinctive sourflavor, both of which result from the lactic acidthat forms when the bacteria ferment the sugars in the cabbage. It is therefore not to be confused with pickled cabbageor coleslaw, which receives its acidic taste from vinegar**Schwarzsauer**

It is stew of goose giblets and blood, usually cooked with dried apples, prunes and pears.

A SAMPLE GERMAN MENU

Linsensuppe Sauerbaaten Spatzle German potato salad Pumpernickir Apfel Strudel

Italy

Italyis located in southern Europeand comprises the long, boot-shaped Italian Peninsula, the land between the peninsula and the Alps, and a number of islands including Sicilyand Sardinia(Corsica, although belonging to the Italian geographical region, has been a part of France since 1769). Its total area is 301,230 square kilometres (116,310 sq mi), of which 294,020 km^2 (113,520 sq mi) is land and 7,210 km^2 is water (2,784 sq mi).

It lies between latitudes 35°and 48° N, and longitudes 6°and 19° E.

Italy borders with Switzerland(740 km/460 mi), France(488 km/303 mi), Austria(430 km/270 mi) and Slovenia(232 km/144 mi). San Marino(39 km/24 mi) and Vatican city(0.44 km/0.27 mi) are both entirely surrounded by Italy.

For culinary purposes, the country can be loosely divided into the South, Central and North. Northern Italy is bordered by France, Switzerland, Austria and Solvenia. Central and Southern Italy is bordered by the Mediterranean Sea, a position that holds great historical importance in terms of exploration and trade.

The generally rugged and mountainous terrain of Italy is home to a population of 58 million people. Politically Italy is divided into twenty regions and each region is unique in its own way. The culinary diversity, specialties and pride of each region are quite remarkable.

HISTORICAL BACKGROUND & REGIONAL CUISINE

Italy has a rich past, at one time, parts of the country were occupied by Etruscans, Spanish, French, Greek, Arabs, Austrian and Germans. Such occupations inevitably shaped the cuisine of Italy today. Italy was made up of separate and disputing states, till it was unified in 1861 by Giuseppe Garibaldi.

Northern Italy

The Romans who ruled Italy and at one time almost all of Europe, for about a thousand years has left a lasting effect on Cookery in Italy, they brought in a lot of local customs and foods of the countries they conquered. The port city of Venice was the centre of trade with the Middle East. This prosperous city had control over the trade of rare foods of the time like sugar, coffee and spices. Western areas of North Italy like Lombardy and Piedmont have strong French and Swiss influences in their cuisine.

Northern Italy is considered the most prosperous area of the country of which the most famous are the Eastern part of Venito known as Emilla-Romagna. The cuisine is dominated by meat and seafood. The green pastures produce a lot of milk, butter and cheese, e.g. Gorgonzola and Mascarpone. Fresh Pasta, polenta and rice are consumed in large quantities. Risotto is the staple of the people of Piedmont. Popular cooking techniques include boiling, stewing and braising. They use a special oven called a Fogher that is used for spit roasting.

Popular pasta shapes of this region include anolini, cappelletti, lasagna, tagliatelle tortelli and tortellini. Other specialities of this region is the Parmigiano-Reggiano(Cheese), Prosciutto di Parma (Ham), and Aceto Balsamico Tradizionale (vinegar).

CENTRAL ITALY

The early settlers on central Italy were the Etruscans who migrated from the Asia Minor as early as 800 BC The Etruscans were an advanced civilization with a major empire. The Romans flourished between the 5th Century BC to 5th Century AD) with Christianity at its core. The Romans built an extensive system of roads and a central market. The great Renaissance originated here in this region and the first ever cooking school was founded in Florence. From the culinary point of view the most significant family in Italy is the Medicis of Florence. It was the Catherine of Medici who single handily shaped the future of Culinary and exported it to France when she married King Henri II.

Central Italy comprises of seven regions of which Roma the capital city of Italy and Christianity is located in the region of Latium. Central Italy is known for its livestock, mainly beef, goat and lamb which are commonly gritted, spit roasted or deep fried

SOUTHERN ITALY

Southern they have been greatly influenced by Greeks and Arabs from North Africa. The regional cuisine began in Southern Italy with the arrival of the Greeks in 415 BC. The Greek introduced wheat cultivation, Bread making, olives, honey and nuts. Romans ruled later but did not contribute much to cuisine except for the introduction of fava beans. Sicily which is at the foot of Italy in only 145 Km from the African continent, and was conquered by the Arabs as early as the ninth century AD They bought in exotic ingredients and planted citrus trees. They also introduced the notion of combining sweet and sour flavours. Saffron, nuts, rice, couscous, sugar cane and ice cream are just a few of the contributions from the Arab world. Olive oil is the preferred fat of the region. Naples at the ankle of the Italian leg is a very historical place; it was the gateway for the entry of Catalan Cookery. Pizza's home is the Neapolitan area of Southern

Italy.

The great difference in Italy's climate and geography are favourable to many different agricultural forms. This means that while a superb cheese is produced from Cow's milk in the north, the south has cheese made from sheep's milk which is just as excellent Northern recipes use butter and cream, the central provinces used lard and olive oil and the south is predominately olive oil.

Respect for the basic produce and a feeling for the freshness and quality of the ingredients determines the lively seasonal variety of dishes. As result the range of products on offer is extensive and high in quality. Unadulterated taste and inspired simplicity are the main characteristics of Italian cookery, as well as health and economical attitude towards food and eating habits.

Coffee with B/F is generally consumed by 10am, followed by Lunch or pranzo which is more prevalent in the rural areas where it is a family affair with substantial 3 or 4 courses. More extensive Lunch is saved for Sundays and other special days. The evening meal is eaten around 8 pm which could again be 3 or 4 courses. A midnight snack is quite common

Antipasta is the Italian word for appetizer or starters they are composed of high quality ingredients like olive which maybe raw, pickled or marinated, toasted slices of bread, salads or sausage or ham in thin slices along with melon and figs

Bread Specialties (PANE)

1. Bruschetta : toasted slices of bread with garlic, olive oil and tomato.
2. Cilindrati : croissants made from thinly rolled bread dough.
3. Grissini Bread sticks from Turin.
4. Crocetta Hot cross Buns

Another famous specialty of Italy is the Pizza. e.g. of Pizza alla :-

- Napolitana consisting of tomatoes, Mozzarella and anchovy fillets.
- Proscuitto Ham
- Funghi- Mashrooms

SPECIALITIES OF ITALY

am is another specialty. Prosciutto de Parma

Italy's most famous ham comes from the province of Parma north-west of BOLOGNA. The quality of PARMA Hams is created with the pigs being fed on barley, corn and fruit.

When slaughtered it must be at least 10 months old, to ensure that the meat is firm and rosy and surrounded by a thick layer of fat. Raw leg should weigh 10 kgs. It is then brined in three phases and then left to dry. They are then matured for a year in cellars with limited supply of air. After 12 months they are ready to eat.

PASTA SECCA (DRY)

Italians are very fond of dry pasta. There are about 300 diff varieties. Pasta is made from durum wheat semolina and can be divided into three categories.

1. PASTA CORTA : Short noodles and may be many shapes such as spirals, wheels, stars, snails, shells and short tube.
2. PASTA LUNGA : long noodles which include the entire spagethi and tagliatelle family- 4 inch and above.
3. PASTA RIPENNA : filled pasta parcels, fortellini and raviolli are the best known.

Some name of pasta

1. BUCATIN : Long smooth hollow noodles.
2. CANNELLONI : Finger length hollow good for filling
3. PENNE : Short pipes with slanting edges.
4. FARFALLA : shaped liked butterflies.
5. SPIRALE : Spiral shapes
6. TAGLINTELLE : Ribbon noodle.
7. LASAGNE : smooth sheets of pasta

GNOOCHI

They are small dumplings or gruels and are a passion for Italians among a wealth of variations a common type is made with mashed potatoes mixed with milk served with a lots of Parmesan, tomato or meat sauce.

Potato may be replaced with semolina, chestnut flour, cornmeal and even pumpkin.

POLENTA

Polenta is an ancient dish made with any grain be it millet, buckwheat, chickpeas or broad beans. After Columbus bought corn to Europe, it became the staple for production of POLENTA as the Polenta made from corn kernels became the most economically viable grain.

Polenta is delicious with rabbit, lamb, game, sausages, cream dishes and fish dishes.

PARMIGINAO REGGIANO

The most famous of all Italian cheese, which has been produced using the same method for seven centuries. Produced in stipulated area which are the provinces of PARMA including Reggio, Emilla, Modena and Mantera on the right bank of the river Po and Bologna on the left bank of River Reno. Cows must be grazed on a meadow or are fed on alfalfa.

Milk is poured into traditional bells shaped copper vats. It is then curdled. The curd Cagliate is then again reheated twice at 45°C and then at 55 °C. The resultant mass is removed in Cheese cloth and deposited in wooden or metal moulds. It is then left in salt solutions for 20-25 days. They are then dried in the sun before being stored in the CASCINA' on wooden shelves to mature slowly regularly turned and brushed. Two gallons of milk produces a pound of cheese they are hard cheeses.

PECORINO

They are produced is south Italy. It is a hard cheese made from sheep's milk and are moulded in basket work cylinders which are woven in SARDINA. When matured the rind is hard and dark. Pecorino Romano is considered the best.

GORGONZOLA

Originally only produced in the little town of the same name near Milan. It is made from full cream pasteurised cow's milk. Milk is heated up to 32° C and curdled with rennin. Spores of pencillum glaucum are also added. They are poured into round Moulds. It is a blue veined cheese.

A sample menu
Minestrone Andalusia
Ravioli Arabeata
Fettuccini carbonara
Pollo alla cacciatore
Medanzane parmigiane
Tiramisu

MERINGUE

Also known as Foam' is a very light item of patisserie made from stiffly beaten egg whites and sugar. Meringue became popular in the 6th century and was popularised by the Queen Marie Antoinette who had a great liking for meringues. The use of meringue by piping was invented by Careme. Meringues are made by incorporating enough sugar to both stabilize and sweeten the meringue.

TYPES OF MERINGUES

There are three types of meringues:-
?Meringues ordinaire or common meringues

Method:-

- Egg whites must be carefully separated and put in a clean bowl; this must be done carefully so that no particles of the egg yolk must mix with the egg white.
- Beat the egg whites until frothy and then start to add the sugar which has been previously ground to a very fine powder, the sugar must be added gradually. Once the sugar is incorporated, whip the meringue to soft, medium or stiff peak, or as required by the recipe.
- This type of meringue can be used to top a pie, to pipe and bake into shells or used to create borders and other decorations. Since the whites are not heated to a safe temperature, this type of meringue should be used for applications where it will be cooked by poaching or baking.

Meringue Swiss

Beat 225 gms of egg whites till frothy, add 450 gms of powdered sugar. Beat over double boiler to the desired peak, according to the recipe.

Italian meringue

- Make sugar syrup using 450 gms sugar and 120 ml of water and boil the mixture upto 116 degrees C.
- Beat 225gm of egg white to the soft peak stage.
- Add sugar syrup to the egg whites in a thick steady stream whilst continuing to beat.

- After all the sugar syrup has been incorporated, continue to beat the mixture to the desired peak.
- The end product has a finer grain and is more stable than the other meringues.
- Italian meringue may also be used to prepare baked shells, cookies or left unbaked to use as a filling or as the base for Italian butter cream.

The addition of some other ingredient or flavouring to meringue can create an almost infinite number of variations, eg, Japonaise where ground almond is added. Small meringues are easier to make than big ones. Very small ones are known as meringuettes or crogugnols,and is used as petit fours.

Dutch calls them schuimpjes.

Large meringues are called Vacherin.

Rules for making meringues:-

- Only absolutely clean and dry bowls preferably ceramic, glass or stainless steel to be used for making meringues.
- Fat inhibits foaming.
- Mild acid like lemon juice or cream of tartar helps foaming.
- Egg whites foam better at room temperature.
- Do not over beat egg whites for they will look dry and curdled.
- Sugar makes the foam stable, but it can also cause weeping because of absorption of water.

Other examples of meringues are Vacherin, Pavlova and Baked Alaska.

What is ORGANOLEPTIC? Organoleptic refers to the involving of sense organs in evaluation of foods, it relates to the perception by sensory organs. Evaluating with the senses of sight, taste and smell for foods and is used particularly of the combination of taste, texture and astringency (perceived by the mouth) and aroma (perceived in the nose).

Sensory evaluation is an invaluable tool to Quality Control as well as Research and Development. Customers perceive product quality with their senses, and as a result, organoleptic evaluations are an essential component of any Quality Control evaluations. All of the technical, chemical and microbiological parameters of a product may well be within specification, but if the product fails to meet sensory expectations, or performs poorly against a competitor, product sales and brand image may well suffer. Organoleptic evaluations can also be used to develop **sensory** profiles when developing new products.

There are three types of testing:

EFFECTIVE TESTING

This type of testing is concerned with obtaining *objective facts* about products. This could range from basic discrimination testing(e.g. Do two or more products differ from each other?) to descriptive profiling(e.g. What are the characteristics of two or more products?). The type of panel required for this type of testing would normally be a trained panel.

Methods for collection and statistical analysis of sensory data include Free choiceprofiling, and Generalized procrustes analysis

AFFECTIVE TESTING

Also known as *consumer testing*, this type of testing is concerned with obtaining *subjective* data, or how well products are likely to be accepted. Usually large (50 or more) panels of untrained personnel are recruited for this type of testing, although smaller focus groupscan be utilised to gain insights into products. The range of testing can vary from simple comparative testing (e.g. which do you prefer, A or B?) to structured questioning regarding the magnitude of acceptance of individual characteristics (e.g. Please rate the "fruity aroma": dislike|neither|like).

Perception

Perceptioninvolves the biochemicaland psychologicaltheories relating to human (and animal) sensations. By understanding the mechanisms involved it may be possible to explain why certain characteristics are preferred over others.

Descriptive analysisinvolves trained panels (6-30 people) who evaluate products by rating the intensity of various characteristics on a scale. Statistical analyses are applied to look for differences among various products for characteristics of interest.

Consumer testing(sometimes called '**hedonic testing**') involves having potential consumers of a product evaluate various products and a small number of items on a **ballot**.

Sensory Evaluation: What is it?

"Sensory" is derived from the Latin "sensus" (= sense) and therefore, "sensory evaluation" is the description and evaluation of food products using the human senses. Accordingly, sensory evaluation is an analytical method in which the human senses serve as a measurement tool to determine the quality and/or to describe the condition of a food product. Prerequisites for the success of this analytical process include: standardization of methods, regular training and performance measurement of testers, a statistical evaluation of test results; and a standardization of terms.

All sensory testing methods are divided into three categories: hedonistic, comparative and descriptive testing. Hedonistic tests are always used within the scope of consumer tests and serve to characterize consumer behavior. On the other hand, comparative and descriptive sensory tests are referred to as "expert tests" because they may only be carried out by trained persons and can give very detailed information about individual product parameters. Selection of a sensory testing method must always take into account the test objective.

One main objective of sensory evaluation is the measurement of sensory attributes and the quantification of the influence of these attributes on consumer acceptance. This aspect is becoming increasingly important because of the interrelationship between enjoyment value and repurchases behavior. Sensory attributes are directly linked to the concept of quality and thereby ultimately contribute to the success or failure of a product.

Organaloptic and sensory evaluation play a very important role in research and development in analyzing new dishes, allows us to understand consumer behavior towards a new dish, facilitates management decision in choosing which new dishes or menus to be introduced, helps management in standardizing menus and dishes and is an important tool for the organization.

SCANDINAVIAN CUISINE

Scandinavian cuisine comprises the cuisine of the countries situated in the extreme North East of Europe and includes Denmark, Norway, Sweden and Finland. These Scandinavian countries share a similar cuisine style and relatively close cuisine development histories.

CULINARY HISTORY

In the 11th-12th century Denmark ruled over Norway and 1389 the Queen of Denmark and Norway became queen of Sweden. Denmark's influence over Sweden and Norway started to diminish in the 19th century, but the food related traditions remained.. Although most European countries consider lunch the main meal of the day, Scandinavian countries place more importance on dinner, which is the most consistent meal of the day. Workers often only have a quick snack for lunch, instead of a sumptuous meal. Many of the cooking styles and dishes used by the Vikings are still present in the Scandinavian cuisine today, and Scandinavians are proud of their Viking heritage, a fact that is also noticed in the way they preserve the authenticity of such foods. The traditional Scandinavian breakfast is very light and fruitive, consisting mainly of some cookies and coffee. Bread is also used, with butterand jam, but in most cases this meal is not considered very important – that's also because Scandinavians usually go to school and work early, at 8 o'clock. Lunch is richer in nutrients than breakfast, but most Scandinavians don't place all that much importance on it – a quick snack or a sandwich will do in most cases. Dinner, however, is served early, around 6 PM, and it is the main meal of the day. All Scandinavian countries see dinner as a family event, where all the members of the family return from school or work and enjoy the meal together. A Scandinavian dinner usually consists of a soup to start and a fish or meat dish for main course. Desert is sometimes served, but it is not a daily dish. Of course, the different Scandinavian countries also have slightly different eating habits. Danes and Norwegians only eat one hot meal a day while Swedes eat more hot meals each day. The cold smorrebrod is usually the lunch of the Danes and Norwegians, while in Sweden children return from school home, around 11 AM, for a hot lunch. A similar custom to the traditional English tea exists in the Scandinavian Peninsula – Scandinavians serve bread, biscuits, cookies, pastry and coffee around 2-3 PM. As for drinks, beer and snaps are enjoyed with the food and dry sherry. Each traditional dish has a special cooking method, which is more or less general in all of the country's regions. Meat is one of the main elements of most Scandinavian dishes and Herringis extremely popular, together with other fish types. Salmon is abundant in the area of the Peninsula, and it constitutes a very popular dish, both on a local and international level. Cold food is often eaten viciously, or "consumed" in the Scandinavian region - smorgasbord is a buffet table consisting mainly of cold dishes of herrings, fish, meat, salad and cheeses. The smorgasbord is accompanied by slices of buttered bread and it constitutes one of the most frequent meals in the Peninsula. Smorgasbord begins with cured herrings and cold fish and meat dishes including roasted meats follow, together with hot or cold vegetables and a salad. Scandinavian dishes are still prepared, even by modern chefs, in the traditional way – using simple tools and basic ingredients, but utilizing them to the maximum, so as to create a delicious and nutritious meal. Whether you are cooking Swedish meats and balls, or "meatballs" the Danish Leverpostej (rough-chopped liver paste served on dark rye bread) or the Norwegian smoked salmon, you will notice that the Scandinavian cuisine produces excellent results with simple and fast cooking methods. Festivities are moments of joy, when the family comes together in all the Scandinavian countries. Christmas is one of the most important holidays of the year. Food is very important on Christmas and on the smorgasbord or dinner table you can expect to find dishes such as: ricepudding, Christmas Ham, stockfish, Herring, cheese and bread, meatballs, small frying sausages, red cabbage, liver pâté, Vealbrawn, spare ribs and the list goes on. Easter is also festively celebrated, although less stress is placed on the culinary aspect, as the religious aura tends to dominate the celebrations.

NORWEGIAN– the cuisine is characterized by a sense of practicality and economy. Norwegians love their meat, whether it is Pork,Vealor fish meat, and you will notice that most of their dishes are concentrated on this main ingredient. The vast wild areas of Norway, and the abundance of fish and game, make such natural food resources a top pick for many traditional dishes. Norwegian cuisine uses elements from various cooking traditions borrowed from their neighbours and developed from their own traditional dishes. The simplicity of the cuisine does not imply a lack of taste, but it does make life easier for the cook. Smoked salmon is probably the most famous type of food product related to Norway; other dishes are **ROMMEGROT**porridge made with sour cream, milk, flavoured with cinnamon and sugar, **FARIKAL** mutton and cabbage stews with black pepper, **PTARMIGAN** meat casserole with cranberries and smoked elk.

DANISH– the cuisine of Denmark is characterized by high levels of meat and animal fat and a rather low level of plants and vegetables. The long winters from the Scandinavian Peninsula shaped the face of the Danish cuisine. Although agriculture is well developed, due to the climate, game and fish are often preferred. Fresh vegetables are rare in the traditional Danish recipes, and many dishes rely on seasonal fruits or vegetables. On the other hand, the climate enables lengthy meet preservation, so smoked meat is one of the most frequently used ingredients in the Danish cuisine. The Danish cuisine is rather conservative, and the numerous islands that form Denmark helped keep the traditional, conservative cooking styles alive until modern times. Some specialities are **FRIKADELLER** minced veal and pork meatballs, HAKKEBIFF minced beef with onions and brown sauce and **RULLEPOELSE** spiced rolled belly of pork. Vegetables used are potatoes, red cabbage and rutabaga. Danish pastries are very famous they may be filled with cream, jam or dried cherries.

SWEDEN– It is considered rude not to finish the food you have on the plate, mainly because, in many cases, you serve yourself and you are responsible for the amount of food you place on your plate. The meals are not very elaborate and many will find them scarce in vegetables. Traditional recipes were influenced by the lack of plants due to the long Swedish winters and many modern dishes still include only small amounts of vegetables. Rutabagais a native turnipthat was among the most popular plant types in Swedish cooking until it got replaced by the Potato. In both major inhabited regions of Sweden – Gothenburg on the west coast and Stockholm on the east – the abundance of fish, mainly Herring, had its influence on traditional cooking. Some specialities— **SLOTTSSTEK** braised beef served with cranberries and potatoes,

LINDSTROM minced beef served with beetroot. Goose is served stuffed with prunes and apples. Sweden has a wide range of pastries flavoured with saffron and cardamons.

FINLAND— Finnish cuisine is characterised by foods with robust flavours, like— **MUSTAKEITTO** a rich soup made of chopped offal cooked with carrot and potatoes, is thickened with blood and garnished with barley balls. **VORSHMACK** a hash of mutton, beef and salted herrings, spiced with garlic and onions and accompanied by **RYPPY** a very strong grain alcohol. The Finns are fond of Swedes, smoked reindeer tongues, raw salmon, burbot roe, crayfish cooked in stock flavoured with fennel and LAKKA a strong liqueur based on Arctic cranberries. Milk is used in the form of buttermilk or in puddings and porridge. Wild mushrooms are widely used in soups, stews, sauces, pickles and salads. The Russian influence is significant with borscht, pashka and blinis being common dishes.

Staling of Bakery Products and Mold Infectnion

There are three ways in which bakery products stale. They are, Starch Retrogradation (firming of the crumb), getting infected by molds and rope; See Below.

In simple terms, staling of crumb (firming of crumb) is the process the starch molecules go through when they shrink upon cooling. Starch molecule consists of a very long chain of Carbon, Hydrogen and Oxygen that are stretched out when warm and feel soft. Upon cooling, the chain shrinks and thus become firm which is called staling. You have probably experienced that when a stale product is warmed, it becomes soft. The starch chain has stretched again. Upon cooling, it shrinks again and become firm.

Anti-Staling Ingredients:

1. Emulsifiers. For the past several years bakers used emulsifiers called bread softeners to produce bread that will remain soft for a longer period of time. It is added to the dough during mixing. Some of the more common ones are monoglycrides, calcium stearoyl lactylate, and sodium stearoyl lactylate. The softening action takes place after the bread is baked. Also, Potato bread will resist staling because potatoes act as anti-staling ingredients to some degree. Some anti-staling ingredients also perform as dough conditioners or dough strengtheners.

2. Enzymes. Enzyme manufacturers are hard at work on generic engineering and protein engineering producing enzymes to extend the shelf life of bread many fold. In a paper presented at the 1999 American Society of Baking's Annual Convention, it was stated that some of these enzymes are available now. However, since every baker wants to have one better, enzyme manufacturers will continue to work on developing better ones. It was also stated that there is a lag time of between 2 and 3 years between the time a specific enzyme is identified and actually having it available for the baker to use.

Advantages of Using Enzymes instead of Chemicals. Since enzymes are produced from natural ingredients, they will find greater acceptance by the housewife than when chemicals are used.

3. Mold and Mold Inhibitors. Sanitation plays a very important role in preventing mold in bread. Mold spores do not survive baking temperatures. The interior of the loaf, when it comes out of the oven is about 210 to 212 degrees F. which will destroy any mold spores which may be present in the dough. Therefore, bread and other bakery products can only be contaminated after they leave the oven.

Some of the more dangerous areas for mold contmination are storage rooms, and slicing machine blades which come in direct contact with the interior of the loaf where there is an abundant supply of food and moisture. Mold spores also thrive in dark places. You can extend the length of time that it takes bakery products to mold by several days by using Mold Inhibitors such as Calcium Propionate for yeast raised doughs and sodium propionate in chemically leavened products. Propionates are present in many foods, but in very small amounts. Swiss Cheese, however is an exception. For this reason, Swiss Cheese rarely molds, unless it is improperly developed. Propionates may be obtained by the oxidization of propyl alcohol, forming propionic acid. The propionic acid is in turn combined with other chemicals to form the well known Sodium and Calcium propionates sold under different Trades Names. Mold Inhibitors react as an alkaline in doughs, and since yeast doesn't like an alkaline condition, Mineral Yeast Foods containing monocalcium phosphate are added to the dough. Monocalcium Phosphate reacts as an acid in doughs therefore counter-acting the alkaline which is formed by the propionates. Also, vinegar can be used at the rate of about 1 pint per 100 pounds of flour. Inhibitors are called inhibitors, because not enough is used to kill the mold. They only retard the growth of molds. Bread will mold eventually if kept in a warm moist invironment. The amounts of Calcium Propionates to use in bread varies with the climate, season of the year, or type of product. Dark Breads require more than White Breads. For average climates, 2.5 to 3.5 ounces are used per 100 pounds of flour in White Breads and 4.0 to 5.0 ounces are used in Dark Breads.

Types and Color of Molds. There are many different types of molds and they have different colors. Mold spores are practically everywhere, because they are very tiny and are carried in the air. They are so tiny that they can only be seen under a microscope. Mold Spores are like seeds that you plant in the garden. When they come in contact with the proper food, moisture and warmth, the spores produce mold plants which you can see with the naked eye.

Rope. Rope is a bread disease caused by the bacteria, Bacillus mesentericus. This disease breaks down the cells of the bread and leaves a sticky, pasty mass. When the crumb is pressed together, and pulled apart, it will stretch into long, sticky, web-like strands. The product will have the odor of over-ripe cantalope. The rope bacteria are too small to see with the naked eye, but they can be seen with a microscope. The bacteria can be present in the ingredients, especially flour and yeast. Unlike mold, rope spores are not destroyed by baking temperatures. Calcium propionate, sodium diacetate or one pint of vinegar per 100 pounds of flour can be used in bread doughs to increase the shelf life of the product. If the bakery is contaminated, thorough cleaning with special chemicals will be necessary and/or the bakery may have to be steam cleaned.

External Bread Faults

Symptom	Causes
Crust too dark	- Oven temperature too high - Excessive milk or sugar. - Excessive baking - Over proofing. time.
Crust too light	- Oven temperature too low. - Insufficient milk or sugar. - Insufficient baking time. - Insufficient - Insufficient mixing. proofing.
Crust broken	- Insufficient proofing -Insufficient liquid.
Crust too hard	- Oven temperature too high - Insufficient proofing. - Insufficient sugar or shortening. - Excessive steam. - Insufficient liquid. - Baking time too long.
Crust too soft	- Oven temperature too low - Excessive sugar/egg yolks/shortening. - Excessive oil/margarine as a wash. - Insufficient steam during baking. - Baking time too short or wrong bread machine setting.

Internal Bread Faults

Symptom	Causes
Coarse and irregular grain	- Improper mixing procedures. - Stiff batter. - Careless or poor depositing in the pans. - Oven too cool, (baked too slowly). - Excessive liquid in the batter. - Improper mixing procedure.
Dense grain	
Off-color breads	- Improper mixing procedure. - Oven too cool, (baked too slowly). - Unclean equipment.
If raisins, nuts or dried fruit sunk to the bottom	- Pieces of fruit were too large and too heavy. - Sugary syrup on the outside of the fruit was not washed off - causing the pieces of fruit to slide through the mixture as it heated. - Washed and dried fruit was not dusted with flour before being added to the mixture. - Bread mixture was over beaten or was too wet so it could not hold the fruit in place. - Oven temperature was too low, causing the mixture to melt before it set to hold the fruit in place.

General Bread Faults

Symptom	Causes
Batter over-flowed the pans	- Wrong adjustments to recipes (too much liquid, flour etc.) - Wrong size pan used. Mixture should fill 2/3 of pan.
Poor flavor	- Improper mixing procedure. - Improper cleaning and greasing of the pans. - Faulty baking conditions. - Improper cleaning of the equipment.
Breads too tough	- Excessive mixing. - Batter too stiff (insufficient water).
Lacks body/structure	- Batter too thin (excessive water). - Excessive mixing - Insufficient liquid.
Dries out too soon	- Excessive baking time. - Insufficient liquid. - Improper mixing procedures. - Cooled in a drafty location.

CHAPTER 5

Food Service

In this chapter of the course, we will be studying the concept of menu in details. You are all aware of menu. When you go to a restaurant, you are presented with a menu. It lists the food available at the place and also the prices of the food items. Depending on your situation you order the food. You may like to have a snack if you don't have appetite or if you don't have time. But, do you know that there are different types of menus? What are these different types of menus called? What is their purpose? Under what situation people prefer one kind of menu? What is the psychology of menu? What is the importance of menu presentation and design?

In this chapter, you will learn about menu planning. Menu planning is not a simple exercise, as it involves making a well-balanced diet, which is a basic requirement for a healthy meal. The main aims of menu planning are to fulfill the needs of the customer, and at the same time within an allotted budget.

You will also learn about the history of menus. In the beginning, menus were lists of food, in seemingly random fashion with the food being raw, prepared or cooked. Individual menus came into use early in the 19th century and courses began to be formulated. The success of a food service operation, no matter what

its size, depends heavily on those who plan the menus and how they do it. While it may seem a simple exercise of providing something to eat and drink, in practice good menu planning requires a lot of skill.

You will also learn that many things have to be kept in mind while planning a menu. The sequencing and meal planning depend entirely on the meal in question, whether it is breakfast, high tea or dinner.

CONDIMENTS AND ACCOMPANIMENTS

Condiments are the food items served with food to add or adjust the taste and flavor or the food. For example, sauces served with steak adds the taste and flavor to the food (steak). Similarly, pickles, chutney, onion, spice, etc are used for the same purpose. These thing go with a very wide variety of the food items. They are not dishes in their own right. They are complementary with the food guest has ordered. No one will order pickle or chutney with roti in a hotel, though in villages farmers are known to eat onion with *bhakari* or roti.

Accompanimnets are the additional items usually served with food. For example, bread and butter is served with salad or soup.

Servers should know the accompaniments and condiments to be served with menu items. It is expected that the condiments and accompaniments are placed before the food and they are kept on the table throughout the course of the meal.

In casual restaurants the condiments are part of the table setup. (For example, you will find onion, pickles, chutney, boat of spices kept on the table even when guest has not ordered any thing in a average restaurant.)

In high value (fine dine) restaurants whese are served in sauce pots or boats and served individually to the guests.

MENU: CONCEPT, TYPES AND FEATURES

CONCEPT OF MENU

A menu can be described as a list of dishes planned for production in a catering operation and may include snacks or beverages. It can be described as a list of items served by a food and beverage outlet. It performs a number of functions:

- Introduces the establishment to the customer
- Reflects the type of customer the establishment wishes to attract
- Satisfies the nutrition and hunger needs of the customer as well as social and psychological needs
- Provides a means of developing good eating habits in people
- Helps in purchase of foods and ingredients
- Determines the type of equipment, Staff skills and the type of supervision required
- Authorizes production of meals in the kitchen
- Helps of organize space and work in store, kitchen and service area
- Determines the style of service to be set up
- Forms the basis for calculation of food and labour cost
- Introduces interesting food combinations of different states, countries and cultures to the customers

WHAT IS 'MENU ENGINEERING' OR 'MENU PSYCHOL OGY'?

Menu engineering can be described as an interdisciplinary field of study devoted to the deliberate and strategic creation of menus. It is also commonly referred to as 'menu psychology'. In general, the ter m menu engineering is used within the hospitality industry (specifically in the context of restaurant), but it can also be applied to any industry that displays, the goal of menu engineering is to buy what you want them to buy and discouraging the purchase of items you do not want them to buy.

The fields of study that contribute the most to menu engineering include the following:

Psychology (perception, attention, emotion/effect)

Managerial accounting (contribution margin and unit cost analysis)

Marketing and strategy (pricing, promotion)

Graphical design (design layout, typography).

What is the goal of menu engineering?

Which subject areas do contribute to menu engineering?

TYPES OF MENUS

These are the major variety of menus. Different types of menu are categorized by how the menu items are listed and priced:

- Table d'hôte
- A la Carte
- Combination

Table d'hôte

This is a French phrase. Table d'hôte literally mea ns 'host's table'. It can be described as a restaur ant terminology to indicate a menu where multicourse meals with only a few choices are charged at a fixed price. Such a menu may also be called prix fixe or 'fixed price'. The terms 'set meal' and 'set menu' are reasonably common as well. As the menu is already set, the cutlery on the table may also already be set for all of the courses.

Table d'hôte menu offers a complete meal for one pr ice. Something like our *thaali* or unlimited *thaali* system. Sometimes, two or more complete meals are offered on the menu, each meal having its own price. Some table d'hôte menus offered limited choi ces to guests within the meal they select, for example, a guest may choose between a soup and a salad, or a restaurant may offer a choice of desserts. But for the most part, a meal on a tabled'hôte menu is set by the planner and guests are given few, if any, choices

Fig Table d'hote menu

A la Carte

Another French phrase, A la carte means 'according to the menu'. It is used in restaurant terminology as follows:

- An option to choose at no extra charge and a side dish to accompany a main course item. With a la Carte menu, food and beverages items are listed and priced separately. Guests need not choose a meal that has been planned for them. Them can choose from the various appetizers, entrees, side dishes and desserts listed to make up their own meal. Prices of the menu items they select are added together to determine the cost of the meal.
- A reference to a list of items that are priced and ordered separately, rather than selected from a list of preset multicourse meals at fixed prices, in contrast to a table d'hôte, at which a menu with limited or no choice is served at a fixed price.

Combination:

Many operations have means that are a combination of the table d'hôte and A la Carte pricing styles. Table d'hôte menus may offer a selection of individ ually priced desserts. A la Carte menus include a choice of vegetables and potatoes or rice with the price of the entrée.

A few operations have combination menus that offer an extensive list of complete meal packages and extensive a la carte selection. Chinese and other ethnic restaurant are most likely to features these combination menus:

CATEGORISAITON AS PER USE

Let us see another way of categorization of menus. Menus are categorized by how often they are used:

Fixed menus:

Let us see what it means. Coffee shops and chain restaurant often use a single menu foe several months (or longer) before replacing it with a new fixed menu. Daily specials may be offered to give frequent guests some new sections, but there is still a set of items that forms the basic menu. Fixed menus work best at restaurant and other food service establishment where guests are not likely to visit frequently, or where there are enough items listed on the menu to offer an acceptable level of variety.

Cycle menus:

This is another type. Cycle menus are designed to provide variety for guests who eat at an operation frequently, or even daily. Non-commercial operations, self-operated, and those that are operated by contract management companies in schools, health care facilities, business and industry facilities and other settings, frequently use cyclic menus. Typical cycle ranges from 1 to 4 weeks, but some are longer. Let us see an important point. Establishing the right cycle length is very important. With too short a cycle, the menus may be repeated too often and guests may become dissatisfied. If the cycle is too long, production and labour costs involved in purchasing, storing and preparing the greater variety of food may be excessive. The optimum cycle length varies by type of operation and how often guests are expected to eat there. Some casino hotels in lows Vegas use a 7-day cycle menu because most guests do not stay long enough to notice the repetition. In a resort, where an average guest stays for two weeks, a 2,3, or 4 week cycle menu may be planned, depending on how concerned the management is with providing variety for guests who stay longer than average. In a large university, a cycle menu of several weeks may be appropriate.

Banquet menu:

We now come to another variety. It can be described as an elaborate table d'hôte menu offering more th an four courses. The dishes are rich in quality and often fairly expensive because a banquet is a formal feast. It is generally given to highlight important events like the visit or head of state, marriage ans so on. The banquet menu is prepared by the F & B manager or the banquet manager in consolation with the chef. A set menu of various price ranges is made and offered to the client who organizes the party after ascertaining prices per head.

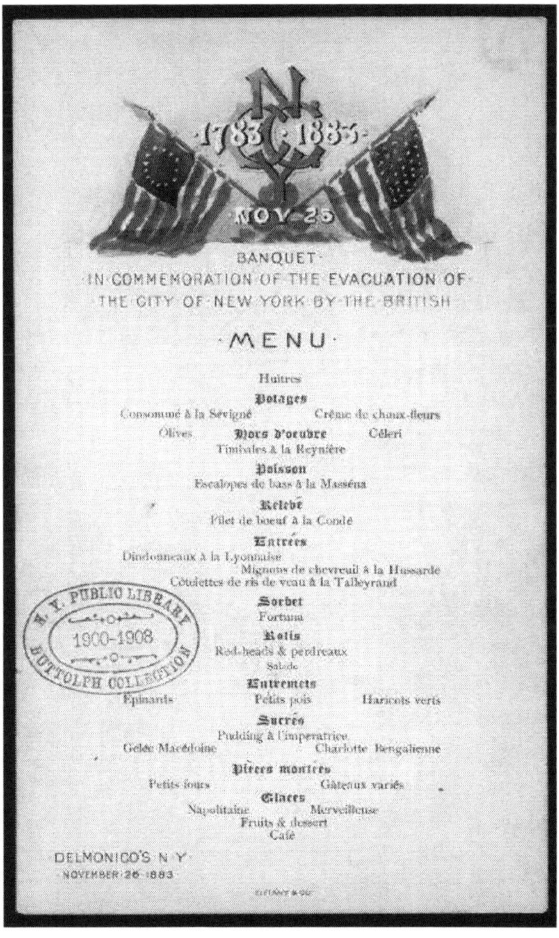
NOV 25
BANQUET
IN COMMEMORATION OF THE EVACUATION OF
THE CITY OF NEW YORK BY THE BRITISH

MENU

Huitres
Potages
Consommé à la Sévigné Crême de choux-fleurs
Olives Hors d'oeuvre Céleri
Timbales à la Reynière
Poisson
Escalopes de bass à la Masséna
Relevé
Filet de boeuf à la Condé
Entrées
Dindonneaux à la Lyonnaise
Mignons de chevreuil à la Hussarde
Côtelettes de ris de veau à la Talleyrand
Sorbet
Fortuna
Rotis
Red-heads & perdreaux
Salade
Entremets
Epinards Petits pois Haricots verts
Sucrés
Pudding à l'imperatrice
Gelée Macédoine Charlotte Bengalienne
Pièces montées
Petits fours Gâteaux variés
Glaces
Napolitaine Merveilleuse
Fruits & dessert
Café

DELMONICO'S N Y
NOVEMBER 26 1883

Fig Banquet menu example

Let us see how the institutions plan their meals. The daily menu used in a cycle can be a la carte or table d'hôte. Schools, hospitals, prisons and other insti tutions may use table d'hôte menus in the cycle: of fer one set meal for each meal period (breakfast, lunch and dinner) each day (although menus offering as choice are also used in many noncommercial operations). Commercial operations that cycle menus use a la carte menus. A hotel restaurant on a 7-day basis could rotate seven different a la carte menus.

We all have seen menus at restaurants. In a restaurant, a menu is a printed brochure or a public display that shows the list of options for a dinner to select. A menu may be a la carte or table d'hote. 'Menu ' can

also be used in a more general sense, synonymous with diet. The selections of foods available are generally based upon a particular location or culture.

CLASSIFICATION AS PER MEAL TIME

The menu for different meals will differ. For example what you eat at breakfast is different than what you at for lunch or dinner. Similarly if you have missed your lunch due to some reason, you may eat a different dish during tea time to make up for the lost opportunity. Let us now look at what the typical menus for these meals are.

BREAKFAST (petit Dejeuner):

Breakfast is called the most important meal of the day. It is the first thing you eat after waking up. Breakfast supplies instant energy thought simple carbohydrates. It should be soft and light, preferably liquid or semisolid because at that time the digestive system is not ready to take solid food, which is difficult to digest. An ideal time for breakfast is 8AM to 10AM. Breakfast may be served in the hotel restaurant or dinning room, in the breakfast room set aside for this meal or in the guest room. The different types of breakfast are continental, American, English, and Indian.

How do we begin the breakfast? The first course is liquid to semisolid like fruit juice, fruit, and cereal with milk, followed by soft protein like egg. Fish and organ meat supplemented with butter, bread and preserves, finished with tea/coffee to stimulate the nervous system.

Breakfast Menu

(i) English breakfast:

The first variety is here. An English breakfast can be described as a very elaborate breakfast. It comprises of ten courses:

- Stewed Fruits: Apples, prunes, figs, pears cut and cooked in sugar syrup (flavoured)
- Cereals: Oatmeal, cornflakes, rice crispies, porridge served with hot/cold milk
- Eggs to order: Omelet, boiled, scrambled, poached, fried eggs
- Fish: smoked or poached- herring, haddock, sardines, salmon
- Meat: Grilled bacon, sausages, ham, salami, kidneys or liver
- Choice of rolls or toast: Toasted white/brown bread, rolls, croissants, muffins, brioche, doughnuts, and Danish pastries.
- Butter and preserves: Butter, jam, honey, marmalade, maple syrup
- Fruits: Melon, papaya, mango, orange, grapefruit, pears
- Choice of juices: Pineapple, grapefruit, tomato, orange, sweet lime, mango
- Beverages: Tea/coffee, milk, cocoa

(ii) American breakfast:

Let us see what it means. It usually starts with a glass of water and then is followed with five courses:

- Beverages: Tea/coffee, milk, cocoa
- Choice of juices: Pineapple, grapefruit, tomato, orange, sweet lime, mango
- Cereals: Oatmeal, cornflakes, rice crispies, porridge served with hot/cold milk
- Choice of breads: Toasted white/brown bread, rolls, croissants, muffins, brioche, doughnuts, and Danish pastries with Butter, jam, honey, marmalade
- Eggs to order: Omelet, boiled, scrambled, poached, fried eggs

(iii) Continental breakfast:

This is the third variety. It can be described as an European breakfast and contains:

- Beverages: Tea/coffee, milk, cocoa. If coffee is served along with continental breakfast, it is known as 'the complet'
- Choice of breads: Toasted white/brown bread, rolls, croissants, muffins, brioche, doughnuts, and Danish pastries with Butter, jam, honey, marmalade
- Choice of juices: Pineapple, grapefruit, tomato, orange, sweet lime, mango

(iv) Indian breakfast

WE are all familiar with the Indian variety. Choices of Indian breakfast: Puri bhaji, stuffed parathas served with curd, idli/uttapam/dosa/served with samber and cocunt chutney, upma, cheela, chana bhatura, choley kulcha

BRUCH OR LOW TEA (midmorning refreshment)

This is combination of lunch and breakfast hence the name. For those who skip their breakfast and want to have a heavy meal toward the later point of the day may take brunch. Brunch is easy to digest as it has light and semisolid food but in substantial quantity and a soup like starter; a dessert may be incorporated in the end. However, heavy main course with accompaniment, and garnishes are replaced by light snacks. Breakfast cereals, jams and jellies are avoided. Waffles and pancakes are often incorporated in the meal. It is taken between 10am and 12noon.

LUNCH

This is what you eat in the noon time. The British enjoys dry, easy-to-eat items like sandwiches and savories with coffee or tea. They avoid lunch. On the other hand, the French, Italian, Spanish, Greek and Portuguese people enjoy an excellent lunch with several courses, followed by a midday nap. An ideal time for lunch is between 12 noon and 3pm. The menu is similar to dinner, i.e., appetizer is preferred to soup, a beer or a soft drink to wet the gullet, fish to heavy roast or braised items. Items with rice are avoidable as they induce sleep or drowsiness.

HIGH TEA

This is what you take late noon time around 5 pm. Any time between 3pm to 5pm is a good time for high tea. An elaborate snacks display with cookies, tea fancies, pastries can be incorporated to satiate the hunger of those who had a light lunch or skipped their lunch. This is but a party suggestion to avoid the regular service of lunch.. A high tea is usually in a modified a la carte from and the menu will offer, in addition to the normal full afternoon tea menu, items such as grills, toasted snacks, fish and meat dishes,salads, cold sweets. The meat dish normally consists of the main pies and patties, while the fish dishes are usually fried or grilled.

High tea menu

A typical high tea menu should look like this:

- Hot butter toast or toast or toasted teacake or crumpets
- Assorted afternoon tea sandwiches
- Smoked salmon, cucumber, tomato, sardine, eggs, gentleman's relish
- Brown and white bread and butter
- Fruit bread and butter
- Chicken patties or lamb pies (tomato ketchup, brown sauce), grilled fish or fried fish (mustard, Worcestershire sauce, vinegar)
- Hot scones (with butter and clotted cream)
- Raspberry or strawberry jams
- Gateaux and pastries

AFTERNOON TEA

Nowadays, the venue of tea is changing from the hotel lounge to coffee shops, cafes and food courts. It can be described as an old and slowly dying English tradition of taking afternoon tea at 4 pm. However, afternoon tea is still served in establishments and in a variety of forms, which may be classified into three types: full afternoon tea, high tea, and reception or buffet tea.

Full tea/evening tea:

Full tea consists of a variety of sandwiches, tea fancies; cookies with other snacks with a pot oh hot tea. Early lunchers and late diners prefer being served full tea. However, it is an essential part of the food cycle of most well off people of the world. It is taken between 3pm and 7pm. Tables are also specifically laid for full tea in restaurants particularly coffee shops.

DINNER

At dinner, people relish and enjoy a meal at leisure because there is no rush for office or business as at breakfast. Hence, the cooks and service staff excel in imposing their skill, art and mettle, at dinner.

SUPPER

Supper is for those who miss their dinner and a light soft meal before bedtime for those who had early dinner.

CHILDREN'S MEAL

Most kid's meals come in bags or cardboard boxes, with a special themed promotion, with activates on the bag a small toy. Typical children's meal includes:

- Toy
- 12 oz (354.8ml) soft drink
- 2.2 oz (62.3g) hamburger
- Small French fries

McDonald's happy meal, Burger king's kids' meal and KFC's laptop meal are examples of meal for kids.

VALUE MEAL

These are the inexpensive variety of meals. Value meals are offered together at a lower price than they would cost individually. Fast food restaurants offer value meals as a common merchandising tactic to facilitate bundling, upselling and price discrimination. The perceived creation of a 'discount' on individual menu items in exchange for the purchase of a 'meal' is also consistent with the loyalty-marketing school of thought. Additionally, the term is based on value theory, which utilizes certain marketing tactics to encourage people to spend more money than they originally intended on their purchase.

CLASSICAL TWELVE COURSE FRENCH MENU

Twelve courses of French menu are as follows:

Course Number	French term for the course	English name for course
1	Hors d' oeuvre froid	Cold appetizer
2	Potage	Soup
3	Poisson	Fish
4	Entrées	Entry of meal
5	Releve	Main course
6	Sorbet	Sherbet
7	Roti	Roast
8	Legume	Vegetable
9	Entremet	Sweet
10	Bonne bouche	Savoury/cheese
11	Dessert	Fruits
12	Café	Coffee

Let us find out about these courses in details.

HORS D'OEUVRE

This is the starter of the meal. It is the first course of the meal and is composed usually of tangy, salty, sour, hot items that help to stimulate appetite. The hors d'oeuvre should have an eye appeal and should be decorative. The d'oeuvre usually applies to a variety of side dishes offered as appetizers such as potato salad, herring, sardines, cold egg dishes, mushrooms, artichoke, asparagus; single items served as a preliminary appetizer course before the soup dishes like melon, caviar, oysters, smoked salmon, salami and sausage.

Let us see another point. France has also adopted a custom of serving hors d'oeuvre as zakuski . Zakuski is made up of hors d'oeuvre washed down with liberal draughts of wine and liquor. Formerly in Russia, this was served in the antechamber adjoining the dinning room.

Cold hors d'oeuvre

1.Salad:

Salad is made of herbs, plants, eggs, meat and fish seasoned with salt, vinegar and pepper, with or without other ingredients. According to Brillat Savrin, 'salads' freshen without enfeebling and fortify wit hout irritating. Salads are divided into two categories – simple and compound.

i) Simple salad: Plain salad could be green salad (raw) or salad of cooked vegetables consisting of one kind of vegetables

ii) Compound salad: Compound salad is a combination of different ingredients such as the following

a) Salade americaine: Cucumber cut in thin slices, previously soaked in salted water then rinsed and seasoned with vinaigrette, surrounded with lettuce hearts with slices of tomatoes and quarters of tomatoes and quarters of hard-boiled eggs.

b) Salad russe: Macedoine (dices) of boiled seasonal vegetables like peas, carrots, turnips, potatoes bound with mayonnaise.

2.Shell fish:

These fish have shells on their outer parts. Like we have bones internally, these fishes have bones externally and flesh inside. Shell fish such as oysters, snails, prawns, crayfish, shrimps, scamps, mussels are served. These could be served from an hors d'oeuvre tray.

3.Eggs:

Eggs could be served cold as a hors d'oeuve for example in the form of:

- Oeuf dur mayonnaise
- Oeuf farcis

4. Fruits:

You can serve various fruits such as avocados, melons, grapefruits, etc.

5. Fruit juices:

You can serve juices too. Assorted fruit juices are served in a pony tumbler underlined with a quarter plate, a doily paper and a tea spoon. Examples are mixed fruit juice cocktail, tomato juice cocktail, grapefruit cocktail.

6. Sea food cocktail:

These cocktails are made with oysters, snails, prawns, crayfish, shrimps, scamps and mussels. Sea food is served with cocktail sauce, in a cocktail cup underlined with a quarter plate and a tea spoon.

7. Canaples:

What are canapés? These are shaped pieces of bread,buttered and treated under salamander or shallow fried, and different toppings are placed on it. A canapé is a small, prepared and unusually decorativefood, held between the fingers and often eaten in one bite. As they are often served during cocktail hours, it is generally desired that a canapé may also be referred to as finger food, although not all finger foods are canapés. Crackers or small slices of bread or toastor puff pastry, cut into various shapes, serve as the base for savory butter or pastes, often topped with savory foods as meat, cheese, fish, caviar, foie, gras, purees or relish.

Examples of canapés are as follows:

- Angles on horseback
- Devils on horseback

8.Galantine:

Galantine is a dish made from boned poultry or meat, stuffed and pressed into symmetrical shape. It is cooked in a gelatin stock

Hot hors d' oeuvres:

After cold hors d'oevres, let us consider hot ones . These are popular during the winters, such as:

1. Beignets or fritters:

A fritter is any kind of food coated in batter and deep fried. The word comes from the Latin frictira 'frying' by way of old French and Middle English.

2. Bouchees or patties:

The original Pattie is a mix of mashed potato and sage blended together and made into a round or square shape, then covered in batter and fried, much like a fish cake. There are different kinds of patties, such as meat patty(corned beef) and cheese patty (cheese and onion) but the most common variety is the standard sage, onion and potato patty

3. Brochttes or skewers:

They are popular dishes that consist of small pieces of grilled, skewered meat. The mea may be marinated in vinegar and spices (such as cumin, pepper and garlic), and while skewers can be made of an type of meat, the most popular are made of beef, lamb, chicken, pork.

4. Croquettes or rissoles:

A croquette can be described as a small fried food roll containing usually as main ingredients mashed potatoes, and/or minced meat (veal, beef, chicken or turkey),shellfish, fish, vegetables and soaked white bread, egg, onion, spices and herbs, wine, milk or any of the combination thereof, sometimes with a filling, often encased in breadcrumbs. The croquette is usually shaped into a cylinder or disk, and then deep fried.

Deluxe hor d' oeuvres

1.Caviar:

Caviar can be described as the processed, salted roe of certain species of fish, most notably sturgeon (black caviar) and salmon (red caviar). It is commercially marketed worldwide as a delicacy and is eaten as a garish or a spread.

2.Snails:

Snails are a delicacy in French cuisine, where they are called escargots. In an English language menu, escargot is generally reserved for snails prepared with traditional French recipes (served in the shell with garlic and parsley butter). Before preparing the snails to eat, the snails should fast for 3 days with only water available. After three days of fasting, the snails should be fed flour and offered water for at least a week. This process is done to cleanse the snails.

3. Smoked salmon:

Smoked salmon can be described as a prepared form of salmon, typically a fillet that has been cured and then got or cold smoked owing to its moderately high price, smoked salmon is considered a delicacy

4. Oysters:

Oysters can be eaten with half shell, raw, smoked, boiled, baked, fried, roasted, stewed, canned, pickled, steamed, broiled or used in a variety of drinks. Preparation of these dishes vary widely. It can be as simple as opening the shell and eating the contents, including the juice. Butter and salt are often added. But, in the case of oysters Rockefeller, preparation can be very elaborate. They are sometimes even served on edible seaweed.

POTAGE OR SOUP

It is an extract of meat, vegetables, fish or poultry in stock or water. It is possible that a soup in its earliest form was a complete meal, because it was found hearty, nourishing, economical and wholesome. Usually soups are served piping hot, but many soups are also served cold.We have learned about the soups in details.

POISSON OR FISH

Poisson is the French word for fish. Don't worry; we don't serve poison in breakfast. Never spell poisson as poison. Fish is the first solid/semisolid diet which is light and soft in texture, easy to digest and takes very little time to cook. The most nourishing fish are river water fish such as heel, lamprey, salmon, trout, mackerel, turbot, herring.

Different type of fish available

i) White flat fish: Brill, sole, pomfret, turbot, common skate, hake, plaice.
ii) White round fish: Cod, hake, lamprey, gudgeon, balluga
iii) Shellfish: Lobster, prawn, shrimps, oyster, mussels, crab, scampi, snails
iv) Oily fish: Anchovy, eel, herring, mackerel, salmon, tuna, trout, sardines, sprats, pilchard

Classes of fish

i) Crustaceans: They have brush-like shells and a covered body. Example are lobster, crab fish, cray, shrimps.
ii) Molluses: They have soft structure, partially or fully enclosed in shells largely made of mineral composition. Examples are oyster, clams, mussels, scallops.

Cuts of fish

- **Darne**: A steak of round fish like cod, salmon
- **Goujons and goujonettes**: Filleted fish cut into strips approximately of 6.8 cm x 1 cm
- **Troncon:** A steak of flat fish like turbot, halibut.
- **Fillet:** Cut of fish from bone. Flat fish can give four fillet and round fish two fillets.
- **Supreme:** Pieces cut from fillets of salmon. Turbot without bone and skin.
- **Paupiette**: Paper-thin fillet of fishlike sole, plaice, whiting spread with stuffing and rolled.
- **Delice:** Fillets of flat fish where the quarter of the head end and the quarter of the tail end of the fillet are folded under the skin and the side is folded inwards.
- **Steaks:** Thick slices of fish on or off the bone

Different kinds of cooked fish

i) Poached fish:

Poached fish is made by cooked it gently in water, which is just below the boiling point (93-95 °C). The liquid is held as close to the boiling point as possible without there being any perceptible movement of the liquid.

ii) Cold fish mousse:

Cold fish mouse is made by poaching and then mincing fish into a paste. Herbs and seasoning is then added to the paste which is then set into various moulds with a binder such as aspic jelly.

iii) Deep fried fish:

Deep fried fish is made by cooking the fish by frying it. It is a popular method for French/Indian cuisine. As the fish is immersed in hot fat, it is essential that the fat is of a good quality and has a high smoking point. The frying pan should have sufficient depth. The size and shape of the food to be fried should be uniform. Fried fish should have good appearance.

iv) Shallow fried fish:

Shallow fried fish is made by cooking the fish by immersing it in fat. The presentation side should always be fried first and then turned, both sides should be browned evenly.

v) Steamed fish:

Let us study this a bit. Steamed fish is made by cooked the fish in moist heat, i.e. direct or indirect steam. Indirect streaming is done when the food is placed in a closed pan or in a streamer, which is surrounded by plenty of stream from fast boiling water. The food item could be protected with greaseproof paper, or cloth or aluminum foil to prevent water from getting into the direct steaming is done by placing the article in a perforated container or on a covered plate over a saucepan of water.

vi) Grilled fish:

Grilled fish is made by placing the fish on grill bars and to the action of radiated heat. Charcoal, cock, gas or electricity subjecting may be used for grilling fish. In an authentic grill, the heat is located below the grill bars, and if the source of heat is above the grill bars, the grilling equipment is called a salamander. The grill bars should be cleaned and oiled, or the bars will rust and food will stick to them. Usually, small items are grilled, the meat is cut, trimmed and slightly flattened with a bat. Then, the meat should be seasoned with salt and pepper and brushed on both sides with oil. The fish is then grilled on the grill bars, turned when half cooked, brushed oil occasionally and cooked to the required degree. Fish are cooked and served with lemon wedges, butter and parsley.

vii) Backed fish:

Backed fish is made by applying of dry heat in an oven. The degree of dryness of heat may be modified by the amount of steam produced from the item baked. During baking, the mixture or moisture in the product expands by air, steam or carbon dioxide.

Shellfish preparation

- Homard Americane
- Homard Cardinal
- Homard Newburg
- Homard Thermidor

Service of poison:

It is served in a hot half plate and the cutlery provided is a fish knife and fish fork on the cover. If fish is served as a main course, then it is served on a large plate with accompaniments and the cutlery provided is fish knife and fish fork.

ENTRÉE

The word entrée literally means 'entrance'. This course was initially served before the roast course or

Roti, but now it is served before the main course or Releve. The following can be served as entrée:

- Hot hors d' oeuvre
- Cereals (rice)
- Egg preparations
- Organ meats and sausages
- Pasta
- Savoury pastries

Some example of pasta products are as follows:

- Fettucini: Flat strips of pasta, approx ½ cm broad
- Macaroni: Hollow, cylindrical small noodles of ½ mm thickness
- Ravioli: Two sheets of pasta stuffed and cut into fancy shapes
- Spaghetti: Solid, cylindrical long noodles
- Lasagne: Thick sheets of pasta approx. 1 inch in thickness
- Canneloni: Stuffed, cylindrical pasta product
- Tahlia Telli: Flat pasta, 16 mm wide made from wh eat
- Fucilli: Pasta with a spiral shape of corkscrew

Special entrée dishes

1. Foie D' Agneau A A Anglaise: Lamb liver cut in slices, grilled and dressed with bacon rashers.
2. Cervelle Frit A A Anglaise: Brain dipped in egg, rolled in breadcrumbs, deep fried and served with tomato sauce.

Entrée are served on a hot half plate, and the cutlery provided are a small knife and a small fork. A dessert spoon is kept on the side board, in case the guest demands it.

RELEVE

Big joints of veal, lamb, meat, poultry, are served with heavy accompaniments and garnish. The accompaniments of Releve are vegetables and potatoes. Potatoes are placed at the 2 o' clock position while the vegetables are placed at 10 o' clock position, in a large hot plate and cutlery provided are a large knife and a large fork.

i) Continental accompaniments: Vegetables and potatoes
ii) Chinese accompaniments: Chinese cruet set comprising of chilli sauce and soya sauce
iii) Indian accompaniments: Achar, papad, chutney and green salad

Different releve preparations

a) Chicken: Poulet Saute Chasseur, Poulet Maryland
b) Lamb: Gigot de Mutton Roti, lamb shaslik
c) Beef: Boeuf Strognoff
d) Veal: Veau Codon Bleau, Escalope De Veau A A Anglaise
e) Pork: Suckling pork

Other meats:

- Hare
- Wild bear
- Horse meat
- Squirrel
- Whale

Releve is served on a hot large plate, and the cutlery provided are a large knife and a large fork.

SORBET

It is the sixth course of the menu and a rest between the main course and Roti 10-12 minutes are allotted for the sorbet service. Russian and Egyptian cigarettes are passed with sorbet. Sorbet is iced water, flavored with champagne or any other liquor. It is sweetened and coloured with fruit and fruit juices

Different sorbet preparations

- Sorbet A A Sicilienne
- Sorbet Alexandra
- Sorbet A A Americain
- Marquise

Sorbet is served in a parfait glass, with a quarter plate and a doily paper as underline. After the clearance of the main course, the dessert cutlery stays on the cover. An ashtray is placed on the cover in the centre. Cigarettes are passed on a quarter plate with a doily paper and a match box.

ROTI

In this course, roasted game birds are served, for example chicken, pigeon, turkey, quail, pheasant, snipe, duck, goose, may be served in this course. It is accompanied by a salad which is served on a half moon shaped plate.

Different roti preparations

- Faisen A A Normande
- Caille En Cocotte
- Dindonneau A A Chipolata

Roti is served on a hot half plate, and the cutlery provided is s small knife and a small fork. A side plate or a quarter plate is put on the side board along with a side knife. If the guest asks for bread, the quarter plate and knife are put on the cover. When serving roast of large birds, the joints may be served on a large plate, and the cutlery provided is a large knife and a large fork. If the roast is part of the main course, it may be served as main dish.

LEGUME

Different vegetables such as mushroom, artichokes, asparagus and carrots are served in this course.

Different legume preparations

i) **Artichaut provencale**: Artichokes are boiled, tossed in butter and cooked in cocote dish with peas and lettuce.

ii) **Artichaut lyommaies:** Artichokes are cut into quarters, tossed in oil with fried onions and garnished with parsley.

iii) **Asperges flamande**: Asparagus is boiled and coated with sauce which is made from butter and egg yolk.

Legumes are served on a cold or hot half plate, depending upon the dish, cutlery provided are a small knife and a small fork.

Vegetables like artichoke and asparagus are eaten with fingers therefore a finger bowl is passed at the end of the meal if serving cold legume, accompaniments are vinaigrette or mayonnaise. Of serving hot legume, accompaniments are hollandaise or beurre noisette.

While serving asparagus, an inverted fork is placed under the plate, so that the plate tilts towards one side, where the appropriate amount of vinaigrette or mayonnaise collects.

ENTREMET

It is a sweet course. Hot or cold puddings, cakes and Indian sweets are served in this course. These days, this course is merged with the dessert course.

i) Crème caramel

ii) Diplomat pudding iii)Soufflé

iv) Baked alaska

v) Gateaux ananas

vi) Fruit and nut cake

vii) Ice cream

Entremet is served on a cold half plate and the cutlery provided is a dissert spoon and a dessert fork. Ice cream is served in an ice cream cup or cocktail cup, with a quarter plate and a doily paper as an underliner with a tea spoon or ice cream spoon.

BONNE BOUCHE

This course comes after the entremets course. It includes many savoury dishes.

Different bonne boucle preparations

- Anchovies on toast
- Roe on toast
- Haddock on toast
- Mushrooms on toast
- Devils on horseback
- Angels on horseback
- Canapés

- Cheeses

Different cheeses

- English: Cheddar, Cheshire, Lancashire, Derby, St ilton, Leicester, Gloucester
- French: Brie, Camembert, Port du Salut, Roquefort , Demi Sel
- Swiss: Gruyere, Emmenthal
- Dutch: Edam, Goda
- Italian: Gorgonzola, Parmesan, Parmesan
- Danish: Danish Blue
- German: Bavarian Blue
- Belgium: Limburger
- Greek: Feta
- American: Brick, Colby
- Scottish: Caboc, **Dunlop Accompaniments of cheese**

i) Special cruet set consisting of salt, pepper and mustard.
ii) Celery is served in a glass bowl on a bed of crushed ice.
iii) Radishes are served, when in season, in a glass bowl.
iv) Castor sugar is passed in sugar dredges for cream cheese.
v) Assorted cheese biscuits like cream crackers are serued.

Bonne bouche is served on a half plate, and the cutlery provided are a small knife and a small fork.

Service of cheese: Cheese is presented on a cheese board or displayed on a trolley. Cheese is served on a quarter plate. It is cut into pieces with the help of a cheese knife. It is picked with the beak of a cheese knife and the ctlery provided is a small knife and a small fork. Cheeses are also provided as dips or accompaniments.

DESSERT

In the dessert course, fresh and dry fruits are served. Fresh fruits are arranged in a fruit basket which is called Corbielle des Fruits. Fresh fruits may be divided into four main categories:

i) Soft fruits: Banana, papaya, grapes
ii) Hard fruits: Pears, apple, mango, etc
iii) Dry fruits: Walnuts, cashew nuts, almonds, pistachio
iv) Citrus fruits: Oranges, sweet limes, grapefruit

Service of dessert:

Fruits may be served in a fruit basket or a half plate. Cutlery provided is a fruit knife and a fruit fork. Grapes are served along with grape scissor and a finger bowl of fresh water to wash the grapes. A nutcracker is passed for nuts. A finger bowl and fresh napkins are passed after the service.

CAFÉ OR COFEE

It is customary to serve coffee at the end of a meal. Coffee could be served with or without milk and with white or brown sugar. There are wide varieties of coffee being served at different time and places. Digest if coffee has a small quantity of digest if and stimulant that ends dinner with a refreshing note. It is a small cup of coffee served in a demitasse which is about 21/2 oz. or 75 ml. it has a compatible saucer and coffee spoon. Frequently it is placed on quarter plate (F & B) to make it look decently large on the table and also to hold any spill while pouring brownies, biscuits and chocolate-flavored liquor are occasionally offered at this stage. Cigar, cognac and liquor are natural accompaniments. Black coffee is most popular after dinner but coffee could be served with or without milk and with white or brown sugar.

CHAPTER 6

Lay Out

Objectives of a good layout:-

The planning of spaces for serving food should be aimed at achieving:-

1. Smooth flow work
2. Prompt & efficient service
3. Effective utilization of space
4. Minimum Investment
5. Profit maximization
6. Less staff movement
7. Ease of supervision
8. Chance of future renovations
9. Aesthetic appeal
10. Efficient flow of Operation
11. Safe working areas
12. Low maintenance cost
13. Follow governing laws (State + Central)
14. Preserving food quality
15. Avoiding queuing problem
16. Maintaining standards of Environmental Hygiene

Steps in Planning Various F&B Outlets (Planning Process)

1. Prepare a prospectus or program guide

The Prospectus must include

i) tittle of the project
ii) reason and need for the project
iii) goals and objectives of the project
iv) policy guidelines of the project
v) procedure to be followed

The prospectus also includes physical and operational characteristics such as style of the building, type of food served, type of service system to be followed, profile of customers etc. it also includes regulatory information such as standards of safety, hygiene, noise control etc.

2. Planning team:-

The planning team is organized and may include some or all of the following

i) Owner or administrator
ii) food service manager or director of food + beverage
iii) design consultant
iv) equipment representative
vi) general manager
vii) builder or contractor
viii) maintenance engineer or chief engineer

3. Conduct a feasibility study:-

A feasibility study is defined as "the collection of data about the market and other factors relating to the operation of the proposed facility to justify the proposed project."

It will include research on:-

i) proposed site
ii) potential customer profile
iii) community growth
iv) building trends
v) competition in the area
vi) possible revenue generating sources like function catering etc.
vii) cost component of the project

4. Menu Analysis:-

Menu Analysis involves identifying the type of menu to be served, food service systems to be followed such as quick-chill method etc. sample menu and menu patterns are designed for this purpose. From this the followed data is derived

i) type of storage needed
ii) portions size of each dish
iii) total number of portions
iv) batch size of all dishes
v) method of cooking and processing
vi) work surface or equipment required
vii) storage or holding equipment required

5. Consider architectural features like Building style and material:-

The style depends on the type of operation, area and menu selected. Material depends on the type of architecture and local weather conditions. If a restaurant is situated near the sea shore or facing a pool, it can go for glass walls to utilize the scene views in its architecture.

Floors:-

While selecting the flooring, the utility, durability, resistance to acids, grease and stains should be considered. The time of the surface selected can have an effect on productivity. Like a hard surface can tire the employees faster. Also carpeted floors may not be the right choice for the use of trolleys or heavy movement. Hard tiles or quarry stones are best suited for kitchen floors as they are smooth, easy to clean and slip resistant.

All the kitchen floor surfaces must be covered 6 inch up at walls and equipment base for sanitation purposes.

Walls, Ceiling and Noise Reduction:-

For choosing walls and ceiling finish aesthetic values, sanitary conditions and noise reduction are considered. The wall finish depends on the amount of natural light available.

Ceramic tiles are best suited for kitchens as they are durable and easy to clean. Tiling is don for upto 1.5 to 2.5 metres to take care of food and water splashes. The height of the ceiling is kept at an average of 4.5 to 6 metres.

Kitchen and dining rooms ceilings and walls are acoustically treated to reduce the noise levels. Ceiling are given a lighter colour than walls as it gives an illusion of space to a room. Sound proof materials are also used to insulate vents, radiators, pipes etc. rubber parts are used in the areas where dishes are washed to prevent excess noise of equipments.

Lighting:-

Correct lighting for the facility is selected. The lighting should be adequate and suitable. It should help to increase the efficiency, as the correct lighting increases workers productivity by 3-4 %. Correct design should allow as much natural light as possible. Light gets reflected from the floors, walls + ceiling and that is to be considered while selecting the lighting.

Direct or down lighting system is used in kitchens to create natural light effect.

Light fixtures should be positioned in such a way that the employees do not work in their shadow. Good lighting reduces eyes strain and increases productivity.

Heating, Ventilation and Air conditioning (HVAC):-

Efficient and effective heating and Ceiling system is required, for the comfort of the guest and employees. It also helps to increase the productivity by 5-15 %.

Proper ventilation has to be ensured in kitchens and consist of exhaust fan system, built into the hoods over cooking equipment and eliminates odour, fumes, moisture + grease vapour. Fans bring in fresh air from outside.

Built-in-refrigeration:-

Proper selection of built-in-refrigeration is ensured keeping into consideration the space available for the purpose in the kitchens.

Plumbing and Electricity:-

Electricity or power requirements are calculated based on the equipment that needs to run. Power requirements of various equipments has to be considered. Concealed wiring is carried out in kitchens and service areas.

Proper drainage and sewage disposal systems has to be ensured and considered.

Budget and Cost Relationship:-

No food service can have an unlimited budget as it would not practical. Hence a balance beds to be made between quality, quantity or space and cost. A well planned and designed facility proves cost effective in the long run.

7. Design Development:

The first step is to determine space allocation, with the help of flow diagrams. All work units along with their roots for supplies and workers are represented schematically in a flow diagrams.

The next step is drawing a blue print to scale for placement of equipment.

The blue print is then submitted and contract documents are formulated for contractors. Tender or bids are called to select the builder or contractor. Once the builder is selected the next stage involves signing a contract with the builder.

Periodic inspections are conducted to ensure that the construction is as per the specifications and the blue print

Factors Affecting Restaurant Planning and Deigning:-

Factors: Internal Factors

i) space available
ii) budget (initial & ongoing)
iii) no. of cover
iv) target market
v) type of service

External Factors

i) market trend
ii) designer
iii) psychological effect on guest
iv) future renovation chances
v) competitor
vi) Govt. rules & regulations

Additional factors

i) Cost of repair and maintenance
ii) Equipment layout
iii) Preference Preference of owner
iv) Division Zone (like smoking zone)
v) low pattern

Major factors affecting Restaurant's Planning & Designing

1.Cost/ funds in Hand:- It means that how much expenses are required or available for the making, renovation or for operating the establishment. The cost factor is always considered on the priority base and will determine the number & types of activities that can be carried out.

2.Space available:- Space is also an important criterion in restaurant planning because different types of seating arrangement require different amount of space. The area of the space at hand will determine the number and extent of activities that can be carried out in it. Besides shape of the space is important in planning work centres efficiently.

3.Style of Service:- Style of Service also affects your restaurant planning. Suppose you want to offer Gueridon service to the guest then it is difficult to put carpet on restaurant floor because it creates problem in rolling of wheels.

A self service facility will require a larger area for the display of foods. If the style of service is buffet, the space for seating should be limited to the sides of the dinning area. Similarly, in a kiosk, only a window counter is sufficient to pass on ready to serve prepared items to customer. In a restaurant equipped for leisurely dinning, at least 50-60 cms space on the table is required per person.

4. Cover:- It means for how many people you are making the restaurant or the number of people or pax can be accommodated at a time in the restaurant. The number of cover always depend upon the available space in the restaurant. But it is always preferable to have the maximum utilisation of the available space which can be achieved by offering different sizes of tables like- offer two, four, six or group tables in your restaurant.

5. Type of Customer:- Type of customer you are catering will have a greater impact on the type of restaurant e.g., for elite class, fine dinning is suitable a cafeteria is suitable for office goers or shoppers.

6. Number, type and size of equipment:- The total number of meals served at any meal time and the menu composition helps to determine the quantities of various dishes to be produced and the size and type of holding and reheating or finishing equipment necessary in the serving area. For a cafeteria Beverage equipment for hot & cold beverages, display cases for snacks, salads & deserts or hot cases for holding food prior to or during service, trolleys for stacking trays if it is self service are required. For seating furniture may be fixed along the sides of dinning rooms or adjustable tables may be used for seating and standing arrangements as required.

7. Man Power:- In case of fast food & other outlets where there is full or semi self service style, the number of skilled staff required is less as the waiting staff have not to serve on the tables. The number of staff are determined by the number of customers to be served at one time, composition of menu, style of service & type of the restaurant.

8. Menu:- during the restaurant planning process, menu is the most important factor because it works as a selling tool plus also merchandising the dishes. The menu has to be planned in accordance to the locality or target market and as per the type of restaurant you intend to plan. It's physical layout like menu paper, language, word font etc should also match with the restaurant's theme.

9. Sanitation and Safety:- sanitation is related with the cleaning aspect of restaurant. If your restaurant is carpeted, it will require more time as well as more man power to clean it. On the other hand, if the floor has hard or marble flooring it can be easily cleaned and there is less chance of spots etc. Safety means security from various future uncertainties like fire, terrorist attacks etc. so the restaurants must be planned in such a way so as to ensure safety & protection of the guests & staff. E.g., fire extinguishers at various places, fire alarms must be put. Emergency exits & evacuation plans must be ensured and put into place.

KITCHEN LAYOUT

The plan or layout of a kitchen will be determined by the catering policy of the establishment. The plan is often limited by space availability. The production area is divided into 3 very distinctive areas.

1. Receiving, Preparation & Storage.
2. Cooking.

3. Service (Dispatching) and wash-up.

As in any other industrial production unit, the kitchen has three functions:

1. Receiving raw materials
2. Transforming them into finished goods
3. Forwarding the products.

The main factors that determine the layout of a kitchen are:

1. Whether the hotel is primarily for guests or if there is a busy chance trade.
2. The locality.
3. The type of customer.
4. The type of menu/service.
5. Seasonal pressure of trade.
6. Possibility of expansion.

Among current trends in cooking, kitchen organization and food service, the following are readily noticeable.

1. Greater mechanization
2. Simpler operations
3. Increased use of convenience foods

The information that will be required before beginning kitchen planning will be:

1. What type of meal is offered?
2. How many persons will he served?
3. Meal timings and how many sittings.
4. What type of service?
5. Will convenience foods be used?
6. Is allowance to be made for special functions/seasons?

Area Requirements: It is possible that kitchen space will be reduced to provide more seating capacity in the restaurant. However cramped, inadequate kitchens will lead to delays and faults in service. This will invariably affect the turnover. Inadequate facilities will also affect staff morale. Kitchen areas will depend on the type of service. Normally a kitchen will occupy between 25%-33% of the space allotted to the restaurant. Whereas 10-12 sq. ft. per cover is the norm in the restaurant, the kitchen space is generally 2½–4 sq. per cover. In smaller establishments this will go up to 6-9 sq. ft. per cover. Generally ¼th the kitchen area is set aside for storage. The remaining is divided between food pre-preparation, cooking and service.

RECEIVING AND PREPARATION AND STORAGE AREAS

Receiving area: The receiving area should be large and convenient enough to receive the volume and type of goods delivered. The receiving clerk must inspect all items before acceptance. The receiving area should be located near the entrance to the storage area so that once checked, goods can be stored quickly.

Delivery Quay: The delivery quay will be situated near the store and will consist of a platform of lorry level for easy unloading. It should be well lit, and fitted with anti-pest fans and an air curtain at the door. A water connection with hosepipe will ensure easy regular cleaning. Trolleys must be kept for easy unloading and cartage.

Gas Bank: If cylinders are used, these must, be kept outside. Incase of a gas tank the distance from the building must be at least 150 yards. A daily check of gas shelters and tank is necessary as a safety measure.

Garbage Disposal: Wet and dry garbage must be stored separately. Wet garbage is stored in containers in a cool area to prevent fermentation and smell. Dry garbage can be incinerated. Disposal of garbage must be on a daily basis. Garbage areas must be cleaned daily, then disinfected and deodorized.

Central stores: Dry stores must be maintained at 70°F (21° C). Lightweight items could be stored on top of shelves and heavy weight items at the bottom. Cases/Cartons can be stored either on shelves or pallets. Nothing should be stored on the floor. 8" height above the floor will ensure easy cleaning. Shelves should not touch the wall. A 2" space must be maintained.

The Cold Room: Many foodstuffs will have to be maintained at refrigerated temperatures. There are two types of cold rooms:

1. Negative cold room (freezer) with an ideal temperature of -18°C.
2. Positive cold room (walk-in) with a temperature of 3°C- 5°C.

Recommended temperatures for various food stuffs:

Meat 0-1°C

Fish 2-3°C

Dairy 4-5°C

Veg. & Fruits 6-7°C

Vegetable Pre-preparation Area: The work here consists of:

1. Washing and Cleaning.
2. Paring and Trimming
3. Cutting, Chopping etc.

Use of frozen vegetables will determine the area required here. This room is sometimes air-conditioned, and in small establishments will be combined with the Butchery.

The Butchery: It is an air-conditioned room for meat pre-preparation. Bone saws, weighing scales and butchers blocks will be provided. The butchery must be situated close to the freezer. Non slip flooring is essential and flycatchers must be installed.

The Larder: The larder must be situated near to but separate from the kitchen. It must be air-conditioned, well lit and well equipped.

COOKING AREA

In this area, raw materials and pre-prepared goods are turned into finished products. This area can range from a simple kitchen to a more complex group or sections or even satellites.

- Pastry/Confectionery - Bakeshop
- Short order kitchen - Pantry
- Hot Kitchen - Main Kitchen

The Bake Shop- The control of costs and quality of desserts and breads sold in hotels is very important for successful operation. In a small hotel, this will be a corner of the main kitchen whereas in big hotels, this will be a separate fully equipped department. There are two sections

Hot: equipped mainly with ovens (single, double decker or triple tier) (convection or conventional), racks, dough mixer, food processor and will provide all bread, cakes and gateaux.

Cold: is equipped with refrigerated marbles, laminators, ice-cream machines, and food processors. It is usually air-conditioned, and provides all the desserts.

The Pantry- As the name suggests all the short orders are executed from here. These will include sandwiches, icecreams and beverages. Quick service equipment, such as toasters, juicers and shakers will be provided.

The Main Kitchen- Known as the heart of the kitchen. The area is divided into work islands where various jobs will be performed.

A) Roasting and Baking
B) Grilling
C) Frying

The equipment must be placed so as to avoid unnecessary movement. Bain Maries must be located near the gas ranges. Exhaust fans are essential. Good lighting, non-slip floors, and easy-to-clean walls are necessary.

In a classical organization the main kitchen is divided according to partie system. But in India it is divided according to the cuisine. E.g. Continental, Chinese, Indian.

SERVICE AND WASH-UP AREA

The Service Area is situated between the kitchen and the restaurant and has the following functions.

1. Cleans dirty equipment corning from the restaurant or floors.
2. Supplies clean equipment to the restaurant and kitchen.
3. Calling point for food orders.
4. Delivery of food.
5. Cashiering.

Issuing meals to the restaurant is carried out in this area. A kitchen clerk called the Aboyeur is stationed at the survey counter throughout the meal period. On receipt of the waiter's check (KOT) he announces in a loud and clear voice the order with special instructions. The section must acknowledge the order in return. Most orders are executed in parts (en suite.)

The Cashier prepares the bills and gives it to the waiter for presentation. The paid check and cash is returned to the cashier who will stamp it with a PAID stamp. A dispense bar is also situated in this area for drinks in the restaurant and in rooms

The Wash-up Area: Dish washing has a high rate of importance because of its significance in sanitation and hygiene. The wash-up area consists of three parts, manned by the kitchen steward.

a) Loading – dirty equipment is pre-washed and loaded on baskets/trays for machine or hand washing.
b) Washing – consists of cleaning, rinsing and sanitizing.
c) Unloading – The clean equipment is kept on racks, picked by waiters or delivered by stewards.

Pre-rinsing calls for water of a warm temperature. 120° F will melt fat but not cook foods firmly onto the surfaces.

The washing temperature must be 140° F hot enough for effective cleaning action. Sanitizing calls for a temperature of 180° F for 10 seconds. In small hotels, dish washing is done manually, but the process is the same. Ideally separate workers should be provided for handling dirty and clean dishes. To ensure effective dish washing water temperatures must be maintained, detergent concentration should be effective and correct handling procedures followed.

RESTAURANT EQUIPMENTS

HOTPLATE POINT

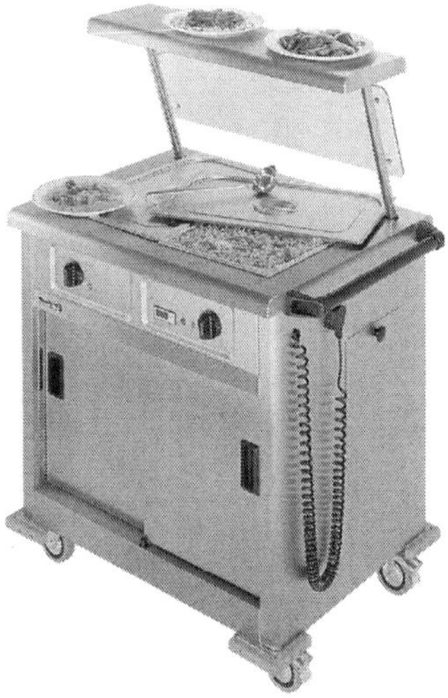

The hotplate is the contact point between the kitchen and theservice staff. It is the point at which both areas must cooperate andcommunicate effectively so that the customer gets the quick andefficient service that he expects.Hot cupboards can be used for either food or plates. Units asa whole are usually made up of a hot cupboard with sliding doors,topped by a heated serving surface. The top may also housecontainers acting as dry or heated brain-maries. Dry heat keeps thefood hot by electric elements or gas flame. The wet heat methodprovides heat via an open tank of water, which itself is heated bygas-fired burners or by an electric immersion heater.

The hot plate or hot cupboard needs to be stocked with all the china and crockery needed for service, e.g soup plates, fish plates, consommé cups, platters, soup cups, tea cups and demitasse. The Aboyeur is in charge, and controls the hotplate over the service period. As an aid to the food service staff the Aboyeur would control the 'off board' which tells the waiter immediately any dish is 'off'. The Aboyeur who controls the hotplate over the service period will initially receive the food check from the waiter. He checks that it is legible and that none of the dishes ordered are 'off' the menu.

WASH-UP AREA

At the service time especially, the wash-up area is one of thebusiest sections. It must be correctly sited to allow a smooth flow ofwork, promoting a fast turnover and efficient service. There are twomethods of washing:

1. The tank method: Using this method, the items are washed ina sink of hot water containing detergent and then placed intoracks and dipped into another sink. This second sink is knownas sterilising tank; the water temperature is very high, atapproximately 75°C. The items are left in here for few minutesthen lifted out. As the water is so hot, the items especially thecrockery, will air dry, making this a more hygienic method (nocloths are needed). The crockery can then be stacked and putaway as required.
2. The machine method: In principle, the machine method is nodifferent from the tank method, except that the whole system isautomated and therefore labour saving.

SILVER ROOM / PLATE ROOM

The silver room holds the stock of silver required for the service of meals. The various types of silver are kept here on labeled shelves, with all the service plates of one size stacked together. Cutlery, flatware, hollowware and other smaller items are usually stored in drawers lined with baize, as this helps to reduce noise, slipping and scratching.

In very large establishments, the silver and the plate room may be two separate units, but in the majority of places they are combined and in some cases, are a part of wash-up.

STILL ROOM

The still room is looked after by a still room supervisor, who is responsible for the staffing, ordering of supplies from the main store and effective control of these items when issued to various departments. In most of the restaurants, the stillroom remains open for long hours. For the efficient running, the staffs normally work on a straight rotating shift basis, doing an early shift one week and a late shift the next. The stillroom staffs are also responsible for the washing up of all their equipments.

Provisions Obtainable from the Stillroom:

The list below gives the provisions that can be obtained from the stillroom:

- Beverages: coffee, tea, chocolate, horlicks, ovaltine and other food drinks.
- Fruit juices: apple, orange, pineapple, grapefruit and other assorted fruit juices.
- Pastries, gateaux and sandwiches
- Rolls, brioche and crossant
- Toast: breakfast toast, melba toast
- Milk, cream and butter
- Toasted scones and teacakes
- Sugar: coffee powder, tea dust, demerara etc.
- Breakfast cereals: cornflakes, weetabixm shredded wheat, rice crispies, muesli etc.
- Preserves: jams, jelly, marmalade, cherry, plum, raspberry, strawberry, apricot and honey.
- Cleaning detergents and scrubbers.

Stillroom Equipments:

A wide range of food items are offered from a stillroom and therefore, to ensure the correct storage, preparation and presentation a considerable amount of equipment is used. The equipment that may be found includes:

- Coffee brewing machine
- Coffee bean grinding machine
- Tea dispenser
- Bread slicing machine
- Salamander
- Hot cupboard
- Steamer and hotwater boiler
- Refrigertors

- Work table and cutting board
- General storage space, shelves and cupboards
- Sinks, washing machines and dish washers.

ANCILLARY DEPARTMENTS

The ancillary department of the restaurant area includes important units in the make-up of a catering establishement, acting as the link between kitchen or food preparation units and the restaurant or food service units. The service areas behind the scener can also be termed as 'back-of-house'. The service areas are stocked with appropriate equipment, depending on the style of operation. The service areas themselves are some of the busiest units of a catering establishment, especially during the service periods. In general, especially in large hotels, five main service areas can be distinguished:

1) Stillroom
2) Silver or plate room
3) Wash-up
4) Hotplate
5) Spare linen store

A well-structured layout of these areas is most important to ensure even flow of work by the various members of staff. However, the layout itself may vary with different catering establishments according to their own needs.

EQUIPMENT HANDLING

Sanitation Standards in Handling Service Equipment

1. Use clean and sanitized glasses, flatware, chinaware and other equipment for service.
2. All service equipment must be wiped dry with clean cloths to avoid watermarks. The cloths used for this purpose must be segregated from other wiping cloths.
3. Bowls should be underlined with appropriate underliner and never to be served with the finger touching the rim.
4. When serving straw serve them with their wrappers or in their respective dispensers.
5. When serving additional utensils or napkin, place them in a small plate to avoid direct contact with hand.
6. The thumb should be kept away from the plate to avoid touching the sauce, meat or dish.
7. When setting up flatware and glasses, avoid leaving finger marks; carry them in trays or with a cloth napkin.
8. Never serve food using cutleries that have fallen on the floor.
9. To avoid contamination, food must be covered when it is not served immediately.

Never serve utensils, cups, glasses or plates that are oily, wet or with fingermarks, spots or lipstick mark.

EQUIPMENT HANDLING

Do's and Dont's of Equipment Handling

1. Dump ice out of the glass; preheat the glass before pouring hot water. Don't pour hot drinks in chilled or cold glasses.
2. Stack dishes according to size and kind. Never stack too high.
3. Handle stemmed glasses by the stem and tumblers by the base. Never handle glasses in bouquet.
4. Remove glass / china from buspan one at a time. Don't unload china, glasses at random.
5. Use ice scooper for scooping ice. Never use the glass for scooping ice.
6. Never put cutlery into glasses, put them in appropriate containers.
7. Make sure of an adequate back-up supply of glassware for rush periods.
8. Always be on the lookout for cracked or chipped glassware and remove them.
9. Never allow glass-to-glass contact on overhead racks, keep distant from each other.
10. Never overload the tray / buspan. Load only what it can conveniently accommodate.
11. Never buss glasses in the sink. Buss them directly onto divider racks.
12. Never stack glasses. Use trays and avoid over crowding them to prevent breakage.

EQUIPMENT HANDLING

Measures to Avoid Breakages

- Use trays when serving and bussing.
- Proper system should be followed in stacking and storing equipment.
- Use appropriate door for entry and exit. A separate door for entering and eiting should be installed to prevent collision.
- Use appropriate glass racks. Make sure that the glasses are conviniently, but not tightly inserted in each rack.
- Buss out glasses separately from chinaware.
- Avoid overloading trays and buspans.

EQUIPMENT HANDLING

Management invests substantial amount in supplies and equipment. Service staffs are, therefore, expected that these equipment are handled gently and carefully. Staff should be sanitation and safety conscious. Equipment should be handled in the right spot stemmed glass by the stem, tumblers by the base, flatware by the handle. Bowls should never be held by the rim, use appropriate underliners. The thumb should never show on the plate.

When setting up cutleries, as well as glasswares, avoid leaving finger marks by using trays or by securing them inside a cloth napkin. To prevent breakage, be conscious of the rules of equipment handling. Breakages are usually caused by the following factors:

1. Mechanical Impact — results from object-to-object collision. This is induced by stacking of glasswares and chinawares, picking of glasses in bouquet, overloading of buspans and trays, putting cutleries inside glasses.
2. Thermal Shock — result of sudden change of temperature. This happens when hot water is placed inside a chilled / cold glass and vice versa, abrupt use of

glasswares after coming of the dishwashing machines, heating chilled bowl in a microwave.

3. Improper Handling and Misuse of Equipment — using the equipment for a purpose it was not intended for such as using a glass to scoop ice, using knives for opening cans, etc.
4. Inattentiveness or Absent-mindedness — accidents often occur when service personnel are absent-minded or are inattentive in executing services especially when they are carrying breakable equipment.
5. Environmental Factors – greasy / wet floor, slippery floor, broken tiles, blind doors.

LINEN

Buffet Cloths

For a buffet table, the minimum size of the tablecloth required is 2 m x 4 m.

Trolley Cloths and Sideboard Cloths

These are usually made from tablecloths well worn and not suitable for use on tables, mended by the housekeeping department and folded to fit a sideboard or trolley.

Waiter's Cloths or Service Cloths A service cloth is a very important part of service equipment as well as being part of the food server's uniform. It must be kept clean and ironed at all times and only used as a service cloth for certain activities such as:

- Carrying hot plates
- Final polishing of plates
- Wiping small spills
- Brushing crumbs onto a service plate
- Wiping the undersides of the plates before placing plates on the table.

Service cloths are also used by every waiter as protection against heat and to keep uniforms clean.

LINEN

Napkins or Serviettes

A napkin or serviette is a rectangle cloth or paper used at the table for wiping the mouth while eating. It is usually small and folded. Conventionally, t he napkin is folded and placed to the left of the place setting, outside the outermost fork. In an ambitious restaurant setting, it may be folded into elaborate shapes and displayed on the empty plate. A napkin may also be held together in a bundle (with cutlery) by a napkin ring. Alternatively, paper napkins may be contained with a napkin holder.

LINEN

Linens are fabric goods, such as tablecloths, napkins and

slip cloths. Linen is a material made from the fibers of the flax plant. Originally, many, such as bed sheets and tablecloths, were made of linen. Today, the term "linen" has come to be applied to all related products even though most are made of cotton, various synthetic materials, or blends. The main items of linen normally found in a restaurant are: tablecloths; slipcloths; buffet cloths; trolley and sideboard cloths; and waiter's cloths or service cloths.

4.9.1 Table Cloths

Table linens made from cotton or linen are not only more absorbent but also last longer. The fibers don't pill or pile as easy as with synthetic table linens and they don't become shiny when exposed to an iron's heat. Egyptian cotton and Irish linen are considered the finest materials for table linens because of their long, durable fibers. White is the most popular color for table linens because it's considered formal. Table linens in off white or ivory are also acceptable. A damask (woven) or embroidered pattern is a perfectly acceptable table cloth.

Types of Tables Size of Tables Size of Table Cloths Square table 76 cm sq 92 cm sq 137 x 137 cm 183 x 183 cm Rectangular table 136 x 76 cm 183 x 137 cm Round table 92 cm diameter 184 cm diameter

Table cloths should be large enough to cover the top as well as a portion of the legs of a table without interfering with the guest's comfort while he is seated at the table.The size of the tablecloth varies according to the size of the table it is required to cover.

Slip Cloths or Naperones

These are designed to be laid over the tablecloth to protect it from spillage and give it a longer life. Using a slip cloth reduces the number of tablecloths used and thus reduces the cost of inventory and laundry. Slip cloths may measure 1 metre square approximately.

OTHER TROLLEYS

CHEESE TROLLEY LIQUEUR TROLLEY

MOBILE BAR

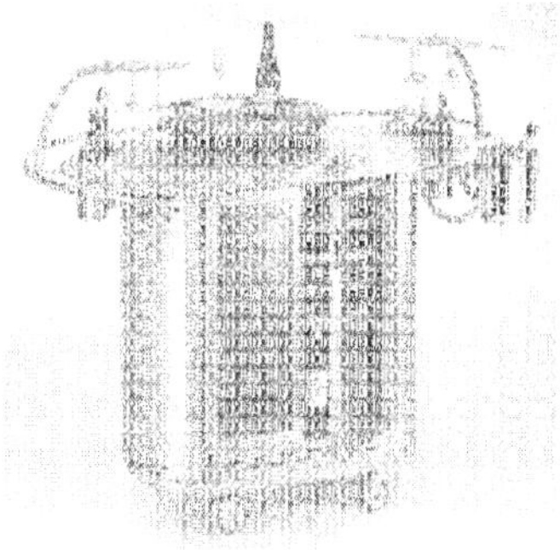

WINE TROLLEY

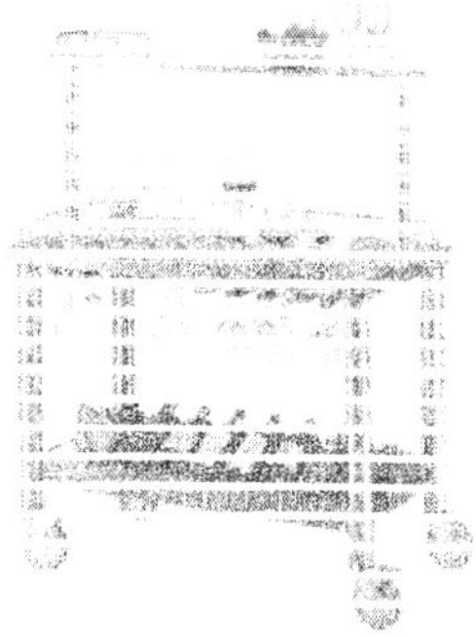

WINE TROLLEY

Hotel & Restaurant Trolleys

TROLLEYS - CARVING TROLLEY

It is used for carving joints of meat at a guest's table. This trolley is seldom used in India.

TROLLEYS - DESSERT TROLLEY

This trolley serves as a visual aid to selling desserts. Guests are more likely to order a dessert if they can see what is available, particularly if it is well presented. Some dessert trolleys are refrigerated. Gateaux, pastries, jellies, tarts, pies, flans and souffles can be served from a dessert trolley.

TROLLEYS - ROOM SERVICE TROLLEY

This trolley is known for its versatility. It is used for the service to guests in their rooms. The waiter sets up the meal and covers on the trolley and wheels it into the guest's room. This trolley may also be used as a dining table in the privacy of the guest's room. Beneath the trolley top, provision is made for mounting a hot case to keep the food warm.

MENU PLANNING

Let us now study the art and science of menu design or menu planning. Planning a menu is a simple exercise that involves applying the knowledge of food, nutrient requirement and individual preferences to plan adequate and acceptable meals.

Let us remember that a well-balanced diet is a basic requirement for a healthy meal. However, a nutritious meal must look, smell and taste good. Balanced diet is defined as 'right kind of foods in the right amounts and proportions, to meet the nutrient needs of the persons'. It helps to decide:

- What to serve
- Where to shop
- How much to spend
- How much to serve
- How much to buy
- How to prepare food
- How to serve meals and at what time?

Menu planning helps in various ways. The chief aims of menu planning are as follows:

- Economies of time, labour and fuel
- Planning meals within budget
- Aiding in the proper purchase, preparation and service of food
- Fulfill the nutritional needs of the customer
- Providing variety in the diet, by making proper selection of foods from within each of the three food groups

- Making meals appealing and palatable by proper selection of food in terms of color, texture and flavor
- Providing nutritious meals taking into account individual preferenc'e
- Planning meals in advance, so that any pre-preparation required cañbe made, and also so that leftovers from previous meals are economically utilized.

Menu

Before studying menu planning, one should get back to of the meaning of a menu. A menu is a list of dishes planned for production in a catering operation and may include full meals, snacks or beverages.

Menu planning may, therefore, appear to be a simple exercise involving putting down whatever items the planner or the cook like and are easy to prepare. Past experience of sales may help them to forecast the quantities of each item that needs to be prepared. They may together decide to keep their outlet open for only a few hours or till the quantity prepared is sold out. If the food is finished and some customers see the 'closed' sign; and thus, customers go away with out being served, the next day the manager may buy the related materials in large Menu Planning quantities. This is often the case with small roadside establishments that do not have much storage space or trained staff but start a business using the hit and trial management techniques.

They may even be faced with the opposite situation where customers did not come again, as they had a bad experience the previous day. This will lead to cooked food being left unsold. All such experiences show that:

- The chefs have to know what the customers like and at what times of the day are suited for those.
- Menus need to be planned for the customer and not the managers or staff of the establishment.
- The staff must know how to prepare the demanded foods well and to the quality standards desired.
- The atmosphere should be light and relaxing and not tense and noisy.
- They need to serve dishes in attractive ways to tempt customers.
- The efforts put in to please customers and satisfy them should also generate profit for the establishment to make it worthwhile.

One can go on thinking of many more factors that need to be consciously or unconsciously considered before a final list of food items or menu could be prepared and offered to customers to choose from at a reasonable price.

Thus, menu planning is not a simple listing of food items. They have to be arrived at after much thought and this complex process is called menu planning.

Let us now see why so much effort needs to be put in by catering managers for writing down a menu. It is because the menu performs a number of useful functions for smooth operation of establishments.

Planing Meal

Before finalizing the items on the menu, every planner must consider the basic factors essential to the situation and the customer for whom the menu is being planned.

The situation

The basic factors to be considered in terms of the situation would be:

(i) The location of the establishment in relation to the market

(ii) Space available for storing food in wholesome condition

(iii) The size of the kitchen and service areas

(iv) The number of staff and their skills

(v) Equipment available in kitchen and service areas (vi The policy of the establishment in terms of:

(a) What type of customers it wishes to attract. This will be basically determined by the pricing policy, in that the higher the prices, richer the customer and the higher his power to pay.

Interior of a five star restaurant.

(b) The extent to which the establishment wishes to invest in catering, in comparison to other areas on expenditure such as furniture, decor, equipment, and so on.

(c) The degree of automation or labour-saving devices desired.

d) Personnel in terms of trained staff or cheaper unskilled labour.

(e) Profit margins.

(f) The type of service, i.e. whether food is served or pre-plated and handed over or packed and delivered.

The customer

We have to value the customers well. Customers are likely to represent people of varying ages, activities, occupations, physiological status and sex. They would also beloig to various religious and cultural backgrounds. Some, perhaps, may have rigid food habits. The following section illustrates how the various requirements form the bases for menu planning. This in indicated in the sample menus given along with the special factors that are considered while planning menus.

Boarding school

Since boarding schools have the responsibility of providing meals to resident school children, the important factors in planning their meals are:

(i) Nutritional balance

(a) School children generally spend a lot of physical energy at play. They are also at various stages of growth and so their general nutritional needs would have to be considered while planning their meals. Some children may have special requirements because of sickness or injury. The considerations would, therefore, emphasize on planning balanced diets suitable to their needs.

(ii) Four-meal pattern

This comprises breakfast, lunch, tea and dinner with bedtime milk or milk-based beverages.

(a) Children are generally restless and do not like to spend too much time at the table. Besides, they feel rushed in the morning because they have to reach school on time. Menus, therefore, have to provide dishes that are not only quick to eat, but satisfying. Perhaps, something they can carry out of the dining hail easily, such as a hamburger or a salad roll; or stuffed parathas, pancakes and whole fruit would be in order.

(b) Children have varying appetites and often prefer snaky meals at frequent intervals, to a few large ones.

(iii) Purchasing power

This may not very important because parents or guardian have already paid the charges in advance before sending children to boarding school and are aware of the quantum of expenses.

iv) Planning

Planning should be done according to the average age of the children. First, their favorite dishes should be cooked. Then a dish that they generally dislike should also be made. This will tempt them to eat whatever food is cooked for them. Similar age groups should be seated together. Service arrangements should be made to help the younger children with the plating of their food. The service should be supervised by teachers who eat with them to set an example of discipline eating of everything offered.

iv) Gender

(a) The tastes and needs of the girls and boys differ. Gender is as important factor to be considered, as girls like very different types of foods than boys. Girls are also less active then boys and eat less, but them like variety in colour, texture and flavors. Boys prefer fast foods and snacks which they can eat while performing activities. A policy of mixing dishes in the menu to suit both sexes is desirable unless their hostels are separate and have separate production and service units.

b) In general, boys prefer food with a higher satiety and caloric value than girls of the same age, who become figure conscious and prefer light, frequent but small meals. Also, girls generally prefer food that is spicier.

(vi) Service methods

Self-service methods should be encouraged while supervision is necessary to ensure every dish is picked and eaten.

(vii) Food safety

Safety of food should be ensured in the production process, service and hygienic 1bits of children who would normally use their hands while eating.

(viii) Eating patterns

(a) Don't be monotonous. Children tend to easily get bored with food. So menus need to provide variety in colour, texture taste and flavour.

(b) The climatic and weather conditions are important considerations too. In very dry and hot weather, children lose a lot of body water and salts through perspiration. The menus then would need to introduce extra liquids and salts, because children do not generally like to drink plain water.

The menu planner, therefore, has to consider all these listed factors when planning menus for children, in addition to making them cost effective, reputing and profitable. The structure of the menu for a children's hostel would, therefore, be follows:

Main dish - Curry

Side dishes - Root vegetable/green/other vegetables

Cereal - Rice/roti /chapatti/poori

Curd - Plain/raita
Salad - Green/mixed /seasonal
Sweet/dessert - Cooked/frozen /topped/fruit
Accompaniments – Papad/pickles/chutney
Meal planning for a school child
A child in the age group of 7 to 12 years is known as

- The rate of growth of a school child is less than the rate of growth of a preschool child.
- Growth continues at a steady pace.
- There will be an improvement in the functioning o f body tissues and organs.
- Growth takes place in the form of development of muscles and bones.
- Preparation for adolescence.

The following should be the weight of boys/girls in the age group of 7—12 years.

Age (Years)	Boys (Kg)	Girls Kg
7 +	24.46	24.45
8 +	26.42	25.97
9+	30.00	29.82
10+	32.29	33.58
11 +	35.26	37.17
12+	38.78	42.97

- Energy
- Iron
- Calcium
- Protein

The important points that should be kept in mind while feeding a school child are:

- Boys have more muscle tissue and less adipose tis sue.
- Girls have more adipose tissue and less muscle ti ssue.
- Shedding of baby teeth takes place and permanent teeth will emerge.
- Boys and girls are engaged in more vigorous activities, may be in the form of sports, so, there is a need for more energy.
- More sweating will take place and hence loss of water, sodium and potassium.
- Fluid intake should be increased.
- Blood volume increases and it pushes up the iron needs.
- Bones will grow due to mineralization of bones.
- Recommended daily intakes (RDI5) for energy, prot ein, calcium, Thiamine (B 1), Riboflavin (B2) and Niacin increases as age increases.
- The RDIs for Vitamin C, folic acid. Vitamin B12, Vitamin A. remains Menu Planning unchanged.
- Iron absorption is more in case of girls.

Meal planning for adolescents

Persons in the age group of 13 to 18 years are called adolescents. During this period, major physical, Mental and emotional changes take place, which are as follows:

- This is a period of rapid physical growth.
- There will be sharp increase in height and weight .
- Growth and development of skeletal system and mus cular system.
- Muscles and bones increase in size and strength.
- Heart, lungs, stomach and kidneys attain their final adult size and level of functioning.
- There will be an increase in blood volume.
- Functional capacity of respiratory. digestive and circulatory system increases.
- Sexual characters will appear.
- Functioning of reproductive system starts.
- The changes in the body structure and functioning are guided by hormones, androgens in males and estrogens in females.
- It is a period of physiological stress for the bo dy, because of the extremely rapid rate of growth. Diet plays a crucial role in promoting and sustaining growth. This is the last chance to catch up growth. The main nutrients required are those that give:
- Iron
- Protein
- Energy
- Calcium

The main points to be considered while planning meals for adolescents are as follows:

- Be careful about dieting, weight reducing techniq ues
- Avoid over-eating
- Exercise is the remedy for over weight

Meal planning for adults

Persons who are more than 20 years old are called as adults. During this period, their growth in terms of body size is completed.

Their:

- In case of young adults, the body has the capacity to reple the worn out tissues.
- There will be a gradual and progressive change in body functioning.
- Breakdown of tissue increases and renewal of wor n out tissue decreases.
- Nutritional needs are for maintenance of body fun ctions.
- In case of older adult, the body has lost the cap acity to replace the worn out tissues.

Changes during ageing

The following changes take place during ageing.

- Kidney functions: There is a marked reduction in the number of functioning of the kidney cells.
- Reduction in the amount of saliva secreted: Hence Swallowing becomes difficult. Teeth become loose: Thus, chewing becomes difficult.

- Digestive tract functioning: The number of taste buds in the mouth decreases. This reduces sensitivity to taste.
- Decreased secretion of digestive juices: So, food is not digested and absorbed properly and it stays longer in the stomach.
- Muscles of digestive tract become weak: Movement of food in the tract slows down and constipation sets in.
- Skeletal system: Skeletal bone loss occurs with a ging.
- Loss of calcium and phosphorus: This results in t hinning of bones. Osteoporosis is a condition in which bones become weak and brittle (mostly in women).

The main nutrient requirements are:

- Energy
- Body building
- Protective/regulatory

CONSIDERATION OF MENU PLANNING

The success of a food service operation, whatever its size, depends heavily on those who plan the menus and how they do it. While it may seem a simple exercise of providing something to eat and drink, in practice good menu planning requires a lot of skill. It is important, therefore, that people responsible for planning menus have a good knowledge of:

1. Food
2. Preparation and service methods
3. Aesthetic presentation
4. Customers

1. Food

This involves knowledge about different types, forms and varieties of foods; their seasonal availability: nutritional and anti-nutritional factors; and the presence of toxic elements in certain food varieties: the edible portion obtained forms each food; taste and flavour differences and how they can best be combined for meals; acceptability and cost factors.

2. Preparation and service methods

Even though a menu planner does not necessarily prepare or serve the food, it is important for him/her to know which food is best prepared and by which method of cooking. This is possible only if the planner knows about the inherent qualities of foods in terms or texture, Composition, colour, flavour and all other chemical and physical properties. Knowledge of the behavior of these characteristics to the application of heat, addition of salts, acids, oils and spices are also very essential to any method of food preparation.

Similarly, knowing what food is suited to what style of service; which flavours Menu Planning blend together best, and how to combine them are the crux of customer's food acceptability,

3. Aesthetic presentation

Whatever may be the colour, taste and flavour of a meal, its appearance on the plate or in the display case determines customer's choice, there are different ways in which simple food can he presented to catch the of customers. Equipped with this knowledge, the menu planner can introduce a variety of form and colour in menus to attract customers and increase acceptability.

4. Customers

It is vital for the menu planner to be familiar with the food expectations of a customer. A general idea of his/her food preferences or favorites, Physiological requirements, paying power, social standing, regional or ethnic backgrounds, and the reasons for eating out are essential for providing customer satisfaction. People eat outside their homes for a number of different reasons and each reason affects their choice of food at a particular time. Office goers, for instance, stopping for a quick lunch would prefer light inexpensive meals, while an executive who is entertaining would choose more elaborately presented items. Similarly, captive customers, such as children in a boarding school, or people in an old age home will necessarily eat from a less selective menu, because they have no choice but to eat what is prepared in the institutional kitchen. Again, people traveling long distances look forward to food because other activities as in a train or an aeroplane are restricted. The menu should, therefore, be interesting in terms of providing variety in form, colour and flavour. In addition, they need to be easy to serve and eat while traveling.

Why Plan Menus

Planning menus is essential when food has to be bought, prepared and served in large quantities to people of varying tastes and requirements. The following are the advantages of planning:

- It has provisions for appetizing, nourishing and attractive meals for customers at a fair price. This is only possible if the meals are planned in advance, so that a price advantage can be obtained by buying seasonal foods and in quantities that carry discounts.
- Planning meals helps determine requirements accurately. Food buying can thus be controlled through advance buying, because quantities are calculated beforehand.
- It ensures that food is not wasted because any leftovers can be creatively incorporated in the next meal on menu which is already planned out.
- Time and effort spent on haphazard ordering, shop ping and receiving of food materials is saved.
- Time and effort spent in preparation and cooking is also minimized because ingredients required for subsequent meals are known in advanced. Garnishes, for instance, can be prepared along with salads at one time. Chopping and cutting separately for each dish is avoided. Time is not lost in waiting for ingredients. as they are already purchased and ready for use.
- Carefully planned menus save fuel and cut down on waste through excessive leftovers: for example, milk may be heated together for the preparation of hot beverages, setting of curds or for preparing cottage cheese, instead of placing the milk in three containers and heating small quantities separately. Similarly, planned menus can help to save on quantities and ingredients e.g. leftover curds many be added to boiling milk for making cottage cheese or paneer instead of

vinegar or lemon juice. Also, the whey obtained need not be wasted, but added to curries, soups, etc.

- Menus help to note favorite dishes and those which did not sell too well in the past. From these records, decisions regarding the number of portions of each item to be prepared for service can be made.
- Planning tends to offer a wider choice of dishes because seasonal varieties of foods can be introduced in advance. This becomes very restricted when preparation has to be done on the bases of spot decisions.
- Advance planning removes a lot of anxiety for the planner and enables clear-cut instructions to be given to staff. This also helps to create harmony among people at work.
- If the planner is absent for a day, customers nee d not have to go hungry or disappointed, because the work goes on according to plan.
- Meal planning helps in the accurate calculation of food costs and inclusion of items that can be profitably sold. It also becomes far easier to fix selling prices in advance for the information of the customer.
- Planning helps to take care f price fluctuations and prevents frequent changes on menu displays as far as the customer is concerned.

Planning menus is thus an important activity for every food service operation, and catering managers need to ensure procedures which can determine how best it can be done.

WELL-PLANNED MENU MAKING

The following sample menus have been suggested for various institutions and occasions to act as guidelines for planning.

Menu A (Boy's Hostel, one day)

Breakfast:

Butter milk and Toast

Lunch

Curd, Chappati, Rice, Vegietable (sauteed)

Tea

Samosa, milkshake

Dinner

Egg Curry (or Veg Kadhi)

Gajar Halva, Dal rice, Palak , Potato sauteed,

Menu B (Girl's Hostel, One day)

Breakfast:

Porridge, egg poached, butter toast, milk

Lunch

Raita, chtney, Curry-pakora, Chappati, Rice, Vegietable (sautéed), pickle

Tea

Cookies, tea/coffee

Dinner

Veg sautéed, Chapatee

Kheer/Halva, Dal rice.

The following factors were taken into consideration in preparing this menu:

(i) The Indian food habits which include a curry, curd, dal preparation (usually consumed in some form at least once a day), and an Indian dessert at dinner.

'ii) Boys need a nutritionally balanced diet provided by food from all food groups in each meal. The satiety value through a fried snack, egg and halwa take care of protein and extra calories for activities, besides providing all the other nutrients.

iii) The menu provides, in this format, a lot of flexibility, so that different currie, haiwas, forms of egg, snacks, fruits and shakes can be provided according to seasonal availability.

iv) Boys do usually not like salads unless they are incorporated in sandwiches or rolls, which can be introduced as snacks, in the form of burgers, kebabs, pakoras, etc.

The difference in Menus A and B is chiefly in the provision of spicy preparations, such as raita, pickle, chutney and assorted pakoras with inclusion of salads for girls. Eggs have been provided in unfired forms in preference to fried forms. This menu is just as flexible as Menu A and can be varied according to the mood of the customer and the availability of ingredients.

It may be noted that Menus A and B are only light, and if a cyclic menu is prepared which is the normal practice in hostels, then specific dishes may be written out for several days in advance.

Menu C:

A conference lunch menu attended by delegates from different countries.

Lunch
Stuffed capsicum and tomatoes
Cottage cheese/Meat ball curry
Mixed vegetable pulao
Pineapple raita
Green salad
Carrot mould with cream
Coffee

The factors taken into consideration while planning are:

(i) The dishes are generally acceptable to persons from all the countries. The menu accomplishes this through:

- The starter and salad which are two items that ar e eaten all over the world.
- The curry selected is familiar to most persons—me at halls served with spaghetti or in tomato sauce are common to most.
- Cottage cheese curry provides vegetarians with an equivalent substitute for meat curry.
- Indian curries are relished by people from all co untries.
- Rice is a common cereal in most countries and peo ple look forward to tasting oriental flavours in the form of pulaos.
- Pineapple raita would provide the familiar flavou r of the fruit.
- Yoghurt can act as a suitable accompaniment to the rice.

- Carrot and halwa molded and served with cream introduces a new form of pudding to foreign palates, while being relished by most Indian.

(ii) The composition of the menu allows for quick service between conference sessions.

(iii) The colour, texture, flavour and attractiveness is taken care of on a buffet table during service.

(iv) There is very little scope for over spicing. For those who wish to add more Spices, these could be placed on the table in the form of chutneys, pickles, papads and cruets of salt and pepper or salad dressings.

While the menu accounts for tastes and habits of the people from all over the world, the Indian touch that many delegates relish is not absent.

Menu D: A canteen menu

Special of the day	pizza	Rs 100.00
Assorted fried snack (with chutney)	1 plate	20.00
Mini meal	plate	40.00
Sandwiches	pack	25.00
Fruit cake	piece	15.00
Tea	cup	5.00
Coffee	cup	8.00
Cold drinks	glass (200ml)	10.00

The factors considered in planning are:

(i) The eating habits of the customers. If it is an office canteen, hot beverages will be demanded throughout the day.

(ii) The purchasing power of customers

(iii) Favorite among customers is included in the days special.

(iv) Easy to serve in disposables.

(v) The satiety value and value for money.

(vi) Minimum on the spot preparation.

(vii) Items that will provide attractive displays.

MENU PRESENTATION

ECONOMIC CONSIDERATIONS

As early as the mid-20th century, some restaurants have relied on "menu specialists" to design and pri nt their menus. Prior to the emergence of digital printing, these niche printing companies printed full-color menus on offset presses. The economics of full-color offset made it impractical to print short press runs.

The solution was to print a "menu shell" with every thing but the prices. The prices would later be printed on a less costly black-only press. In a typical order, the printer might produce 600 menu shells, then finish and laminate 150 menus with prices. When the restaurant needed to reorder, the printer would add prices and laminate some of the remaining shells.

With the advent of digital presses, it became practical in the 1990s to print full-color menus affordably in short press runs, sometimes as few as 25 menus. Because of limits on sheet size, larger laminated menus were impractical for single-location independent re to produce press runs of as few as 300 menus, but some restaurants may want to place far fewer menus into service. Some menu printers continue to use shells. The disadvantage for the restaurant is that it is unable to update anything but prices without creating a new shell.

During the economic crisis in the 1970s, many restaurants found that they were having to incur costs from having to reprint the menu as inflation caused prices to increase. Economists noted this transaction cost, and it has become part of economic theory, under the term "menu costs." As a general economic phenomenon, "menu costs" can be experienced by a range of businesses beyond restaurants; for example, during a period of inflation, any company that prints catalogues or product price lists will have to reprint these items with new price figures.

To avoid having to reprint the menus throughout the year as prices changed, some restaurants began to display their menus on chalkboards, with the menu items and prices written in chalk. This way, the restaurant could easily modify the prices without going to the expense of reprinting the paper menus. A similar tactic continued to be used in the 2000s with certain items that are sensitive to changing supply, fuel costs, and so on: the use of the term "market price" or "Please ask server" instead of stating the price. This allows restaurants to modify the price of lobster, fresh fish and other foods subject to rapid changes in cost.

The latest trend in menus is the advent of handheld tablets that hold the menu and the guests can browse through that and look at the photographs of the dishes.

Writing style

The main categories within a typical menu in the US are "appetizers," "side orders and a la carte," "entrées," "desserts" and "beverages." Sides and ala carte may include such items as soups, salads and dips. There may be special age-restricted sections for "seniors" or for children, presenting smaller portions at lower prices. Any of these sections may be pulled out as a separate menu, such as desserts and/or beverages, or a wine list. Children's menus may also be presented as placemats with games and puzzles to help keep children entertained.

Menus can provide other useful information to diners. Some menus describe the chef's or proprietor's food philosophy, the chef's resume, or the mission statement of the restaurant. Menus often present a restaurant's policies about ID checks for alcohol, lost items, or gratuities for larger parties. In the United States, county health departments frequently require restaurants to include health warnings about raw or undercooked meat, poultry, eggs and seafood.

Types of Menu Presentations

1. Paper

Menus vary in length and detail depending on the type of restaurant. The simplest hand-held menus are printed on a single sheet of paper, though menus with multiple pages or "views" are common. In some cafeteria-style restaurants and chain restaurants, a single-page menu may double as a disposable placemat. To protect a menu from spills and wear, it may be protected by heat-sealed vinyl page protectors, laminating or menu covers. Restaurants weigh their positioning in the marketplace (e.g. fine dining, fast food, informal) in deciding which style of menu to use.

While some restaurants may use a single menu as the sole way of communicating information about menu items to customers, in other cases, the meal menu is supplemented with ancillary menus, such as:

- An appetizer menu (nachos, chips and salsa, vegetables and dip, etc.)
- A wine list
- A liquor and mixed drinks menu
- A beer list
- A dessert menu (which may also include a list of tea and coffee options)

Some restaurants use only text in their menus. In other cases, restaurants include illustrations and photos, either of the dishes or of an element of the culture which is associated with the restaurant. An example of the latter is in cases where a Lebanese kebab restaurant decorates its menu with photos of Lebanese mountains and beaches. Particularly with the ancillary menu types, the menu may be provided in alternative formats, because these menus (other than wine lists) tend to be much shorter than food menus. For example, an appetizer menu or a dessert menu may be displayed on a folded paper table tent, a hard plastic table stand, a flipchart style wooden "table stand," or even, in the case of a pizza restaurant with a limited wine selection, a wine list glued to an empty bottle.

Take-out restaurants often leave paper menus in the lobbies and doorsteps of nearby homes as advertisement. The first to do so may have been New York City's Empire Szechuan chain, founded in 1976. The chain and other restaurants' aggressive menu distribution in the Upper West Side of Manhattan caused the "Menu Wars" of the 1990s, including invasions of Empire Szechuan by the "Menu Vigilantes", the revoking of its cafe license, several lawsuits, and physical attacks on menu distributors.

2. Menu board

Some restaurants – typically fast-food restaurants and cafeteria-style establishments – provide their menu in a large poster or display board format up high on the wall or above the service counter. This way, all of the patrons can see all of the choices, and the restaurant does not have to provide printed menus. This large format menu may also be set up outside (see the next section). The simplest large format menu boards have the menu printed or painted on a large flat board. More expensive large format menu boards include boards that have a metal housing, a translucent surface, and a backlight (which facilitates the reading of the menu in low light), and boards that have removable numbers for the prices. This enables the restaurant to change prices without having to have the board reprinted or repainted.

Some restaurants such as cafes and small eateries use a large chalkboard to display the entire menu. The advantage of using a chalkboard is that the menu items and prices can be changed; the downside is that the chalk may be hard to read in lower light or glare, and the restaurant has to have a staff member who has attractive, clear handwriting.

A high-tech successor to the chalkboard menu is the 'write-on wipe-off' illuminated sign, using LED technology. The text appears in a vibrant color against a black background.

3. Outdoor

Some restaurants provide a copy of their menu outside the restaurant. Fast-food restaurants that have a drive-through or walk-up window will often put the entire menu on a board, lit-up sign, or poster outside, so that patrons can select their meal choices. High-end restaurants may also provide a copy of their menu outside the restaurant, with the pages of the menu placed in a lit-up glass display case; this way, prospective patrons can see if the menu choice is to their liking. As well, some mid-level and high-end restaurants may provide a partial indication of their menu listings–the "specials"–on a chalkboard displayed outside the restaurant. The chalkboard will typically provide a list of seasonal items or dishes that are the specialty of the chef which are only available for a few days.

Fig :Menu cards - Presi Corp.

4. Digital displays

With the invention of LCD and Plasma displays, some menus have moved from a static printed model, to one which can change dynamically. By using a flat LCD screen and a computer server, menus can be digitally displayed allowing moving images, animated effects and the ability to edit details and prices.

For fast food restaurants, a benefit is the ability to update prices and menu items as frequently as needed, across an entire chain. Digital menu boards also allow restaurant owners to control the day parting of their menus, converting from a breakfast menu in the late morning. Some platforms support the ability allow local operators to control their own pricing while the design aesthetic is controlled by the corporate entity. Various software tools and hardware developments have been created for the specific purpose of managing a digital menu board system. Digital menu screens can also alternate between displaying the full menu and showing video commercials to promote specific dishes or menu items.

5. Online menu

Websites featuring online restaurant menus have been on the Internet for nearly a decade. In recent years, however, more and more restaurants outside of large metropolitan areas have been able to feature their menus online as a result of this trend.

Several restaurant-owned and startup online food ordering websites already included menus on their websites, yet due to the limitations of which restaurants could handle online orders, many restaurants were left invisible to the Internet aside from an address listing. Multiple companies came up with the idea of posting menus online simultaneously, and it is difficult to ascertain who was first. Menus and online food ordering have been available online since at least 1997. Since 1997, hundreds of online restaurant menu web sites have appeared on the Internet. Some sites are city-specific, some list by region, state or province.

6. SECRET MENU

Another phenomenon is the so-called "secret menu" where some fast food restaurants are known for having unofficial and unadvertised selections that customers learn by word of mouth. Fast food restaurants will often prepare variations on items already available, but to have them all on the menu would create clutter. Chipotle

Mexican Grill is well known for having a simple five item menu, but some might not know they offer quesadillas and single tacos, despite neither being on the menu board.

In-N-Out Burger has a very simple menu of burgers, fries, sodas, and shakes, but has a wide variety of "secret" styles of preparations, the most famous being "Animal Style" burgers and fries. This can also occur in high-end restaurants, which may be willing to prepare certain items which are not listed on the menu (e.g., dishes that have long been favorites of regular clientele). Sometimes restaurants may name foods often ordered by regular clientele after them, for either convenience or prestige.

LAYOUT OF TABLE

Points to be while laying a table

When we lay out the table we have to be aware of some of the important things. We list them for you here:

1. The chairs, sideboard and trolleys should be spotlessly cleaned.
2. The table and chairs should be kept in proper place according to the lay out of the restaurant or according to the requirement of the day.
3. Table on which tablecloth is to be used should be covered with baize cloth which is of a thick, soft material like velvet.
4. Table should be 30" from the ground and the cha ir seat should be 18" high from the ground level.
5. For square, round and rectangular table, a square or rectangular clothe should be used. The length and width of the cloth should be two feet extra from the table-top dimension. If a square table cloth is to be used on a round table, the four corners of the table cloth should just brush the floor. The four corner of the tablecloth should be well hemmed to give a near tidy appearance. Spoilt, crumpled or form cloth should never be used. When spreading a tablecloth one should make sure that the right side is on the top. Different types of cloth material used are cotton or line. The damask is the best material for table linen. It is mixture of cotton and linen, with geometrical designs and has the strength of cotton and texture of linen.
6. Occasionally, a decoration piece can be placed on which a flower arrangement can be done but arrangement should have a low flower vase. Large flower arrangements in the vase prevent customers sitting opposite each other from conversing. Heavily sainted flowers should never be used as they adversely effect the flavour of the food.
7. Each cover should be well balanced and never be overcrowded with cutlery crockery and glassware. Covers: It is the space required on the table for laying cutlery, crockery and glassware for one person.
   Normally, each cover requires 24"x15" and 27"x15" space for banquet.
8. Knives and spoons are placed on the right hand side of the cover whereas forks are placed on the left-hand side of the cover. Dessert spoon and forks for the sweet are placed on the top on the cover. A side plate is placed on the extreme left-hand side of the cover with small knife or side knife. The cutting edge of all the knives should be towards the let-hand side of the cover. The water tumbler should be placed on the right hand side of the cover near the tip of the first

knife. The butter should be placed on a quarter plate along with a butter spreader in the center on the table. A napkin is placed in the center of cover or side plate but rarely in the tumbler as this practice is unhygienic.

9. Two opposite covers should be exactly opposite to each other, namely the large knife should be in link of the fork of the opposite cover. Only necessary cutlery for the meal should be placed. The order of laying the cutlery should be from outside to inside of the sequence in which they are to be used
10. Salt and pepper cellars are placed between two or four covers.
11. Crockery used in the restaurant should be spotlessly clean, glassware and cutlery well-polished. Chipped and cracked crockery and glassware should never be used.
12. While placing the plate and glassware on the table see that the monogram is directly facing the customer.
13. The crockery should be carried on the salver or on a large plate covered with a waiter's cloth or napkin. The cutlery should never be handled in the bare hand. Crockery should be handled with clean waiter clothe and in no case should the waiter touch prongs, bowls of spoons, blades of knife. Glassware should be handled from the base and never from the brim. The plates should be covered with a waiter's with a waiter's cloth.
14. Menu card should either be placed on the menu cared stand or on the sideboard or on the menu card holder placed on the table.
15. The cutlery for hors d'oeuvres fish knife and fish fork can laid in advance on the cover or can be brought on the same plate which is used for the hors d'oeuvres course. Generally, this is done when there is a fish in the course as well.
16. All the cutlery, crockery should be placed approx. ¼ to ½ inches away from the edges of the table.

MENU

Menu is the priced list of food and beverage items available in food and beverage outlets. Menu is also termed as "Bill of Fare" or "Price List" of food and beverage items. This is one of the most important parts of modern catering operation. A menu has to be well designed since it acts as a selling tool. It helps the guests to select what they like to eat and drink.

Types of Menu

Basically, there are two types of menu.

1. À la Carte

À la Carte means "from the card" which is a multiple choice menu, in which each item is listed down in specific sequence with individual price. The guest is then charged only for the items consumed or ordered.

2. Table d' hote

The literal meaning of Table d' hote is "Table of the host." It refers to a menu of limited choices, which is planned in advance for specific function or meal. It usually includes 4 to 5 courses at fixed price.

COVER

Cover is a place allotted in a table for an individual customer with all the accessories required for the meal, which includes flatware, glassware and chinaware along with linen, etc. Mostly cover will occupy 183 ´243 on the table for each person. The capacity of an outlet is determined by the number of covers it surrounds.

Types of Cover and Layout

There are mainly two types of covers (Although cover may be laid in many different manners in different restaurants depending upon the requirement of the menu and style of service)

1. À la Carte Cover: This type of cover setting usually has a standard cover laid down for the entire course. It will consist of the items listed below. The cutlery is placed from out to inside according to the course being served. As in À la Carte menu, orders are placed on the spot. Other cutlery which are required for specific courses are supplied along with the dish.

Following are the requirements for an À la Carte Cover.

1. Serviette/Napkin
2. AP Knife
3. AP Fork
4. Side Plate
5. Side Knife
6. Wine Glass (optional)
7. Water goblet
8. Desert spoon and fork

1. Table D' hote Cover: As we know that table d' hote is a fixed menu in which all major courses are included. Here, the cover is set according to the menu.

The cover setting includes.

1. Serviette
2. Soup Spoon
3. Dinner Knife
4. Dinner Fork
5. Appetizer Knife
6. Appetizer Fork
7. Dessert Spoon
8. Dessert Fork
9. Side Plate
10. Butter Knife
11. Wine Glass (optional)
12. Water Goblet

Table Accompaniments

While preparing for service, all other items which are required to be placed on table during the service should also be prepared and kept ready on the side boards. These generally include:

1. Bread Roll Basket
2. Butter chiplets with ice
3. Soup Sticks
4. Cayenne Pepper
5. Sauces like tobasco, barbecue sauce, etc.
6. Pepper mill
7. Chutneys, pickles, etc.

Service Equipments

All equipments required for the service must be kept ready after the covers are set so that there will not be any problem or hindrance in service in last minute. These include the following:

i. Service salver: A round tray, which is used during the service for:
ii. Carrying of clean glassware.
1. Placing and removing of clean cutlery and crockery from the table.
2. Tea and coffee cups.
3. Under plates or saucers.

Important points while Laying of a Table

It is a very important task and must be handled meticulously. The steps for lying of a table include the following:

1. Place all the tables and chairs in their correct positions.
2. Clean the table tops.
3. Lay a correct size of moultan for even balance of the cover to be laid out.
4. Place a table cloth ensuring that the cloth is clean and free of stains.
5. Always ensure that the corners of the table cloth are covering the legs of the table.
6. The fall of the table cloth should be even and equal on sides, usually between 10 to 12 inches.
7. Place a slip cloth on top of the table cloth for protection.
8. All covers should be laid out preferably facing the centre entrance of the restaurant. *(see cover layout)*
9. Check all cutlery and crockery for cleanliness. They should be sparkling clean and wiped. Chipped crockery should not be used.
10. The monograms/logos on the crockery should face the guest.
11. Napkin folds should be appropriate to the time of the day and service style and must face the guest.

ii. **Service Platters:** These are the platters with serviette and used for:
- Placing and removing cutlery on the table
- Crumbing of the table.
- Clearing of accompaniments from the table.

iii. **Extra Serviette Folds:** As there may be two or more service rounds, folded napkins are kept ready for the next service on hand so that as soon as the customer finishes his/her meal the table can be set immediately for next.

iv. **Extra Cutlery/Crockery**

Important points while laying a cover

Once your table has been set, the cover has to be laid down. This is very important factor which does not only improve the presentation of the table but also shows the professionalism of the restaurant.

1. The covers to be laid on the table must be facing each other and should be parallel.
2. All cutleries must be placed at least ½" away from the edge of the table.
3. Forks are laid on the left-hand side of the cover (except in case of pastry fork, oyster fork, etc) which are placed on right side, whereas the dessert fork is placed on top of the cover.
4. All spoons and knives are placed on the right-hand side of the cover (except dessert spoon which is placed on top of the cover). Blades of the knives should face the left-hand side.
5. The water tumbler is placed on the right hand side, on the tip of the large knife.
6. The side-knife is placed on the side plate.
7. It is to be remembered that if the courses are too many only up to 3 knives (for 3 courses) should be placed on the table. The balance should be brought in later for the subsequent courses.
8. For dinner, the napkin fold is placed in the glass, whereas for lunch, it is placed on the cover itself.
9. Cutlery is laid according to the sequence of the course.
10. Check and lay down all filled cruet sets in the centre of the table, along with ashtray, bud vase, etc.

Index

H

I

J

K

L